Homeschool Packet

for

Advanced Mathematics

An Incremental Development, Second Edition

John H. Saxon, Jr.

Answers

Contents

ISBN 1-56577-485-X

9 781565 774858

Advanced Mathematics: An Incremental Development
Second Edition

Homeschool Packet

Copyright © 1998 by Saxon Publishers, Inc.

Printed in the United States of America.

ISBN: 1-56577-159-1 Home Study Packet
ISBN: 1-56577-485-X Answer Book

Prepress Manager: J. Travis Rose

Production Coordinator: Joan Coleman

17 18   0748   19 18

4500698987

┌─── *Reaching us via the Internet* ───┐
www.saxonpublishers.com
E-mail: info@saxonpublishers.com
└──────────────────────────────────────┘

Using Saxon Materials in a Homeschool Environment

Introduction

This guide to using the Saxon Homeschool Math and Physics programs has been designed to help homeschoolers using our *Math 54* through *Calculus* and *Physics* get the most benefit from our program. Please read through this carefully and consider the advice given. Among all of the available learning programs, the Saxon program is unique. Some of this advice is common sense. However, many of these guidelines are specific to the Saxon program and require special attention by the parent-teacher and the student.

Materials Available

The basic package Saxon Publishers offers for homeschool students for grades four and above consists of a student textbook, test booklet, and answer booklet. The test booklets for *Math 54* through *Math 87* include test forms, facts practice problems, answer grids, and all activity masters needed. The answer booklet includes answers to all the problems in the textbook, answers to the facts practice problems, and solutions to the tests.

Also available from Saxon Publishers are solutions manuals for *Algebra 1/2* through *Calculus* and *Physics*. The solutions manuals contain step-by-step solutions for each problem in every lesson. These manuals are highly recommended as a powerful tool to aid in evaluating the student or to assist the student in developing solution strategies. To order any of our materials, please consult our catalog or call our customer service department at (800) 416-8171.

If you have access to the Internet, you can take advantage of our online services. Our World Wide Web site contains our latest catalogs, teacher resources, in-service information, errata, and much more. You can visit our site at **http://www.saxonhomeschool.com.** You can also contact us by E-mail to get general or specific help. For general help, our E-mail address is **info@saxonhomeschool.com.** For help with specific math questions, please send E-mail to **mathhelp@saxonhomeschool.com.**

Planning the Course

The first step when planning a course of study is to determine a schedule for how many lessons will be taught each week. To do this, find the total number of lessons in the textbook being studied. All lessons should be taken into account, including the review lessons, the numbered lessons, and any extra sections to be studied. Next, divide the total number of lessons by the amount of time desired to complete the textbook. For example, if you are beginning the *Advanced Mathematics* program, its textbook has 125 lessons. Dividing the total number of lessons by the total number of weeks in a regular school year (estimated at 36 weeks) gives you approximately 3.47 lessons per week. This means you will need to complete 3 to 4 lessons per week in order to cover every lesson in the textbook within a school year. A student will most likely be able to complete lessons in a shorter period of time at the beginning of a book and will take longer for each lesson towards the end. A similar strategy can be used to develop a time schedule to meet your own specific needs. Once you have developed your schedule, try to maintain a constant pace. *This is a very important point.* If a student's study schedule is broken up or erratic, his or her quality of learning will suffer.

It is also important to assure that the student is adequately prepared for each successive textbook. Knowledge of the basic addition, subtraction, multiplication, and division facts is crucial for success in mathematics. The Saxon Middle Grade Series, which includes *Math 54* through *Math 87*, continually practices these facts to ensure full mastery. To assist in this process we use several methods. For instance, fact cards, called *Middle Grades Basic Facts*, are available in our catalog. We also employ facts practice problems which are incorporated into the test booklets. These facts are designed to be practiced as speed drills so that the student becomes progressively faster at answering each fact. Regular practice with these facts will allow for a smoother transition between textbooks.

Teaching the Lessons

Though the textbook is the main tool for student learning, the help of a knowledgeable and concerned parent-teacher enhances the learning process. **The parent-teacher must assume responsibility for the student's education.** This can best be accomplished by ensuring that the student demonstrates competency in each area of study before continuing to the next, and making sure that the student completes all assignments. **Do not allow the student to do independent study.**

Part of the parent-teacher's responsibility lies in being prepared. Each lesson should be read and fully understood by the parent-teacher before being taught. This will ensure that any questions that may arise can be answered quickly and accurately. If, after reading the lesson, the parent-teacher is uncomfortable with any material, further assistance should be sought through other knowledgeable sources.

Each lesson is designed to be taught within fifteen to twenty minutes. This allows more time for actual problem solving by the student. During the lecture period, all lesson material should be presented and any example problems should be demonstrated. The student should also maintain a notebook that includes any relevant information presented in the lesson. For example, any formulas, definitions, or strategies should be written in the notebook for quick and easy reference in future problem sets. Especially important are bold words or sentences and boxed items. The notebook should be maintained daily in an organized fashion. After the lecture, the student should work the practice problems first to make sure that he/she has grasped the basic concepts discussed in that lesson. With the remaining time allotted (preferably 40–60 minutes, depending on the subject matter), the student should begin the problem set. The parent-teacher should be available for assistance and guidance during this period. When this time period has expired, instruct the student to complete the remaining problems before the next lecture. It is important that the student be responsible for completing **all** the problems in the problem sets. Only in this way will the student succeed in mathematics.

Assigning the Problem Sets

Before working the problem sets, there are several things of which the parent-teacher and student should be aware. First of all, it is impossible to construct an example problem for each type of problem in the problem sets. Many problems are designed to extend the concepts already learned by the student. If the student cannot work a problem, he or she should first return to the lesson or lessons relevant to that problem in order to gain further insight. After reviewing the lesson, if the student is still having problems, he or she should then seek parent-teacher assistance. It is important that the student develop an individual problem-solving strategy. The student should copy the problem, write legibly, and show all of his or her work. The student should attempt to solve the problem using clear, logical steps. The steps that a student uses to solve the problem should be evident in his or her solution. A final point to consider is when to use a calculator. A calculator should only be used in problems involving complicated decimal computations, radicals, trigonometric functions, or logarithmic functions.

When the student has completed an assigned problem set, it must be evaluated by the parent-teacher. If time allows, check each problem to ensure that all work was shown and that the correct answer was obtained; otherwise, spot-check an assortment of problems. When comparing the student's answers to the answer booklet or solutions manual, be aware of equivalent forms of the same answer (e.g., $\frac{3}{2} = 1\frac{1}{2} = 1.5$). These equivalent forms are usually counted correct unless the problem asks for a specific form. Also, recognize that problems involving rounding or estimation may not exactly match the given answer, but should be relatively close. Each problem with an incorrect answer must be examined to determine where the error occurred. Review all errors with the student to determine whether the error was a computational error or a conceptual error. Any concepts not understood by the student should be re-taught as soon as possible so that the student will be able to work related problems in the future. If the parent-teacher and student, after referring back to the relevant lesson or lessons, still have questions regarding a specific problem in the textbook, they may seek further help from the *Saxon Publishers Math Helpline*.

Saxon Publishers Math Helpline

(405) 573-6451

The helpline is designed solely to answer questions concerning lessons and problem sets in Saxon textbooks. Help is available each weekday from 2:00 p.m. to 5:00 p.m. (CST).

Before calling our helpline, please make every attempt to solve your problem. Keep in mind that many mathematical concepts may not be obvious upon first reading, but do become familiar with rereading and practice.

Assessing the Student

After a concept has been practiced, the student has an opportunity to demonstrate his/her competency of the learned material. Two methods of assessing the student are facts practices and tests. Facts practice is a component of the Saxon Middle Grades Series and for *Math 54* and *Math 65* in particular. Facts practice sheets are designed to be given at the beginning of each lecture period and then reviewed with the student. The student should keep track of his or her time and get progressively faster as the course continues.

The second method of assessment is tests. Tests are provided that contain problems similar to those that have been practiced for at least several lessons. In *Math 54* through *Math 87*, tests are given every five lessons, beginning with Lesson 10. In *Algebra 1/2* through *Calculus*, tests are given every four lessons. Testing schedules are provided in the Homeschool Packets.

On these tests, the student will use the same problem-solving methods and strategies used for the homework. The test problems should be copied and worked on a separate sheet of paper. *This sheet of paper should not be scratch paper.* Allowing the use of scratch paper may falsely convey that it is acceptable for the student to be messy and disorganized. The sheet(s) of paper should be $8\frac{1}{2}$" × 11" ruled notebook paper or any type of standard graph paper, such as 1-cm grid paper. The student should write legibly and in an organized manner, precisely showing each step taken to determine the answer. It is important for the student to show all work so that understanding and strategy can be analyzed.

Each test problem should be graded by comparing the student's answer with the answer provided. If an answer does not match, determine where the mistake was made. After grading, review the test with the student and allow him or her to decide whether the mistakes were computational or conceptual. Be sure to let the student determine the location and type of mistake. The parent-teacher should only verify or reinforce the student's conclusion. Addition and subtraction errors, incorrectly copied problems, and careless mistakes are considered to be computational mistakes. Emphasize to the student that computational mistakes can be avoided by careful review of his or her solutions before completing the assignment. Conceptual mistakes, however, are usually caused by a lack of understanding of the material and should be promptly dealt with by reviewing and practicing the problematic concepts in the relevant lesson(s). Also, in order to see if the same type of problem is being missed repeatedly, the parent-teacher should both save and refer to old tests. If such a situation is discovered, the cause should be determined before continuing.

Getting Started

Consult these guidelines regularly for assistance and direction. Before beginning, remember that the Saxon program is meant to be flexible. The parent-teacher and student must decide what they are capable of accomplishing. Establish a schedule that works for you and your student. Do not try to go too fast. The main objectives are consistency and completion of the entire textbook, including every problem. Even if a student is familiar with a topic, do not skip that particular lesson. Review can only help with future learning. Remember, mathematics is not difficult. Mathematics is just different. Practice and dedication will turn things unfamiliar and different into things familiar.

Acknowledgments

The following Saxon employees were instrumental in the development of this Homeschool Packet, and we gratefully acknowledge their contributions: Coen Barnes, Mary Burleson, Edward Burr, Adriana Castaneda, and Erin McCain for working the solutions and proofing the various revisions; David LeBlanc and Angela Johnson for typesetting the packet; Aaron Lauve for creating the artwork; and Emerson Mounger for creating the cover art.

Reference Sheet

Planning the Course

- Determine the number of weeks you have to complete the book.
- Determine the total number of lessons in the book.
- Divide the number of lessons by the number of weeks.
- Be sure to complete about the same number of lessons each week.

Teaching the Lessons

- Be sure that the student completes all assignments.
- Do not allow the student to do independent study.
- Read and understand each lesson before teaching it.
- Teach for only 15–20 minutes.
- Have the student keep a notebook.
- Make sure that the student completes all practice problems.
- Make sure that all problems in the problem set are completed.

Assigning the Problem Sets

- Have the student refer to previous material, if necessary.
- Assist the student in developing a logical problem-solving strategy.
- Allow calculators only with complicated problems.
- Watch out for equivalent answers $\left(\text{e.g., } \frac{3}{2} = 1\frac{1}{2} = 1.5\right)$.
- Watch out for estimated answers; close ones are counted correct.
- Review all errors with the student.

Assessing the Student

- Use facts practice with Saxon Middle Grades Series.
- Do not allow scratch paper on tests.
- Allow the student to determine problem areas.
- Reteach any misunderstood concepts.

Contacting Us

- *Customer Service*: (800) 416-8171
- *Saxon Math Helpline*: (405) 573-6451
- *WWW*: http://www.saxonhomeschool.com
- *E-mail*: info@saxonhomeschool.com
  mathhelp@saxonhomeschool.com

Test 1

1. (1)

$$3(90 - A) = (180 - A) - 60$$
$$270 - 3A = 120 - A$$
$$2A = 150$$
$$A = \mathbf{75°}$$

2. (R)

$$\frac{s}{t} = \frac{8}{5}$$
$$\frac{1400}{t} = \frac{8}{5}$$
$$8t = 7000$$
$$t = \mathbf{875}$$

3. (R)

$$\frac{72}{100} = \frac{936}{T}$$
$$72T = 93{,}600$$
$$T = \mathbf{1300}$$

4. (4)

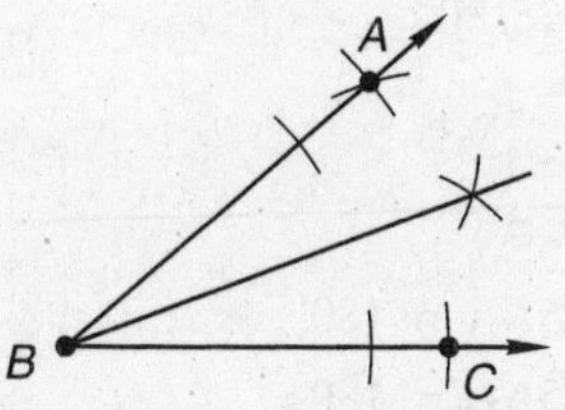

5. (4)

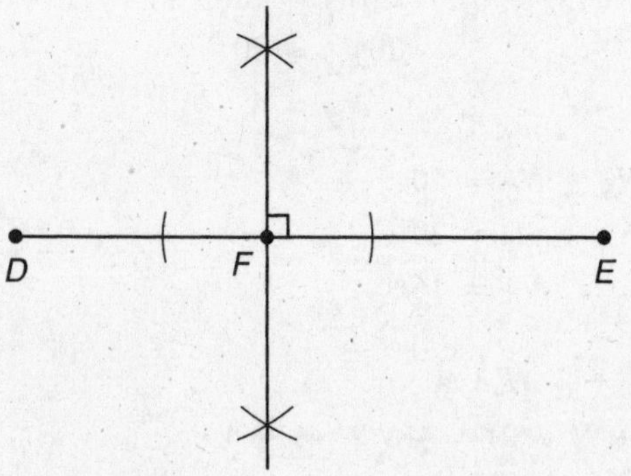

6. (4)

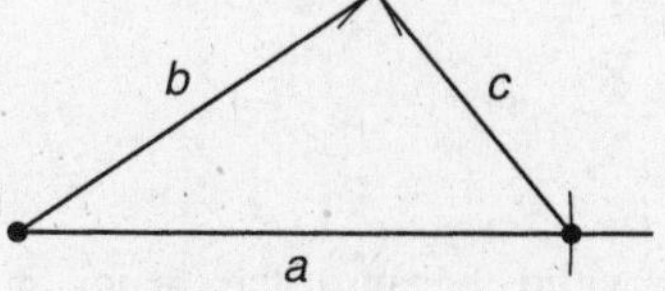

7. (R)

$$x - 3y = 0$$
$$x = 3y$$

$$2x + 6y = -36$$
$$2(3y) + 6y = -36$$
$$12y = -36$$
$$y = \mathbf{-3}$$

$$x = 3y$$
$$x = 3(-3)$$
$$x = \mathbf{-9}$$

8. (R)

$$6\left(x + x^0 - 1\right) = 2(-x + 8)$$
$$6x + 6 - 6 = -2x + 16$$
$$8x = 16$$
$$x = \mathbf{2}$$

9. (R)

$$\frac{5}{x(x+1)} + \frac{4}{(x+1)} + \frac{3}{x}$$
$$= \frac{5 + 4x + 3(x+1)}{x(x+1)} = \mathbf{\frac{7x + 8}{x^2 + x}}$$

10. (R)

$$\frac{4p^3s^{-5}}{p^{-3}s}\left(\frac{2^{-1}p^{-2}s}{p^3} + \frac{p^2s^3}{s^{-3}}\right)$$
$$= \frac{4p^6}{s^6}\left(\frac{s}{2p^5} + p^2s^6\right) = \mathbf{\frac{2p}{s^5} + 4p^8}$$

11. (3)

$$c^2 \bigcirc a^2 + b^2$$
$$8^2 \bigcirc 6^2 + 5^2$$
$$64 \bigcirc 36 + 25$$
$$64 > 61$$

Since the square of the largest side is greater than the sum of the squares of the other two sides, the triangle is an **obtuse triangle.**

12. (3)

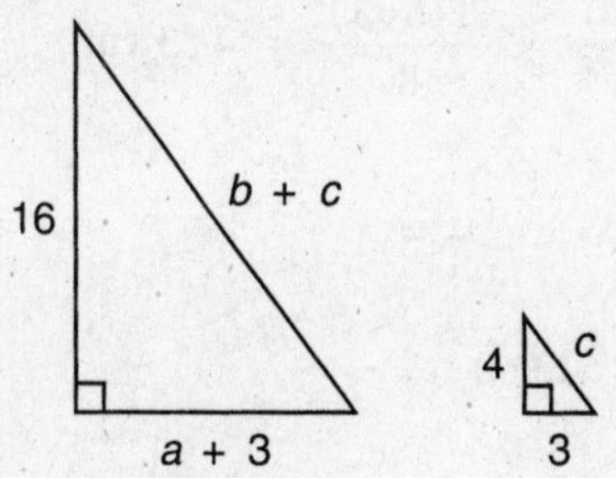

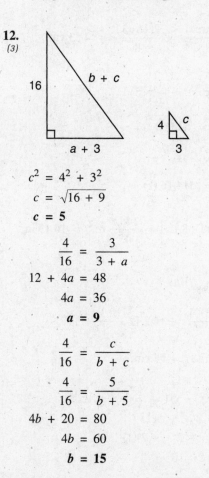

$$c^2 = 4^2 + 3^2$$
$$c = \sqrt{16 + 9}$$
$$\mathbf{c = 5}$$

$$\frac{4}{16} = \frac{3}{3 + a}$$
$$12 + 4a = 48$$
$$4a = 36$$
$$\mathbf{a = 9}$$

$$\frac{4}{16} = \frac{c}{b + c}$$
$$\frac{4}{16} = \frac{5}{b + 5}$$
$$4b + 20 = 80$$
$$4b = 60$$
$$\mathbf{b = 15}$$

Test 2

13.
(3)
$$3 \cdot \overline{SF} = 9$$
$$\overline{SF} = 3$$
$$x = 5 \cdot \overline{SF}$$
$$x = 5 \cdot (3)$$
$$x = 15$$
$$y \cdot \overline{SF} = 20$$
$$y \cdot (3) = 20$$
$$y = \frac{20}{3}$$

14.
(1)
$$\frac{7}{8} = \frac{3}{z}$$
$$7z = 24$$
$$z = \frac{24}{7}$$

15.
(1)
$$x + 150 = 180$$
$$x = 30$$
$$y = 150$$

16.
(1)
$$B = \frac{24}{3} = 8$$
$$\text{Area} = \frac{1}{2}BH$$
$$H = \frac{(2)(\text{Area})}{B} = \frac{2(16\sqrt{3})}{8} = 4\sqrt{3}\ \text{cm}$$

17.
(2)
$$V_{\text{sphere}} = \frac{4}{3}\pi r^3 = \frac{4}{3}\pi(5)^3$$
$$= \frac{500\pi}{3}\ \text{ft}^3 = 523.60\ \text{ft}^3$$
$$A_{\text{sphere}} = 4\pi r^2 = 4\pi(5)^2$$
$$= 100\pi\ \text{ft}^2 = 314.16\ \text{ft}^2$$

18.
(1)
$$A = 2\left[\frac{73}{360}\pi(\sqrt{8})^2\right] = \frac{146\pi}{45}\ \text{m}^2 = 10.19\ \text{m}^2$$

19.
(2)
$$V_{\text{cone}} = \frac{1}{3}(A_{\text{base}})(h)$$
$$= \frac{1}{3}\left[\frac{(3)(4)}{2} + (6)(4) + \frac{(3)(4)}{2}\right](8)$$
$$= \frac{1}{3}(36)(8) = 96\ \text{cm}^3$$

20.
(R)
$$x^3 - 3y^3 + 2(x - y)(x^2 + 3xy + y^2)^0$$
$$= x^3 - 3y^3 + 2(x - y)(1)$$
$$= (3)^3 - 3(2)^3 + 2(3 - 2)(1)$$
$$= 27 - 24 + 2 = 5$$

1.
(R)
(a) $\begin{cases} \dfrac{b}{g} = \dfrac{14}{3} \\ \\ 4g = b - 6 \end{cases}$
(b)

(a) $\dfrac{b}{g} = \dfrac{14}{3}$
$$b = \frac{14g}{3}$$

(b) $4g = b - 6$
$$4g = \frac{14g}{3} - 6$$
$$12g = 14g - 18$$
$$2g = 18$$
$$g = 9$$

2.
(R)
(a) $\begin{cases} N_N + N_Q = 20 \\ 5N_N + 25N_Q = 180 \end{cases}$
(b)

(a) $N_N + N_Q = 20$
$$N_N = 20 - N_Q$$

(b)
$$5N_N + 25N_Q = 180$$
$$5(20 - N_Q) + 25N_Q = 180$$
$$100 - 5N_Q + 25N_Q = 180$$
$$20N_Q = 80$$
$$N_Q = 4$$

(a) $N_N + N_Q = 20$
$$N_N + (4) = 20$$
$$N_N = 16$$

3.
(7)
$$N, N + 2, N + 4$$
$$3(N + N + 2) = 4(N + 4) - 4$$
$$6N + 6 = 4N + 16 - 4$$
$$2N = 6$$
$$N = 3$$

3, 5, 7

4. The argument is **valid** because the major premise
(7) identified a property of the set of all athletes, and the minor premise identified Mark as a member of this set.

5. **If an object is not a ball, then it is not round.**
(7)

6.
(6)
$$\frac{1}{3} + \frac{2}{x + 1} = \frac{4}{9}$$
$$\frac{2}{x + 1} = \frac{1}{9}$$
$$x + 1 = 18$$
$$x = 17$$

7. $\sqrt{2x - 1} - \sqrt{9} = 4$
(6)
$$\sqrt{2x - 1} = 4 + \sqrt{9}$$
$$\sqrt{2x - 1} = 7$$
$$2x - 1 = 49$$
$$2x = 50$$
$$x = \mathbf{25}$$

8. (a) $\begin{cases} x + y + z = 4 \\ 2x - 3y - z = 1 \\ 4x + y - 2z = 16 \end{cases}$
(6) (b)
   (c)

(a) $x + y + z = 4$
(b) $\underline{2x - 3y - z = 1}$
(d) $3x - 2y = 5$

2(a) $2x + 2y + 2z = 8$
 (c) $\underline{4x + y - 2z = 16}$
 (e) $6x + 3y = 24$

3(d) $9x - 6y = 15$
2(e) $\underline{12x + 6y = 48}$
     $21x = 63$
           $x = \mathbf{3}$

(d) $3x - 2y = 5$
$$3(3) - 2y = 5$$
$$2y = 4$$
$$y = \mathbf{2}$$

(a) $x + y + z = 4$
$$(3) + (2) + z = 4$$
$$z = \mathbf{-1}$$

9. $(\sqrt{7} - \sqrt{3})(\sqrt{7} + \sqrt{3})$
(5)
$$= (\sqrt{7})^2 - \sqrt{21} + \sqrt{21} - (\sqrt{3})^2$$
$$= 7 - 3 = \mathbf{4}$$

10. $\dfrac{\sqrt[3]{x^2 y^4}\, x^{-2} y}{\sqrt{x^4 y^6 (xy)^{-2}}} = \dfrac{x^{2/3} y^{4/3} yxy}{x^2 y^3 x^2} = \dfrac{x^{5/3} y^{10/3}}{x^4 y^3}$
(5)
$$= \mathbf{x^{-7/3} y^{1/3}}$$

11. $3i^2 + 5i^4 - 4i^3 + 6$
(5)
$$= 3(ii) + 5(ii)(ii) - 4i(ii) + 6$$
$$= 3(-1) + 5(-1)(-1) - 4i(-1) + 6$$
$$= -3 + 5 + 4i + 6 = \mathbf{8 + 4i}$$

12. $(i - 5)(i - 3) = i^2 - 5i - 3i + 15$
(5)
$$= -1 - 5i - 3i + 15 = \mathbf{14 - 8i}$$

13. $(AB)^2 = 5^2 + d^2$
(5)
$$AB = \sqrt{25 + d^2}$$
$$(AC)^2 = (AB)^2 + 2^2$$
$$(AC)^2 = (25 + d^2) + 4$$
$$AC = \sqrt{29 + d^2}\ \mathbf{m}$$

14. $A_{\text{shaded region}} = A_{\text{rectangle}} - A_{\text{circle}}$
(1)
$$= lw - \pi r^2$$
$$= 4(7 + 2) - \pi(2)^2$$
$$= \mathbf{(36 - 4\pi)\ ft^2 = 23.43\ ft^2}$$

15. $\dfrac{4x + 3}{5} = \dfrac{2x}{2}$
(8)
$$2(4x + 3) = 5(2x)$$
$$8x + 6 = 10x$$
$$2x = 6$$
$$x = \mathbf{3}$$

16. $\dfrac{7}{5} = \dfrac{4}{x}$
(8)
$$7x = 20$$
$$x = \mathbf{\dfrac{20}{7}}$$

17. $\dfrac{\text{Side}_1}{\text{Side}_2} = \dfrac{4}{1}$
(5)
$$\dfrac{\text{Area}_1}{\text{Area}_2} = \left(\dfrac{\text{Side}_1}{\text{Side}_2}\right)^2 = \left(\dfrac{4}{1}\right)^2 = \mathbf{\dfrac{16}{1}}$$

18.
(4)
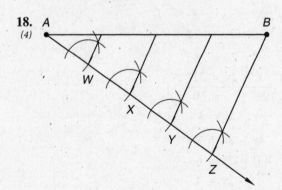

19.
(8)
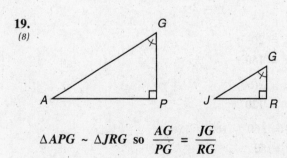

$$\triangle APG \sim \triangle JRG \text{ so } \dfrac{AG}{PG} = \dfrac{JG}{RG}$$

20.
$$A_{\text{surface}} = \pi r^2 + \pi r l$$
$$= \pi(2)^2 + \pi(2)(9)$$
$$= 4\pi + 18\pi$$
$$= 22\pi \text{ cm}^2 = 69.12 \text{ cm}^2$$
(2)

Test 3

1.
(R)
$$\frac{s}{d} = \frac{11}{4}$$
$$\frac{s}{s+d} = \frac{11}{11+4}$$
$$\frac{s}{270} = \frac{11}{15}$$
$$15s = 2970$$
$$s = 198$$

2. Exterior = **360°**
(12) Interior = $(N-2)180° = (12-2)180° = $ **1800°**

3. (a) $\begin{cases} N_M + N_C = 54 \\ 3N_C = N_M + 10 \end{cases}$
(R) (b)

(b) $3N_C = N_M + 10$
$$N_M = 3N_C - 10$$

(a) $N_M + N_C = 54$
$$(3N_C - 10) + N_C = 54$$
$$4N_C = 64$$
$$N_C = 16$$

(a) $N_M + N_C = 54$
$$N_M + (16) = 54$$
$$N_M = 38$$

4. (a) $\begin{cases} 4x - 2y = 8 \\ 6x + 2y = 22 \end{cases}$
(11) (b)

(a) $4x - 2y = 8$
(b) $\underline{6x + 2y = 22}$
$$10x \quad\quad = 30$$
$$x = 3$$

(a) $4x - 2y = 8$
$$4(3) - 2y = 8$$
$$2y = 4$$
$$y = 2$$

5. $x = 2(80)$
(11) $x = 160$

$y = 2(60)$
$y = 120$

$z = 360 - 160 - 120$
$z = 80$

6.
(11)
$$ax^2 + bx + c = 0$$
$$x^2 + \frac{b}{a}x + \frac{c}{a} = 0$$
$$\left(x^2 + \frac{b}{a}x \quad\right) = -\frac{c}{a}$$
$$\left(x^2 + \frac{b}{a}x + \frac{b^2}{4a^2}\right) = \frac{b^2}{4a^2} - \frac{c}{a}$$
$$\left(x + \frac{b}{2a}\right)^2 = \frac{b^2 - 4ac}{4a^2}$$
$$x + \frac{b}{2a} = \pm\sqrt{\frac{b^2 - 4ac}{4a^2}}$$
$$x = -\frac{b}{2a} \pm \sqrt{\frac{b^2 - 4ac}{4a^2}}$$
$$x = \frac{-b \pm \sqrt{b^2 - 4ac}}{2a}$$

7.
(11)
$$4x^2 = 2x - 3$$
$$4x^2 - 2x + 3 = 0$$
$$a = 4, \ b = -2, \ c = 3$$
$$x = \frac{-(-2) \pm \sqrt{(-2)^2 - 4(4)(3)}}{2(4)} = \frac{2 \pm \sqrt{-44}}{8}$$
$$x = \frac{2}{8} \pm \frac{2\sqrt{11}i}{8} = \frac{1}{4} \pm \frac{\sqrt{11}}{4}i$$

8.
(10)
$$3 + 2x^2 = -8x$$
$$2x^2 + 8x = -3$$
$$\left(x^2 + 4x \quad\right) = -\frac{3}{2}$$
$$\left(x^2 + 4x + 4\right) = 4 - \frac{3}{2}$$
$$(x + 2)^2 = \frac{5}{2}$$
$$x + 2 = \pm\sqrt{\frac{5}{2}}$$
$$x = -2 \pm \sqrt{\frac{5}{2}}$$

9.
(6)
$$\sqrt{8n + 9} + \sqrt{8n} = 9$$
$$\sqrt{8n + 9} = 9 - \sqrt{8n}$$
$$8n + 9 = 81 - 18\sqrt{8n} + 8n$$
$$18\sqrt{8n} = 72$$
$$\sqrt{8n} = 4$$
$$8n = 16$$
$$n = 2$$

10.
(5)
$\sqrt{3}\sqrt{-12} - \sqrt{12}\sqrt{-3}\sqrt{3} + 3\sqrt{-3}\sqrt{-3}$

$= \sqrt{3}(2\sqrt{3}i) - (2\sqrt{3})(\sqrt{3}i)\sqrt{3} + 3(\sqrt{3}i)^2$

$= 6i - 6\sqrt{3}i + 9i^2$

$= 6i - 6\sqrt{3}i + 9(-1)$

$= \mathbf{6i(1 - \sqrt{3}) - 9}$

11.
(7)
The argument is **invalid** because the major premise identified a property of the set of all French teachers, and the minor premise did not identify the tutor as a member of this set.

12.
(3)

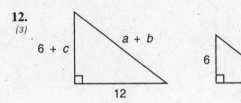

$a^2 = 6^2 + 8^2$

$a = \sqrt{6^2 + 8^2}$

$\mathbf{a = 10}$

$\dfrac{8}{12} = \dfrac{a}{a + b}$

$\dfrac{8}{12} = \dfrac{10}{10 + b}$

$80 + 8b = 120$

$8b = 40$

$\mathbf{b = 5}$

$\dfrac{8}{12} = \dfrac{6}{6 + c}$

$48 + 8c = 72$

$8c = 24$

$\mathbf{c = 3}$

13.
(5)
$\dfrac{a^{-3} + n^{-2}}{a^2 n^{-3}} = \dfrac{a^{-3}}{a^2 n^{-3}} + \dfrac{n^{-2}}{a^2 n^{-3}}$

$= \dfrac{n^3}{a^2 a^3} + \dfrac{n^3}{a^2 n^2} = \dfrac{n^3}{a^5} + \dfrac{n}{a^2}$

$= \dfrac{\mathbf{n^3 + a^3 n}}{\mathbf{a^5}}$

14.
(5)
$\dfrac{\sqrt[3]{a^{-9}b^6}(\sqrt{b})^{-1}}{\sqrt{a^4 b^2}(a^{-2}b^3)^2} = \dfrac{a^{-3}b^2 b^{-1/2}}{a^2 b a^{-4}b^6}$

$= \dfrac{a^4 b^2}{a^2 a^3 b b^6 b^{1/2}} = \dfrac{a^4 b^2}{a^5 b^{15/2}}$

$= \mathbf{a^{-1}b^{-11/2}}$

15.
(10)
$\dfrac{2i^3 + 3 - 2i}{3 - i} = \dfrac{2i(-1) + 3 - 2i}{3 - i}$

$= \dfrac{3 - 4i}{3 - i} \cdot \dfrac{3 + i}{3 + i} = \dfrac{9 + 3i - 12i - 4i^2}{9 + 3i - 3i - i^2}$

$= \dfrac{9 - 9i - 4(-1)}{9 - (-1)} = \dfrac{13 - 9i}{10} = \mathbf{\dfrac{13}{10} - \dfrac{9}{10}i}$

16.
(2)
$V_{\text{sphere}} = \dfrac{4}{3}\pi r^3 = \dfrac{4}{3}\pi(15)^3$

$= \mathbf{4500\pi \ in.^3} = \mathbf{14,137.17 \ in.^3}$

$A_{\text{sphere}} = 4\pi r^2 = 4\pi(15)^2 = \mathbf{900\pi \ in.^2} = \mathbf{2827.43 \ in.^2}$

17.
(9)
1.

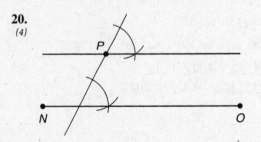

2. $\triangle SRQ \cong \triangle SPQ$ by *SAS* congruency postulate

3. $\overline{SR} \cong \overline{SP}$ by *CPCTC*

18.
(9)
SAS congruency postulate

19.
(4)

20.
(4)

Test 4

1.
(R)
$T_1 = 1200 - 360 = 840$

$\dfrac{T_2}{1600} = \dfrac{T_1}{1200}$

$\dfrac{T_2}{1600} = \dfrac{840}{1200}$

$1200 T_2 = 1,344,000$

$\mathbf{T_2 = 1120 \ grams}$

2.
(14)

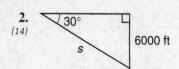

$$\sin 30° = \frac{6000}{s}$$

$$s = \frac{6000}{\sin 30°}$$

$$s = \mathbf{12,000 \ ft}$$

3. $2y - x = 5$
(10)

$$2y = x + 5$$

$$y = \frac{1}{2}x + \frac{5}{2}$$

Perpendicular lines have slopes that are negative reciprocals of each other.

$$y = -2x + b$$
$$4 = -2(-3) + b$$
$$b = 4 - 6$$
$$b = -2$$
$$\mathbf{y = -2x - 2}$$

4.
(14)

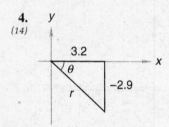

$$r = \sqrt{(3.2)^2 + (2.9)^2} = 4.32$$

$$\tan \theta = \frac{2.9}{3.2}$$

$$\theta = 42.18°$$

The polar angle is $360° - 42.18° = 317.82°$.

$4.32\underline{/317.82°}$; $4.32\underline{/-42.18°}$
$-4.32\underline{/137.82°}$; $-4.32\underline{/-222.18°}$

5.
(14)

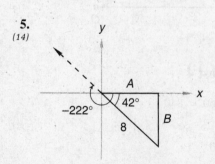

$$A = 8 \cos 42° = 5.95$$

$$B = 8 \sin 42° = 5.35$$

$$\mathbf{5.95\hat{i} - 5.35\hat{j}}$$

6. $\left(5x^{3/2} - 3y^{7/2}\right)\left(5x^{3/2} + 3y^{7/2}\right)$
(5)

$$= \left(5x^{3/2}\right)^2 - \left(3y^{7/2}\right)^2 = \mathbf{25x^3 - 9y^7}$$

7. (a) $\begin{cases} \dfrac{1}{4}y - \dfrac{1}{2}z = \dfrac{1}{2} \\ (b) \ \ 0.5x - 0.5y = -1 \\ (c) \ \ \dfrac{1}{3}x - z = -1 \end{cases}$
(6)

$$\begin{array}{r} 2(b) \quad x - y \qquad\quad = -2 \\ -3(c) \ \underline{\ -x \qquad + 3z = \ 3} \\ (d) \qquad -y + 3z = \ 1 \end{array}$$

$$\begin{array}{r} (d) \ -y + 3z = 1 \\ 4(a) \ \underline{\ \ y - 2z = 2} \\ z = \mathbf{3} \end{array}$$

$$\begin{array}{r} 4(a) \quad y - 2z = 2 \\ y - 2(3) = 2 \\ y = \mathbf{8} \end{array}$$

$$\begin{array}{r} 2(b) \quad x - y = -2 \\ x - (8) = -2 \\ x = \mathbf{6} \end{array}$$

8.
(16)
$$a = n\left(\frac{br}{g} - \frac{d}{p}\right)$$

$$a = \frac{brn}{g} - \frac{nd}{p}$$

$$a = \frac{brnp - gnd}{gp}$$

$$agp = brnp - gnd$$

$$agp + gnd = brnp$$

$$g(ap + nd) = brnp$$

$$\mathbf{g = \frac{brnp}{ap + nd}}$$

9. $\dfrac{3 + 7\sqrt{3}}{3\sqrt{3} + 5} = \dfrac{3 + 7\sqrt{3}}{3\sqrt{3} + 5} \cdot \dfrac{3\sqrt{3} - 5}{3\sqrt{3} - 5}$
(10)

$$= \frac{9\sqrt{3} - 15 + 21(3) - 35\sqrt{3}}{9(3) - 15\sqrt{3} + 15\sqrt{3} - 25}$$

$$= \frac{48 - 26\sqrt{3}}{2} = \mathbf{24 - 13\sqrt{3}}$$

10. $\dfrac{m^{-5}n^6 - n^4m^{-4}}{m^{-3}n^2} = \dfrac{m^{-5}n^6}{m^{-3}n^2} - \dfrac{n^4m^{-4}}{m^{-3}n^2}$
(5)

$$= \frac{m^3n^6}{m^5n^2} - \frac{m^3n^4}{m^4n^2} = \frac{n^4}{m^2} - \frac{n^2}{m}$$

$$= \frac{n^4 - n^2m}{m^2}$$

11.
(15)

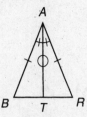

STATEMENTS	REASONS
1. $\overline{BA} \cong \overline{RA}$	1. Given
2. $\overline{AT}$ bisects $\angle BAR$	2. Given
3. $\angle BAT \cong \angle RAT$	3. A bisector divides an angle into two congruent angles.
4. $\overline{AT} \cong \overline{AT}$	4. Reflexive axiom
5. $\triangle BAT \cong \triangle RAT$	5. *SAS* congruency postulate
6. $\overline{BT} \cong \overline{RT}$	6. *CPCTC*

12.
(8)

$$\frac{5}{4} = \frac{x}{8}$$

$$4x = 40$$

$$x = \mathbf{10}$$

13.
(3)

$$\frac{6}{a} = \frac{a}{13}$$

$$a^2 = 78$$

$$a = \mathbf{\sqrt{78}}$$

$$h^2 = \left(\sqrt{78}\right)^2 - 6^2$$

$$h = \sqrt{78 - 36}$$

$$h = \mathbf{\sqrt{42}}$$

$$b^2 = 7^2 + \left(\sqrt{42}\right)^2$$

$$b = \sqrt{49 + 42}$$

$$b = \mathbf{\sqrt{91}}$$

14.
(5)

$$\sqrt{3}\sqrt{5}\sqrt{-3}\sqrt{-5} - \sqrt{3}\sqrt{5}i\sqrt{3}\sqrt{5}i^3 - \sqrt{-36}$$

$$= \sqrt{3}\sqrt{3}\sqrt{5}\sqrt{5}i^2 - \sqrt{3}\sqrt{3}\sqrt{5}\sqrt{5}i^4 - 6i$$

$$= (3)(5)(-1) - (3)(5)(-1)(-1) - 6i = \mathbf{-30 - 6i}$$

15. $x = \dfrac{130 + 150}{2} = \mathbf{140}$
(13)

16. $x = \dfrac{40 - 20}{2} = \mathbf{10}$
(13)

17.
(11,13)

$$3 \cdot x = 6 \cdot 2$$

$$3x = 12$$

$$x = \mathbf{4}$$

18.
(13)

$$4(4 + x) = 6(6 + 14)$$

$$16 + 4x = 36 + 84$$

$$4x = 104$$

$$x = \mathbf{26}$$

19. **All mathematicians are engineers.** The argument is
(7) **valid.** Bobby belongs to the set identified by the contrapositive.

20.
(R)

$$\frac{85 + 74 + 91 + 93 + x}{5} = 82$$

$$\frac{343 + x}{5} = 82$$

$$343 + x = 410$$

$$x = \mathbf{67}$$

Test 5

1. (a)
(20)

$$\tan 30° = \frac{1}{\sqrt{3}}$$

$$\frac{\sqrt{3}}{2} \tan 30° = \frac{\sqrt{3}}{2}\left(\frac{1}{\sqrt{3}}\right) = \mathbf{\frac{1}{2}}$$

(b)

$$\cos 60° = \frac{1}{2}$$

$$2\sqrt{3} \cos 60° = 2\sqrt{3}\left(\frac{1}{2}\right) = \mathbf{\sqrt{3}}$$

(c)

$$\sin 45° = \frac{1}{\sqrt{2}}$$

$$\frac{\sqrt{2}}{2} \sin 45° = \frac{\sqrt{2}}{2}\left(\frac{1}{\sqrt{2}}\right) = \mathbf{\frac{1}{2}}$$

2. Glycol$_1$ + glycol$_2$ = total glycol
(18)

$$0.79(P_N) + 0.34(72) = 0.63(P_N + 72)$$

$$0.79P_N + 24.48 = 0.63P_N + 45.36$$

$$0.16P_N = 20.88$$

$$P_N = \mathbf{130.50 \text{ liters}}$$

3.
(17)

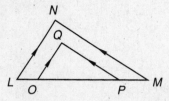

Statements	Reasons
1. $\overline{NL} \parallel \overline{QO}$	1. Given
2. $\angle L \cong \angle QOP$	2. If two parallel lines are cut by a transversal, then each pair of corresponding angles is congruent.
3. $\overline{MN} \parallel \overline{PQ}$	3. Given
4. $\angle M \cong \angle QPO$	4. If two parallel lines are cut by a transversal, then each pair of corresponding angles is congruent.
5. $\angle N \cong \angle Q$	5. $AA \rightarrow AAA$
6. $\triangle LMN \sim \triangle OPQ$	6. AAA

4. (a) $\begin{cases} x^2 + y^2 = 18 \\ y - x = 4 \end{cases}$
(19) (b)

(b) $y - x = 4$

$$y = x + 4$$

(a)
$$x^2 + y^2 = 18$$
$$x^2 + (x + 4)^2 = 18$$
$$x^2 + x^2 + 8x + 16 = 18$$
$$2x^2 + 8x - 2 = 0$$
$$x^2 + 4x - 1 = 0$$

$$x = \frac{-4 \pm \sqrt{4^2 - 4(1)(-1)}}{2(1)} = \frac{-4 \pm \sqrt{20}}{2} = -2 \pm \sqrt{5}$$

For $x = -2 + \sqrt{5}$

(b)
$$y - x = 4$$
$$y - (-2 + \sqrt{5}) = 4$$
$$y = 2 + \sqrt{5}$$

For $x = -2 - \sqrt{5}$

(b)
$$y - x = 4$$
$$y - (-2 - \sqrt{5}) = 4$$
$$y = 2 - \sqrt{5}$$

$$(-2 + \sqrt{5}, \ 2 + \sqrt{5}), (-2 - \sqrt{5}, \ 2 - \sqrt{5})$$

5.
(16)

$$\begin{array}{r} x^2 - x - 4 \\ x - 4 \overline{)x^3 - 5x^2 + 0x + 9} \\ \underline{x^3 - 4x^2} \\ -x^2 + 0x \\ \underline{-x^2 + 4x} \\ -4x + 9 \\ \underline{-4x + 16} \\ -7 \end{array}$$

$$\frac{x^3 - 5x^2 + 9}{x - 4} = x^2 - x - 4 - \frac{7}{x - 4}$$

6. $72x^3z^{12} - 9y^9$
(19)
$$= 9(8x^3z^{12} - y^9)$$
$$= 9\left[(2xz^4)^3 - (y^3)^3\right]$$
$$= 9(2xz^4 - y^3)(4x^2z^8 + 2xy^3z^4 + y^6)$$

7. $10x^{5n+3} - 25x^{7n+5} = 2(5x^{5n}x^3) - 5^2x^{7n}x^5$
(19)
$$= 5x^{5n}x^3(2 - 5x^{2n}x^2) = 5x^{5n+3}(2 - 5x^{2n+2})$$

8. $\dfrac{3i^2 - 2i^3 + i^4}{2 + 2i + \sqrt{-36}} = \dfrac{3(-1) - 2i(-1) + (-1)(-1)}{2 + 2i + 6i}$
(10)

$$= \frac{-2 + 2i}{2 + 8i} \cdot \frac{2 - 8i}{2 - 8i} = \frac{-4 + 4i + 16i - 16i^2}{4 - 64i^2}$$

$$= \frac{-4 + 20i - 16(-1)}{4 - 64(-1)} = \frac{12 + 20i}{68} = \frac{3}{17} + \frac{5}{17}i$$

9. $W = \dfrac{kY^3}{P}$
(18)

$$250 = \frac{k(5)^3}{8}$$
$$k = 16$$

$$W = \frac{16Y^3}{P} = \frac{16(7)^3}{4} = \textbf{1372 whites}$$

10. $\dfrac{\dfrac{m}{\dfrac{m}{y} + x} + m}{ } = \dfrac{\dfrac{m}{\dfrac{m + xy}{y}} + m}{ } = \dfrac{\dfrac{m}{\dfrac{my}{m + xy}} + m}{ }$
(16)

$$= \frac{m}{\dfrac{my + m(m + xy)}{m + xy}} = \frac{m(m + xy)}{my + m^2 + mxy}$$

$$= \frac{m(m + xy)}{m(y + m + xy)} = \frac{m + xy}{y + m + xy}$$

11. $\dfrac{\dfrac{4z}{xy} + \dfrac{2y}{z}}{\dfrac{2z}{x} + \dfrac{x}{y}} \cdot \dfrac{\dfrac{xyz}{1}}{\dfrac{xyz}{1}} = \dfrac{4z^2 + 2xy^2}{2yz^2 + x^2z}$
(16)

12. $(4x^4y^2)^{-2}\left(\dfrac{4x^2y}{xy^2}\right)^2 = \dfrac{16x^4y^2}{16x^8y^4x^2y^4} = \dfrac{1}{x^6y^6}$
(5)

13. (a) $\begin{cases} T + U = 8 \\ 10U + T = 18 + 10T + U \end{cases}$
(18) (b)

(b) $10U + T = 18 + 10T + U$

$$9U - 9T = 18$$
$$U - T = 2$$
$$U = T + 2$$

(a) $T + U = 8$

$T + (T + 2) = 8$

$2T = 6$

$T = 3$

(a) $T + U = 8$

$(3) + U = 8$

$U = 5$

The original number was **35**.

14.
(14)

200 ft h

60°

$\sin 60° = \dfrac{h}{200}$

$h = 200 \sin 60°$

$h = \textbf{173.21 ft}$

15. $OG = MO = 5$
(3)

$r = MG = \sqrt{5^2 + 5^2} = 5\sqrt{2}$

$A_{\text{shaded region}} = A_{\text{circle}} - A_{\text{square}}$

$= \pi r^2 - lw$

$= \pi(5\sqrt{2})^2 - (10)(10)$

$= \mathbf{50\pi - 100 = 57.08}$

16.
(15)

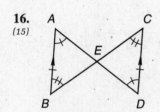

STATEMENTS	REASONS
1. $\overline{AB} \parallel \overline{DC}$	1. Given
2. $\angle A \cong \angle D$ and $\angle B \cong \angle C$	2. If two parallel lines are cut by a transversal, each pair of alternate interior angles is congruent.
3. $\angle AEB \cong \angle DEC$	3. Vertical angles are congruent.
4. $\overline{AB} \cong \overline{DC}$	4. Given
5. $\triangle AEB \cong \triangle DEC$	5. *AAAS* congruency postulate

17. $\dfrac{y^{4m} - x^{4n}}{y^{2m} - x^{2n}} = \dfrac{(y^{2m})^2 - (x^{2n})^2}{y^{2m} - x^{2n}}$
(19)

$= \dfrac{(y^{2m} - x^{2n})(y^{2m} + x^{2n})}{(y^{2m} - x^{2n})}$

$= \mathbf{y^{2m} + x^{2n}}$

18. $x + 2y = 3$
(10)

$2y = -x + 3$

$y = -\dfrac{1}{2}x + \dfrac{3}{2}$

Parallel lines have identical slopes.

$y = -\dfrac{1}{2}x + b$

$(6) = -\dfrac{1}{2}(-2) + b$

$b = 5$

$y = \mathbf{-\dfrac{1}{2}x + 5}$

19. $\dfrac{170 - x}{2} = 60$
(13)

$170 - x = 120$

$x = \mathbf{50}$

20. $4 \cdot x = 8 \cdot 6$
(11,13)

$4x = 48$

$x = \mathbf{12}$

Test 6

1. (a) $\begin{cases} T + U = 15 \\ 10U + T = 27 + 10T + U \end{cases}$
(18)

(b) $10U + T = 27 + 10T + U$

$9U - 9T = 27$

$U - T = 3$

$U = T + 3$

(a) $T + U = 15$

$T + (T + 3) = 15$

$2T = 12$

$T = 6$

(a) $T + U = 15$

$(6) + U = 15$

$U = 9$

The original number was **69**.

2. (a) **Function**
(21)

(b) **Not a function**

(c) **Function**

(d) **Function**

3. (a)
(22)

-2 -1 0 1 2 3 4 5 6 7 8

(b)

-2 -1 0 1 2 3 4 5 6 7 8

4.
(14)

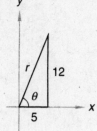

$$r = \sqrt{5^2 + 12^2} = 13$$

$$\tan \theta = \frac{12}{5}$$

$$\theta = 67.38°$$

13$\underline{/67.38°}$; 13$\underline{/-292.62°}$;
−13$\underline{/247.38°}$; −13$\underline{/-112.62°}$

5. $f(x) = x^2 + 2x - 6$
(21)

   (a) $f(-4) = (-4)^2 + 2(-4) - 6 = 16 - 8 - 6 = \mathbf{2}$

   (b) $f(8) = 8^2 + 2(8) - 6 = 64 + 16 - 6 = \mathbf{74}$

6. (a) $125p^3b^6 - 216k^9 = \left(5pb^2\right)^3 - \left(6k^3\right)^3$
(19)
$$= \left(5pb^2 - 6k^3\right)\left(25p^2b^4 + 30pb^2k^3 + 36k^6\right)$$

   (b) $x^{4b} - y^{4c} = \left(x^{2b} - y^{2c}\right)\left(x^{2b} + y^{2c}\right)$
$$= \left(x^b - y^c\right)\left(x^b + y^c\right)\left(x^{2b} + y^{2c}\right)$$

7. $H_{\text{cone}} = \sqrt{\left(5\sqrt{2}\right)^2 - (5)^2} = 5$
(2)
$$V_{\text{solid}} = V_{\text{cone}} + V_{\text{cylinder}} + V_{\text{hemisphere}}$$

$$= \frac{1}{3}\pi(5)^2(5) + \pi(5)^2(8) + \frac{1}{2}\left[\frac{4}{3}\pi(5)^3\right]$$

$$= \frac{125\pi}{3} + 200\pi + \frac{250\pi}{3}$$

$$= \mathbf{325\pi \ cm^3 = 1021.02 \ cm^3}$$

8. (a) $f(x) = \sqrt{x + 5}$
(21)
$$x + 5 \geq 0$$
$$x \geq -5$$

   Domain of $f = \left\{x \in \mathbb{R} \mid x \geq -5\right\}$

   (b) $g(x) = \dfrac{1}{x^2 - 9} = \dfrac{1}{(x + 3)(x - 3)}$

   $(x + 3)(x - 3) \neq 0$
$$x \neq 3, -3$$

   Domain of $g = \left\{x \in \mathbb{R} \mid x \neq 3, -3\right\}$

9.
(14)

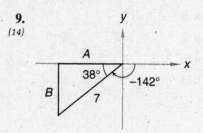

$$A = 7 \cos 38° = 5.52$$
$$B = 7 \sin 38° = 4.31$$
$$\mathbf{-5.52\hat{i} - 4.31\hat{j}}$$

10. $5x^{4n+2} + 15x^{2n+1}$
(19)
$$= 5x^{4n}x^2 + (5)(3)x^{2n}x$$
$$= 5x^{2n}x\left(x^{2n}x + 3\right)$$
$$= \mathbf{5x^{2n+1}\left(x^{2n+1} + 3\right)}$$

11. $y = 7^x$
(23)

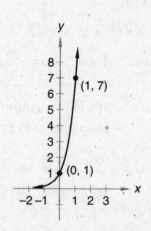

12. $y = \left(\dfrac{1}{9}\right)^x$
(23)

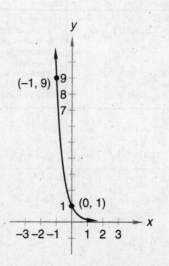

13.
(21)

(a) **Function, 1 to 1**

(b) **Not a function**

(c) **Function, 1 to 1**

(d) **Function, 1 to 1**

14.
(18)

(a) $\begin{cases} N_N + N_D + N_Q = 30 \\ 5N_N + 10N_D + 25N_Q = 425 \\ N_Q = N_D \end{cases}$

(b)

(c)

(a) $N_N + N_D + N_Q = 30$

$N_N + N_D + (N_D) = 30$

$N_N = 30 - 2N_D$

(b) $5N_N + 10N_D + 25N_Q = 425$

$5(30 - 2N_D) + 10N_D + 25(N_D) = 425$

$150 - 10N_D + 10N_D + 25N_D = 425$

$25N_D = 275$

$N_D = 11$

(c) $N_Q = N_D$

$N_Q = 11$

(a) $N_N + N_D + N_Q = 30$

$N_N + (11) + (11) = 30$

$N_N = 8$

15.
(15)

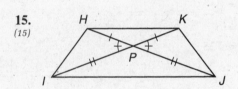

STATEMENTS	REASONS
1. $\overline{HP} \cong \overline{KP}$	1. Given
2. $\overline{IP} \cong \overline{JP}$	2. Given
3. $\angle HPI \cong \angle KPJ$	3. Vertical angles are congruent.
4. $\triangle HPI \cong \triangle KPJ$	4. *SAS* congruency postulate

16.
(19)

(a) $\begin{cases} x^2 + y^2 = 8 \\ x^2 - y^2 = 4 \end{cases}$

(b)

(a) $x^2 + y^2 = 8$

(b) $\dfrac{x^2 - y^2 = 4}{2x^2 \quad\quad = 12}$

$x^2 = 6$

$x = \pm\sqrt{6}$

For $x = \sqrt{6}$

(a) $x^2 + y^2 = 8$

$(\sqrt{6})^2 + y^2 = 8$

$6 + y^2 = 8$

$y^2 = 2$

$y = \pm\sqrt{2}$

For $x = -\sqrt{6}$

(a) $x^2 + y^2 = 8$

$(-\sqrt{6})^2 + y^2 = 8$

$6 + y^2 = 8$

$y^2 = 2$

$y = \pm\sqrt{2}$

$(\sqrt{6}, \sqrt{2}), (\sqrt{6}, -\sqrt{2}), (-\sqrt{6}, \sqrt{2}), (-\sqrt{6}, -\sqrt{2})$

17.
(5)

$(a - b)(a^{-1}b + ab^{-1})^{-1} = \dfrac{(a - b)}{\dfrac{b}{a} + \dfrac{a}{b}}$

$= \dfrac{a - b}{\dfrac{b^2 + a^2}{ab}} = \dfrac{(a - b)ab}{b^2 + a^2}$

18.
(24)

$\tan 30° = \dfrac{1}{\sqrt{3}}$

$\sin 60° = \dfrac{\sqrt{3}}{2}$

$\cos 45° = \dfrac{1}{\sqrt{2}}$

$\dfrac{\sqrt{3}}{2} \tan 30° + \sqrt{3} \sin 60° - \sqrt{2} \cos 45°$

$= \dfrac{\sqrt{3}}{2}\left(\dfrac{1}{\sqrt{3}}\right) + \sqrt{3}\left(\dfrac{\sqrt{3}}{2}\right) - \sqrt{2}\left(\dfrac{1}{\sqrt{2}}\right)$

$= \dfrac{1}{2} + \dfrac{3}{2} - 1 = 1$

19.
(2)

$V_{\text{sphere}} = \dfrac{4}{3}\pi r^3$

$288\pi = \dfrac{4}{3}\pi r^3$

$r^3 = 216$

$r = 6 \text{ ft}$

$A_{\text{sphere}} = 4\pi r^2 = 4\pi(6)^2 = 144\pi \text{ ft}^2 = 452.39 \text{ ft}^2$

20.
(18)

$0.45(89) = 0.40(P_N + 89)$

$40.05 = 0.40P_N + 35.60$

$0.40P_N = 4.45$

$P_N = 11.13 \text{ liters}$

Test 7

1.
(24)

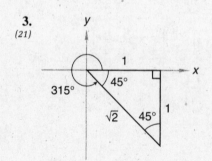

$$\sin 45° = \frac{1}{\sqrt{2}}$$

$$\cos 60° = \frac{1}{2}$$

$$\tan 30° = \frac{1}{\sqrt{3}}$$

$$\frac{1}{\sqrt{2}} \sin 45° + 4 \cos 60° - \frac{\sqrt{3}}{2} \tan 30°$$

$$= \frac{1}{\sqrt{2}} \left(\frac{1}{\sqrt{2}} \right) + 4 \left(\frac{1}{2} \right) - \frac{\sqrt{3}}{2} \left(\frac{1}{\sqrt{3}} \right)$$

$$= \frac{1}{2} + 2 - \frac{1}{2} = \mathbf{2}$$

2.
(21)
$$f(x) = \frac{\sqrt{x - 10}}{x^2 - x - 6} = \frac{\sqrt{x - 10}}{(x + 2)(x - 3)}$$

$$(x + 2)(x - 3) \neq 0$$

$$x \neq -2, 3$$

$$x - 10 \geq 0$$

$$x \geq 10$$

Domain of $f = \left\{ x \in \mathbb{R} \mid x \geq \mathbf{10} \right\}$

3.
(21)

$$f(315°) = 6 \sin (315°)$$

$$= 6 \left(-\frac{1}{\sqrt{2}} \right) = -\frac{6}{\sqrt{2}} = \mathbf{-3\sqrt{2}}$$

4.
(28)
$$\frac{10!}{4!6!} = \frac{10 \cdot 9 \cdot 8 \cdot 7 \cdot 6!}{4 \cdot 3 \cdot 2 \cdot 1 \cdot 6!} = \mathbf{210}$$

5.
(21)
$$f(x) = x^2 + x$$

$$f(x - h) = (x - h)^2 + (x - h)$$

$$= \mathbf{x^2 - 2xh + h^2 + x - h}$$

6.
(25)
(a) $\begin{cases} A_N - 5 = 2(J_N - 5) \\ J_N + 15 = A_N - 10 \end{cases}$
(b)

(b) $J_N + 15 = A_N - 10$

$$A_N = J_N + 25$$

(a) $\qquad A_N - 5 = 2(J_N - 5)$

$$(J_N + 25) - 5 = 2J_N - 10$$

$$J_N = \mathbf{30}$$

7.
(26)
(a) $\log_x 4 = \frac{1}{2}$

$$x^{1/2} = 4$$

$$x = \mathbf{16}$$

(b) $\log_4 \frac{1}{64} = x$

$$4^x = \frac{1}{64}$$

$$4^x = \frac{1}{4^3}$$

$$4^x = 4^{-3}$$

$$x = \mathbf{-3}$$

(c) $\log_5 x = 3$

$$x = 5^3$$

$$x = \mathbf{125}$$

8.
(16)
$$3q = \frac{5}{6s} \left(\frac{3z}{t} + \frac{5m}{p} \right)$$

$$3q = \frac{15z}{6st} + \frac{25m}{6sp}$$

$$3q = \frac{15pz + 25mt}{6pst}$$

$$18pstq = 15pz + 25mt$$

$$p(18stq - 15z) = 25mt$$

$$p = \frac{\mathbf{25mt}}{\mathbf{18stq - 15z}}$$

9.
(5,10)
$$\frac{\sqrt{5}\sqrt{-5} - \sqrt{-36} + \sqrt{16}\sqrt{-16}\sqrt{-16}}{3 + 4i^3}$$

$$= \frac{5i - 6i + 64i^2}{3 + 4i^3} = \frac{-64 - i}{3 - 4i}$$

$$= \frac{-64 - i}{3 - 4i} \cdot \frac{3 + 4i}{3 + 4i} = \frac{-192 - 256i - 3i - 4i^2}{9 - 16i^2}$$

$$= \frac{-188 - 259i}{25} = \mathbf{-\frac{188}{25} - \frac{259}{25}i}$$

10. $y = \dfrac{1}{x - 3}$
(22)

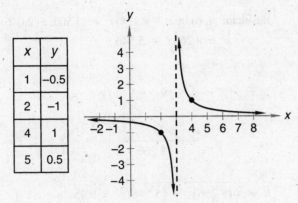

x	y
1	-0.5
2	-1
4	1
5	0.5

14. $A = \dfrac{kB^2}{W}$
(18)

$60 = \dfrac{k(4)^2}{(8)}$

$k = 30$

$A = \dfrac{30B^2}{W} = \dfrac{30(6)^2}{3} = \mathbf{360\ apples}$

15. $4x^{3n+1} - 32x^{5n+3} = 2^2x^{3n}x - 2^5x^{5n}x^3$
(19)

$= 2^2x^{3n}x\left(1 - 2^3x^{2n}x^2\right) = 4x^{3n+1}\left(1 - 8x^{2n+2}\right)$

16. $216a^3b^9 - 64c^6d^9$
(19)

$= \left(6ab^3\right)^3 - \left(4c^2d^3\right)^3$

$= (6ab^3 - 4c^2d^3)(36a^2b^6 + 24ab^3c^2d^3 + 16c^4d^6)$

17. (a) **Not a function**
(21)

(b) **Function, not 1 to 1**

(c) **Function, not 1 to 1**

(d) **Function, 1 to 1**

11. $R_JT_J + R_MT_M = 1\ \text{lawn}$
(25)

$\left(\dfrac{1}{40}\dfrac{\text{lawn}}{\text{min}}\right)(T + 10\ \text{min}) + \left(\dfrac{1}{20}\dfrac{\text{lawn}}{\text{min}}\right)T = 1\ \text{lawn}$

$\left(\dfrac{1}{40}\dfrac{\text{lawn}}{\text{min}}\right)T + \dfrac{1}{4}\ \text{lawn} + \left(\dfrac{1}{20}\dfrac{\text{lawn}}{\text{min}}\right)T = 1\ \text{lawn}$

$\left(\dfrac{3}{40}\dfrac{\text{lawn}}{\text{min}}\right)T = \dfrac{3}{4}\ \text{lawn}$

$T = \mathbf{10\ min}$

18. $\dfrac{y^{c+5}\left(\sqrt{x^8}\right)^{3c}}{x^{3c-6}} = \dfrac{y^{c+5}\left(x^4\right)^{3c}}{x^{3c-6}}$
(5)

$= y^{c+5}x^{12c}x^{-3c+6} = \mathbf{x^{9c+6}y^{c+5}}$

12.
(15)

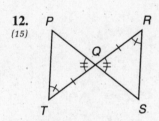

STATEMENTS	REASONS
1. Q is the midpoint of $\overline{RT}$	1. Given
2. $\overline{RQ} \cong \overline{TQ}$	2. A midpoint divides a segment into two congruent segments.
3. $\angle R \cong \angle T$	3. Given
4. $\angle PQT \cong \angle SQR$	4. Vertical angles are congruent.
5. $\angle P \cong \angle S$	5. If two angles in one triangle are congruent to two angles in a second triangle, then the third angles are congruent.
6. $\triangle PTQ \cong \triangle SRQ$	6. AAAS congruency postulate
7. $\overline{PT} \cong \overline{SR}$	7. CPCTC

19. (a) $(fg)(x) = 3x^2(3 - x) = 9x^2 - 3x^3$
(24)

$(fg)(5) = 9(5)^2 - 3(5)^3 = 225 - 375 = \mathbf{-150}$

(b) $(f/g)(x) = \dfrac{3x^2}{3 - x}$

$(f/g)(5) = \dfrac{3(5)^2}{3 - 5} = \mathbf{-\dfrac{75}{2}}$

(c) $(f \circ g)(x) = 3(3 - x)^2 = 27 - 18x + 3x^2$

$(f \circ g)(5) = 27 - 18(5) + 3(5)^2$

$= 27 - 90 + 75 = \mathbf{12}$

13. $RWT = J$
(25)

$R(10)(3) = 2$

$R = \dfrac{2}{30}\ \dfrac{\text{sports car}}{\text{man-day}}$

$RWT = J$

$\left(\dfrac{2}{30}\right)(10 + 5)T = 9$

$T = \mathbf{9\ days}$

20. Distance $= d$ m, rate $= s\ \dfrac{\text{m}}{\text{min}}$, time $= \dfrac{d}{s}$ min
(28)

New distance $= d$ m

New time $= \left(\dfrac{d}{s} - 9\right) = \dfrac{d - 9s}{s}$ min

New rate $= \dfrac{d}{\dfrac{d - 9s}{s}} = \dfrac{ds}{d - 9s}\ \dfrac{\text{m}}{\text{min}}$

Test 8

1. Rate $= n \dfrac{\text{mi}}{\text{hr}}$, time $= t$ hr, distance $= nt$ mi
(28)

New distance $= (nt + 30)$ mi

New rate $= (n + 15) \dfrac{\text{mi}}{\text{hr}}$

New time $= \dfrac{nt + 30 \text{ mi}}{n + 15 \dfrac{\text{mi}}{\text{hr}}} = \dfrac{nt + 30}{n + 15}$ **hr**

2. $\dfrac{7!}{4!3!} = \dfrac{7 \cdot 6 \cdot 5 \cdot 4!}{3 \cdot 2 \cdot 1 \cdot 4!} = \mathbf{35}$
(28)

3. $f(x) = \dfrac{\sqrt{x - 12}}{x^2 - 2x - 24} = \dfrac{\sqrt{x - 12}}{(x - 6)(x + 4)}$
(21)

$(x - 6)(x + 4) \neq 0$

$\qquad x \neq -4, 6$

$x - 12 \geq 0$

$\qquad x \geq 12$

Domain of $f = \left\{ x \in \mathbb{R} \mid x \geq 12 \right\}$

4.
(24,29)

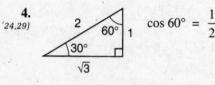

$\cos 60° = \dfrac{1}{2}$

$\sin 330° = -\dfrac{1}{2}$

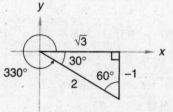

$\cos 90° + \sin 330° + \sin 90° + \cos 60°$

$= 0 + \left(-\dfrac{1}{2}\right) + (1) + \left(\dfrac{1}{2}\right) = \mathbf{1}$

5.
(30)

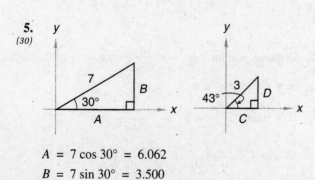

$A = 7 \cos 30° = 6.062$

$B = 7 \sin 30° = 3.500$

$C = 3 \cos 43° = 2.194$

$D = 3 \sin 43° = 2.046$

Resultant $= (6.062 + 2.194)\,\hat{i} + (3.500 + 2.046)\,\hat{j}$

$\qquad\qquad = 8.256\,\hat{i} + 5.546\,\hat{j}$

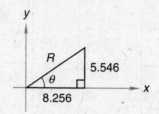

$R = \sqrt{(8.256)^2 + (5.546)^2} = 9.95$

$\tan \theta = \dfrac{5.546}{8.256}$

$\qquad \theta = 33.89°$

9.95 / 33.89°

6. $N, N + 1, N + 2$
(7)

$N(N + 1) + 37 = (N + 2)^2$

$N^2 + N + 37 = N^2 + 4N + 4$

$\qquad\qquad 3N = 33$

$\qquad\qquad\ N = 11$

11, 12, 13

7. (a) $y = x^2$
(22)

x	y
-2	4
-1	1
1	1
2	4

(b) $y = \dfrac{1}{x^2}$

x	y
-2	$\frac{1}{4}$
-1	1
1	1
2	$\frac{1}{4}$

8. (a)
(32)

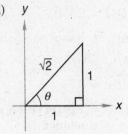

$$-90° \leq \theta \leq 90°$$

$$\text{Arcsin } \frac{1}{\sqrt{2}} = \mathbf{45°}$$

(b)

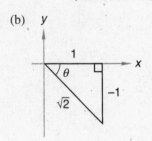

$$-90° \leq \theta \leq 90°$$

$$\text{Arcsin } \left(-\frac{1}{\sqrt{2}}\right) = \mathbf{-45°}$$

9. Replace $f(x)$ with $-g(x)$
(31)

$$-g(x) = |x|$$
$$\mathbf{g(x) = -|x|}$$

10. $3a^{7n+4} - 81a^{3n+4} = 3a^{7n}a^4 - 3^4 a^{3n}a^4$
(19)
$$= 3a^{3n}a^4(a^{4n} - 3^3) = \mathbf{3a^{3n+4}(a^{4n} - 27)}$$

11.
(16)
$$\frac{1}{\frac{4x}{\frac{2}{a}+3} + 2b} = \frac{1}{\frac{4x}{\frac{2+3a}{a}} + 2b} = \frac{1}{\frac{4ax}{2+3a} + 2b}$$

$$= \frac{1}{\frac{4ax + 2b(2+3a)}{2+3a}} = \mathbf{\frac{2+3a}{4ax + 4b + 6ab}}$$

12. (a) $\log_x 121 = 2$
(26)
$$x^2 = 121$$
$$x = \mathbf{11}$$

(b) $\log_4 \frac{1}{256} = x$

$$4^x = \frac{1}{256}$$
$$4^x = \frac{1}{4^4}$$
$$4^x = 4^{-4}$$
$$x = \mathbf{-4}$$

(c) $\log_{1/3} x = 5$

$$x = \left(\frac{1}{3}\right)^5$$

$$x = \mathbf{\frac{1}{243}}$$

13. (a) $\begin{cases} J_N = A_N + 7 \\ \frac{1}{2}J_N = A_N - 12 \end{cases}$
(25) (b)

(a) $\quad J_N = A_N + 7$
$$A_N = J_N - 7$$

(b) $\frac{1}{2}J_N = A_N - 12$

$$\frac{1}{2}J_N = (J_N - 7) - 12$$

$$\frac{1}{2}J_N = 19$$

$$J_N = \mathbf{38}$$

14.
(15)

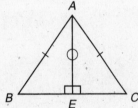

STATEMENTS	REASONS
1. $\overline{AE} \perp \overline{BC}$	1. Given
2. $\angle AEB$ and $\angle AEC$ are right angles.	2. Perpendicular lines intersect to form right angles.
3. $\triangle AEB$ and $\triangle AEC$ are right triangles.	3. A triangle which contains a right angle is a right triangle.
4. $\overline{AB} \cong \overline{AC}$	4. Given
5. $\overline{AE} \cong \overline{AE}$	5. Reflexive axiom
6. $\triangle AEB \cong \triangle AEC$	6. HL congruency postulate

15.
(5)
$$\frac{(\sqrt{h})^{2b+4} h^{3+2b}}{h^{b+1}} = \frac{(h^{1/2})^{2b+4} h^{3+2b}}{h^{b+1}}$$

$$= \frac{h^{b+2} h^{3+2b}}{h^{b+1}} = h^{b+2} h^{3+2b} h^{-b-1} = \mathbf{h^{2b+4}}$$

16. $y = 5x + 4$
(32)
$$5x = y - 4$$

$$x = \frac{1}{5}y - \frac{4}{5}$$

Interchange x and y.

$$y = \mathbf{\frac{1}{5}x - \frac{4}{5}}$$

17. (a) $\begin{cases} y^2 + x^2 = 4 \\ 3x - y = -2 \end{cases}$
(19)

(b) $3x - y = -2$

$\quad y = 3x + 2$

(a) $\qquad y^2 + x^2 = 4$

$(3x + 2)^2 + x^2 = 4$

$9x^2 + 12x + 4 + x^2 = 4$

$\qquad 10x^2 + 12x = 0$

$\qquad x^2 + \dfrac{6}{5}x = 0$

$\qquad x\left(x + \dfrac{6}{5}\right) = 0$

$\qquad x = 0, -\dfrac{6}{5}$

For $x = 0$

(b) $\quad 3x - y = -2$

$\quad 3(0) - y = -2$

$\qquad y = 2$

For $x = -\dfrac{6}{5}$

(b) $\quad 3x - y = -2$

$\quad 3\left(-\dfrac{6}{5}\right) - y = -2$

$\quad -\dfrac{18}{5} - y = -2$

$\qquad y = -\dfrac{8}{5}$

$\left(0, 2\right), \left(-\dfrac{6}{5}, -\dfrac{8}{5}\right)$

18. $\dfrac{\sqrt{4}\sqrt{-4}\sqrt{3}\sqrt{-3} - \sqrt{-36} + \sqrt{-4}\sqrt{4}}{1 + \sqrt{-9}\, i^3}$
(5,10)

$= \dfrac{12i^2 - 6i + 4i}{1 + 3i^4} = \dfrac{-12 - 2i}{4} = \mathbf{-3 - \dfrac{1}{2}i}$

19. $f(x) = x^2 - 2x + 7$
(21)

$f(x + h) - f(x)$

$= (x + h)^2 - 2(x + h) + 7 - \left(x^2 - 2x + 7\right)$

$= x^2 + 2xh + h^2 - 2x - 2h + 7 - x^2 + 2x - 7$

$= \mathbf{h^2 + 2xh - 2h}$

20. (a) $\begin{cases} 0.2(P_N) + 0.6(D_N) = 0.4(4) \\ P_N + D_N = 4 \end{cases}$
(18)

(b) $P_N + D_N = 4$

$\qquad P_N = 4 - D_N$

(a) $\quad 0.2(P_N) + 0.6(D_N) = 0.4(4)$

$0.2(4 - D_N) + 0.6D_N = 1.6$

$0.8 - 0.2D_N + 0.6D_N = 1.6$

$\qquad 0.4D_N = 0.8$

$\qquad D_N = \textbf{2 gal of 60\% benzene}$
$\qquad\qquad\qquad \textbf{solution}$

$P_N = 4 - D_N$

$P_N = 4 - (2)$

$P_N = \textbf{2 gal of 20\% benzene solution}$

Test 9

1. (a) $\begin{cases} (H + W)T_D = D_D \\ (H - W)T_U = D_U \end{cases}$
(36) (b)

$H = 5W,\ T_U = T_D + 2$

(a) $\quad (H + W)T_D = D_D$

$[(5W) + W]T_D = 600$

$\qquad 6WT_D = 600$

$\qquad WT_D = 100$

(b) $\qquad (H - W)T_U = D_U$

$[(5W) - W](T_D + 2) = 800$

$\qquad 4W(T_D + 2) = 800$

$\qquad 4WT_D + 8W = 800$

$\qquad 4(100) + 8W = 800$

$\qquad 8W = 400$

$\qquad W = 50$

$H = 5W = 5(50) = \textbf{250 mph}$

2. Number $= -2\dfrac{2}{5} + \dfrac{3}{5}(\Delta C)$
(35)

$= -2\dfrac{2}{5} + \dfrac{3}{5}\left[6\dfrac{4}{5} - \left(-2\dfrac{2}{5}\right)\right]$

$= -2\dfrac{2}{5} + \dfrac{3}{5}\left(\dfrac{46}{5}\right)$

$= -\dfrac{60}{25} + \dfrac{138}{25} = \dfrac{\mathbf{78}}{\mathbf{25}}$

3.
(30)

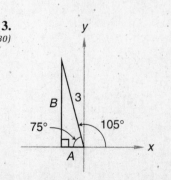

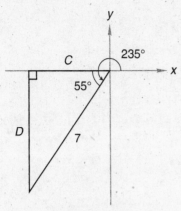

$A = 3 \cos 75° = 0.776$

$B = 3 \sin 75° = 2.898$

$C = 7 \cos 55° = 4.015$

$D = 7 \sin 55° = 5.734$

Resultant $= (-0.776 - 4.015)\hat{i} + (2.898 - 5.734)\hat{j}$
$= -4.791\hat{i} - 2.836\hat{j}$

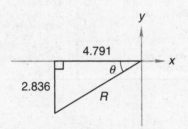

$R = \sqrt{(4.791)^2 + (2.836)^2} = 5.57$

$\tan \theta = \dfrac{2.836}{4.791}$

$\theta = 30.62°$

The polar angle is measured from the positive x axis and is $180° + 30.62° = 210.62°$.

Resultant $= 5.57\underline{/210.62°}$

Equilibrant $= \mathbf{5.57\underline{/30.62°}}$

4. $A_1 = L \times W$
(5)

$A_2 = (L + 0.2L)(W - 0.1W)$

$= LW - 0.1LW + 0.2LW - 0.02LW$

$= LW + 0.08LW$

The area increases by 8%.

5. $\dfrac{12!}{5!7!} = \dfrac{12 \cdot 11 \cdot 10 \cdot 9 \cdot 8 \cdot 7!}{5 \cdot 4 \cdot 3 \cdot 2 \cdot 1 \cdot 7!} = \mathbf{792}$
(28)

6. $\displaystyle\sum_{j=0}^{2} \dfrac{4^j}{4 + j} = \dfrac{4^0}{4 + 0} + \dfrac{4^1}{4 + 1} + \dfrac{4^2}{4 + 2}$
(34)

$= \dfrac{1}{4} + \dfrac{4}{5} + \dfrac{16}{6} = \dfrac{\mathbf{223}}{\mathbf{60}}$

7. $f(x) = \dfrac{1}{x}$
(21)

$f(x + h) - f(x) = \dfrac{1}{x + h} - \dfrac{1}{x}$

$= \dfrac{x - (x + h)}{x(x + h)} = -\dfrac{h}{x(x + h)}$

8. $24x^3y^9 - 81a^6b^{15}$
(19)

$= 3\left(8x^3y^9 - 27a^6b^{15}\right)$

$= 3\left[\left(2xy^3\right)^3 - \left(3a^2b^5\right)^3\right]$

$= \mathbf{3\left(2xy^3 - 3a^2b^5\right)\left(4x^2y^6 + 6xy^3a^2b^5 + 9a^4b^{10}\right)}$

9. $f(480°) + k(390°) = \sin 480° + \tan 390°$
(24,36)

$= \sin 60° + \tan 30° = \dfrac{\sqrt{3}}{2} + \dfrac{1}{\sqrt{3}} = \dfrac{\mathbf{5\sqrt{3}}}{\mathbf{6}}$

10. (a)
(32)

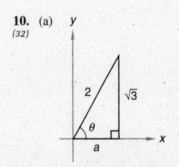

$-90° \le \theta \le 90°$

$a = \sqrt{2^2 - \left(\sqrt{3}\right)^2} = 1$

$\cos\left(\text{Arcsin } \dfrac{\sqrt{3}}{2}\right) = \dfrac{\mathbf{1}}{\mathbf{2}}$

(b)

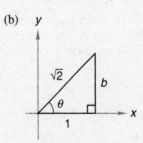

$0° \le \theta \le 180°$

$b = \sqrt{\left(\sqrt{2}\right)^2 - (1)^2} = 1$

$\tan\left(\text{Arccos } \dfrac{1}{\sqrt{2}}\right) = \mathbf{1}$

11.
(34) Choose two ordered pairs from the graph of the line: (45, 6) and (120, 24).

$$m = \frac{24 - 6}{120 - 45} = \frac{18}{75} = \frac{6}{25}$$

$$C = \frac{6}{25}Z + b$$

$$6 = \frac{6}{25}(45) + b$$

$$b = -\frac{24}{5}$$

$$C = \frac{6}{25}Z - \frac{24}{5}$$

12.
(28) Distance $= s$ ft, rate $= y\ \dfrac{\text{ft}}{\text{min}}$, time $= \dfrac{s}{y}$ min

New distance $= s$ ft

New time $= \left(\dfrac{s}{y} - 10\right) = \dfrac{s - 10y}{y}$ min

New rate $= \dfrac{s}{\dfrac{s - 10y}{y}} = \dfrac{sy}{s - 10y}\ \dfrac{\text{ft}}{\text{min}}$

13.
(25)
$$RWT = A$$
$$R(6)(2) = 24$$
$$R = 2\ \frac{\text{articles}}{\text{reporter-day}}$$

$$RWT = A$$
$$(2)(12)T = 120$$
$$T = \textbf{5 days}$$

14.
(25)
$$R_O T_O + R_D T_D = 32 \text{ lines}$$
$$\left(\frac{8}{10}\frac{\text{line}}{\text{min}}\right)T + \left(\frac{12}{15}\frac{\text{line}}{\text{min}}\right)T = 32 \text{ lines}$$
$$\left(\frac{8}{5}\frac{\text{lines}}{\text{min}}\right)T = 32 \text{ lines}$$
$$T = \textbf{20 min}$$

15.
(21)
$$f(x) = \frac{\sqrt{x-8}}{x^2 - 6x - 16} = \frac{\sqrt{x-8}}{(x-8)(x+2)}$$

$$(x-8)(x+2) \neq 0$$
$$x \neq -2, 8$$

$$x - 8 \geq 0$$
$$x \geq 8$$

Domain of $f = \left\{x \in \mathbb{R} \mid x > 8\right\}$

16.
(32)
$$y = \frac{11}{12}x - \frac{1}{4}$$
$$\frac{11}{12}x = y + \frac{1}{4}$$
$$x = \frac{12}{11}y + \frac{3}{11}$$

Interchange x and y.

$$y = \frac{12}{11}x + \frac{3}{11}$$

17.
(30)

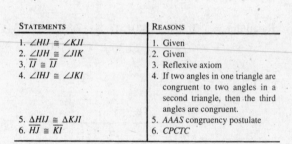

STATEMENTS	REASONS
1. $\angle HIJ \cong \angle KJI$	1. Given
2. $\angle IJH \cong \angle JIK$	2. Given
3. $\overline{IJ} \cong \overline{IJ}$	3. Reflexive axiom
4. $\angle IHJ \cong \angle JKI$	4. If two angles in one triangle are congruent to two angles in a second triangle, then the third angles are congruent.
5. $\triangle HIJ \cong \triangle KJI$	5. *AAAS* congruency postulate
6. $\overline{HJ} \cong \overline{KI}$	6. *CPCTC*

18.
(26) (a) $\log_x \dfrac{125}{216} = 3$

$$x^3 = \frac{125}{216}$$
$$x^3 = \frac{5^3}{6^3}$$
$$x^3 = \left(\frac{5}{6}\right)^3$$
$$x = \frac{\textbf{5}}{\textbf{6}}$$

(b) $\log_2 \dfrac{1}{8} = x$

$$2^x = \frac{1}{8}$$
$$2^x = \frac{1}{2^3}$$
$$2^x = 2^{-3}$$
$$x = \textbf{-3}$$

(c) $\log_{1/4} x = -3$

$$x = \left(\frac{1}{4}\right)^{-3}$$
$$x = 4^3$$
$$x = \textbf{64}$$

19. Replace $f(x)$ with $-g(x)$
(31)

$$-g(x) = \frac{1}{\sqrt{x}}$$

$$g(x) = -\frac{1}{\sqrt{x}}$$

20. $\quad EF = \frac{1}{2}\left(\text{base}_1 + \text{base}_2\right)$
(33)

$$3x + 9 = \frac{1}{2}\left[(6x - 1) + (2x - 3)\right]$$

$$3x + 9 = 4x - 2$$

$$x = 11$$

Test 10

1. Overall average rate $= \dfrac{\text{overall distance}}{\text{overall time}}$
(38)

$$3\,\frac{\text{mi}}{\text{hr}} = \frac{16\,\text{mi} + 8\,\text{mi} + 6\,\text{mi}}{\text{overall time}}$$

$$3\,\frac{\text{mi}}{\text{hr}} = \frac{30\,\text{mi}}{\text{overall time}}$$

Overall time $= 10\,\text{hr}$

$$\text{Time}_1 = \frac{16\,\text{mi}}{4\,\frac{\text{mi}}{\text{hr}}} = 4\,\text{hr}$$

$$\text{Time}_2 = \frac{8\,\text{mi}}{2\,\frac{\text{mi}}{\text{hr}}} = 4\,\text{hr}$$

$$\text{Time}_3 = \text{overall time} - \text{Time}_1 - \text{Time}_2$$
$$= 10\,\text{hr} - 4\,\text{hr} - 4\,\text{hr}$$
$$= 2\,\text{hr}$$

Rate of third leg $= \dfrac{6\,\text{mi}}{2\,\text{hr}} = 3\,\dfrac{\text{mi}}{\text{hr}}$

2. Choose two ordered pairs from the graph of the line:
(34) (3, 100) and (9, 20).

$$m = \frac{20 - 100}{9 - 3} = -\frac{80}{6} = -\frac{40}{3}$$

$$Z = -\frac{40}{3}P + b$$

$$20 = -\frac{40}{3}(9) + b$$

$$b = 140$$

$$Z = -\frac{40}{3}P + 140$$

3. $\sqrt{(x - 6)^2 + (y - 5)^2} = \sqrt{(x)^2 + (y + 3)^2}$
(37)

$$(x - 6)^2 + (y - 5)^2 = x^2 + (y + 3)^2$$

$$x^2 - 12x + 36 + y^2 - 10y + 25$$

$$= x^2 + y^2 + 6y + 9$$

$$-16y = 12x - 52$$

$$y = -\frac{3}{4}x + \frac{13}{4}$$

4. $5 \cdot 5 \cdot 5 \cdot 5 \cdot 5 \cdot 5 = \mathbf{15{,}625}$
(38)

5. $(x + 2)(x - 7) = 0$
(38) $x^2 - 5x - 14 = 0$

6. $f(x) = 4x^2 - 3$
(21)

$$\frac{f(x + h) - f(x)}{h}$$

$$= \frac{4(x + h)^2 - 3 - \left(4x^2 - 3\right)}{h}$$

$$= \frac{4x^2 + 8xh + 4h^2 - 3 - 4x^2 + 3}{h}$$

$$= \frac{8xh + 4h^2}{h} = 8x + 4h$$

7. $\displaystyle\sum_{k=5}^{8}\left(\frac{k^2}{2} - 3k\right)$
(34)

$$= \left[\frac{5^2}{2} - 3(5)\right] + \left[\frac{6^2}{2} - 3(6)\right]$$

$$+ \left[\frac{7^2}{2} - 3(7)\right] + \left[\frac{8^2}{2} - 3(8)\right]$$

$$= \frac{25}{2} - 15 + \frac{36}{2} - 18 + \frac{49}{2} - 21 + \frac{64}{2} - 24$$

$$= \frac{174}{2} - 78 = \mathbf{9}$$

8. $54°\left(\dfrac{\pi}{180°}\right)(10) = 3\pi = \mathbf{9.42\ in.}$
(39)

9. $x = \dfrac{x_1 + x_2}{2} = \dfrac{8 + (-2)}{2} = 3$
(37)

$$y = \frac{y_1 + y_2}{2} = \frac{3 + (-5)}{2} = -1$$

Midpoint $= \mathbf{(3, -1)}$

10. $\log_{63} 4 + \log_{63} 6 = \log_{63}(10 + x)$
(40)

$$\log_{63}(4 \cdot 6) = \log_{63}(10 + x)$$

$$24 = 10 + x$$

$$x = \mathbf{14}$$

11. $\log_{30}(3x + 9) - \log_{30} 3 = \log_{30} 12$
(40)

$$\log_{30}\left(\frac{3x + 9}{3}\right) = \log_{30} 12$$

$$\frac{3x + 9}{3} = 12$$

$$3x + 9 = 36$$

$$3x = 27$$

$$x = \mathbf{9}$$

12. $2\log_b x = \log_b 49$
(40)

$$\log_b x^2 = \log_b 49$$

$$x^2 = 49$$

$$x^2 = 7^2$$

$$x = \mathbf{7}$$

13. $\log_2 \dfrac{1}{64} = x$
(26)

$$2^x = \frac{1}{64}$$

$$2^x = \frac{1}{2^6}$$

$$2^x = 2^{-6}$$

$$x = \mathbf{-6}$$

14. $\cos 2\pi + \sin \dfrac{\pi}{6} - \tan \dfrac{3\pi}{4}$
(36,39)

$$= \cos 2(180°) + \sin\left(\frac{180°}{6}\right) - \tan\left(\frac{3(180°)}{4}\right)$$

$$= \cos 360° + \sin 30° - \tan 135°$$

$$= \cos 360° + \sin 30° - (-\tan 45°)$$

$$= 1 + \frac{1}{2} - (-1) = \mathbf{\frac{5}{2}}$$

15.
(32)

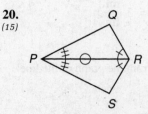

$-90° \leq \theta \leq 90°$

$$a = \sqrt{5^2 - 3^2} = 4$$

$$\tan\left(\text{Arcsin } \frac{3}{5}\right) = \mathbf{\frac{3}{4}}$$

16. $y - y_1 = m(x - x_1)$
(39)

$$y - 6 = -4(x + 2)$$

$$y - 6 = -4x - 8$$

$$\mathbf{4x + y + 2 = 0}$$

$$4x + y + 2 = 0$$

$$4x + y = -2$$

$$-2x + \frac{y}{-2} = 1$$

$$\frac{x}{-\dfrac{1}{2}} + \frac{y}{-2} = \mathbf{1}$$

17. Distance $= y$ mi, rate $= t\,\dfrac{\text{mi}}{\text{hr}}$, time $= \dfrac{y}{t}$ hr
(28)

New distance $= y$ mi

New time $= \left(\dfrac{y}{t} - 3\right) = \dfrac{y - 3t}{t}$ hr

New rate $= \dfrac{y}{\dfrac{y - 3t}{t}} = \mathbf{\dfrac{yt}{y - 3t}\,\dfrac{mi}{hr}}$

18. $R_R T_R + R_L T_L = 32$ desks
(25)

$$\left(\frac{4}{1}\,\frac{\text{desks}}{\text{day}}\right)T + \left(\frac{4}{2}\,\frac{\text{desks}}{\text{day}}\right)(T + 1) = 32 \text{ desks}$$

$$\left(4\,\frac{\text{desks}}{\text{day}}\right)T + \left(2\,\frac{\text{desks}}{\text{day}}\right)T + 2 \text{ desks} = 32 \text{ desks}$$

$$\left(6\,\frac{\text{desks}}{\text{day}}\right)T = 30 \text{ desks}$$

$$T = \mathbf{5 \text{ days}}$$

19. Replace y with $y - 2$.
(31)

$$y - 2 = x^2$$

$$\mathbf{y = x^2 + 2}$$

20.
(15)

STATEMENTS	REASONS
1. $\overline{PR}$ bisects $\angle QRS$	1. Given
2. $\overline{PR}$ bisects $\angle QPS$	2. Given
3. $\angle QPR \cong \angle SPR$ and $\angle QRP \cong \angle SRP$	3. An angle bisector divides an angle into two congruent angles.
4. $\overline{PR} \cong \overline{PR}$	4. Reflexive axiom
5. $\angle Q \cong \angle S$	5. If two angles in one triangle are congruent to two angles in another triangle, then the third angles are congruent.
6. $\triangle RQP \cong \triangle RSP$	6. $AAAS$ congruency postulate

Test 11

1. Rate $= \dfrac{d}{m} \dfrac{\text{dollars}}{\text{microscope}}$
(44)

New rate $= \dfrac{d}{m} - 20 = \dfrac{d - 20m}{m} \dfrac{\text{dollars}}{\text{microscope}}$

New rate $\times N = $ price

$\left(\dfrac{d - 20m}{m}\right)N = 2000$

$N = \dfrac{2000m}{d - 20m}$ **microscopes**

2. $60°\left(\dfrac{\pi}{180°}\right)(120) = 40\pi = $ **125.66 in.**
(39)

3. $y = \left(\dfrac{1}{4}\right)^{-2x} = \left[\left(\dfrac{1}{4}\right)^{-2}\right]^x = 16^x$
(42)

4. $_nP_r = \dfrac{n!}{(n - r)!}$
(41)

$_7P_6 - {_7P_3} = \dfrac{7!}{(7 - 6)!} - \dfrac{7!}{(7 - 3)!}$

$= \dfrac{7!}{1!} - \dfrac{7!}{4!}$

$= $ **4830**

5. (a) $4\log_2 x = 2\log_2 16$
(26,40)

$\log_2 x^4 = \log_2 16^2$

$x^4 = 256$

$x^4 = 4^4$

$x = $ **4**

(b) $\log_x 216 = 3$

$x^3 = 216$

$x^3 = 6^3$

$x = $ **6**

(c) $\log_7 \dfrac{1}{49} = x$

$7^x = \dfrac{1}{49}$

$7^x = \dfrac{1}{7^2}$

$7^x = 7^{-2}$

$x = $ **–2**

6. (a) $0° \leq \theta \leq 180°$
(32)

Arccos $1 = $ **0°**

(b) $-90° \leq \theta \leq 90°$

Arcsin $(-1) = $ **–90°**

(c)

$-90° \leq \theta \leq 90°$

$a = \sqrt{5^2 - 3^2} = 4$

$\cos\left[\text{Arcsin}\left(-\dfrac{3}{5}\right)\right] = \dfrac{4}{5}$

7. $\log_3 3^6 + \log_4 4^5 - \log_6 6^9 = 6 + 5 - 9 = $ **2**
(40)

8. $\log_6 (x + 10) - \log_6 (x - 1) = \log_6 12$
(40)

$\log_6 \dfrac{(x + 10)}{(x - 1)} = \log_6 12$

$\dfrac{(x + 10)}{(x - 1)} = 12$

$x + 10 = 12x - 12$

$11x = 22$

$x = $ **2**

9. $f(x) = \dfrac{\sqrt{3 - x}}{x^3 - 2x^2 - 8x} = \dfrac{\sqrt{3 - x}}{x(x^2 - 2x - 8)}$
(21)

$= \dfrac{\sqrt{3 - x}}{x(x - 4)(x + 2)}$

$x(x - 4)(x + 2) \neq 0$

$x \neq 0, 4, -2$

$3 - x \geq 0$

$x \leq 3$

Domain of $f = \left\{x \in \mathbb{R} \mid x \leq 3, x \neq 0, -2\right\}$

10. $\displaystyle\sum_{n=3}^{5}\left(2n-3n^2\right)$
(34)

$= \left[2(3)-3(3)^2\right] + \left[2(4)-3(4)^2\right] + \left[2(5)-3(5)^2\right]$

$= (-21) + (-40) + (-65)$

$= \mathbf{-126}$

11. (a) $f(x) = |x+3| - 1$
(22)

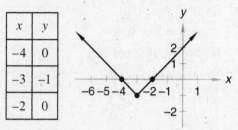

(b) $g(x) = \dfrac{1}{|x+3|-1}$

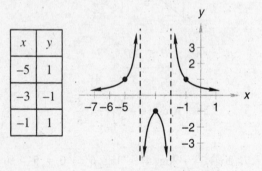

12. $\sqrt{(x-4)^2+(y+3)^2}$
(37)

$\qquad = \sqrt{(x+4)^2+(y-1)^2}$

$(x-4)^2+(y+3)^2$

$\qquad\qquad = (x+4)^2+(y-1)^2$

$x^2 - 8x + 16 + y^2 + 6y + 9$

$\qquad\qquad = x^2 + 8x + 16 + y^2 - 2y + 1$

$8y = 16x - 8$

$y = \mathbf{2x - 1}$

13. $f(x) = \dfrac{1}{x-3}$ and $g(x) = \dfrac{3x+1}{x}$
(40)

$f(g(x)) = \dfrac{1}{\left(\dfrac{3x+1}{x}\right)-3}$

$= \dfrac{1}{\dfrac{3x+1-3x}{x}} = \dfrac{1}{\dfrac{1}{x}} = x$

$g(f(x)) = \dfrac{3\left(\dfrac{1}{x-3}\right)+1}{\dfrac{1}{x-3}}$

$= \dfrac{\dfrac{3+x-3}{x-3}}{\dfrac{1}{x-3}} = \dfrac{x(x-3)}{x-3} = x$

$f(g(x)) = g(f(x)) = x$

Yes, f and g are inverse functions.

14. $(x-h)^2 + (y-k)^2 = r^2$
(42)

$(x-3)^2 + (y+8)^2 = 6^2$

15.
(15)

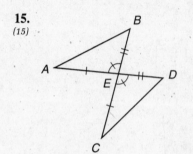

STATEMENTS	REASONS
1. $\overline{AE} \cong \overline{CE}$	1. Given
2. $\overline{BE} \cong \overline{DE}$	2. Given
3. $\angle CED \cong \angle AEB$	3. Vertical angles are congruent.
4. $\triangle CED \cong \triangle AEB$	4. *SAS* congruency postulate
5. $\angle A \cong \angle C$	5. *CPCTC*

16. $\sin \dfrac{8\pi}{3} - \tan \dfrac{7\pi}{6} = \sin \dfrac{8(180°)}{3} - \tan \dfrac{7(180°)}{6}$
(39)

$= \sin 480° - \tan 210° = \sin 60° - \tan 30°$

$= \dfrac{\sqrt{3}}{2} - \dfrac{1}{\sqrt{3}} = \dfrac{\sqrt{3}}{6}$

17. $RPT = S$
(44)

$R(24)(t) = m$

$R = \dfrac{m}{24t} \dfrac{\text{solutions}}{\text{pupil-hr}}$

$RPT = S$

$\left(\dfrac{m}{24t}\right)(24-4)T = 60$

$T = \dfrac{60(24t)}{20(m)}$

$T = \dfrac{72t}{m} \text{ hr}$

18. $\sec 660° + \cot 405° = \sec 60° + \cot 45°$
(41)

$= \dfrac{1}{\cos 60°} + \dfrac{1}{\tan 45°} = 2 + 1 = \mathbf{3}$

19. $x = \dfrac{x_1 + x_2}{2} = \dfrac{8 + 12}{2} = \dfrac{20}{2} = 10$
(37)

$y = \dfrac{y_1 + y_2}{2} = \dfrac{3 + 5}{2} = \dfrac{8}{2} = 4$

Midpoint = (10, 4)

20. Function $= -\sin\theta$
(43)

Amplitude $= 6$

$y = -6\sin\theta$

Test 12

1. $x_m = \dfrac{x_1 + x_2}{2} = \dfrac{-2 + (-8)}{2} = -5$
(39,48)

$y_m = \dfrac{y_1 + y_2}{2} = \dfrac{3 + 1}{2} = 2$

$(-5, 2)$

$m = \dfrac{-1}{\left(\dfrac{y_2 - y_1}{x_2 - x_1}\right)} = \dfrac{-1}{\left(\dfrac{1 - 3}{-8 - (-2)}\right)} = \dfrac{-1}{\dfrac{2}{6}} = -3$

$y = -3x + b$

$(2) = -3(-5) + b$

$b = -13$

$y = -3x - 13$

$3x + y = -13$

$\dfrac{x}{-\dfrac{13}{3}} + \dfrac{y}{-13} = 1$

2.
(45)

PHYSICS						GEOMETRY				
6	5	4	3	2	1	5	4	3	2	1

$\longrightarrow \quad 6! \times 5! = 86{,}400$

GEOMETRY					PHYSICS					
5	4	3	2	1	6	5	4	3	2	1

$\longrightarrow \quad 5! \times 6! = 86{,}400$

$86{,}400 + 86{,}400 = \mathbf{172{,}800}$

3. $R_A T_A + R_J T_J = 26 \text{ rings}$
(25)

$\left(\dfrac{3}{6}\dfrac{\text{ring}}{\text{hr}}\right)(T + 3\text{ hr}) + \left(\dfrac{5}{4}\dfrac{\text{rings}}{\text{hr}}\right)T = 26 \text{ rings}$

$\left(\dfrac{1}{2}\dfrac{\text{ring}}{\text{hr}}\right)T + \dfrac{3}{2}\text{ hr} + \left(\dfrac{5}{4}\dfrac{\text{rings}}{\text{hr}}\right)T = 26 \text{ rings}$

$\left(\dfrac{7}{4}\dfrac{\text{rings}}{\text{hr}}\right)T = \dfrac{49}{2}\text{ rings}$

$T = \mathbf{14\ hr}$

4. $\text{Alcohol}_1 - \text{Alcohol}_{\text{extracted}} = \text{Alcohol}_2$
(18)

$0.7(600) - A_e = 0.4\big(600 - A_e\big)$

$420 - A_e = 240 - 0.4A_e$

$0.6A_e = 180$

$A_e = \mathbf{300\ L}$

5. $x^2 + 3x + 9 = 0$
(46)

$x = \dfrac{-(3) \pm \sqrt{(3)^2 - 4(1)(9)}}{2(1)}$

$x = \dfrac{-3 \pm \sqrt{-27}}{2} = -\dfrac{3}{2} \pm \dfrac{3\sqrt{3}}{2}i$

$\left(x + \dfrac{3}{2} - \dfrac{3\sqrt{3}}{2}i\right)\left(x + \dfrac{3}{2} + \dfrac{3\sqrt{3}}{2}i\right)$

6. $[x - (3 + 2i)][x - (3 - 2i)] = 0$
(46)

$(x - 3 - 2i)(x - 3 + 2i) = 0$

$x^2 - 3x - 2xi - 3x + 9 + 6i + 2xi - 6i - 4i^2 = 0$

$\mathbf{x^2 - 6x + 13 = 0}$

7. (a) **x axis, yes**
(31)
    y axis, no

    origin, no

(b) **x axis, no**

    y axis, yes

    origin, no

8. (a)
(32,47)

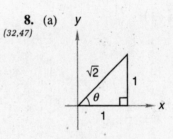

$-90° < \theta < 90°$

Arctan $1 = \mathbf{45°}$

(b)

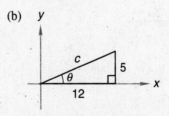

$-90° < \theta < 90°$

$c = \sqrt{5^2 + 12^2} = 13$

$\sin\left(\text{Arctan }\dfrac{5}{12}\right) = \dfrac{\mathbf{5}}{\mathbf{13}}$

9.
(40)
$$\frac{1}{2} \log_{12} 4 + \log_{12}(x + 2) = \log_{12} 16$$
$$\log_{12}\left[4^{1/2}(x + 2)\right] = \log_{12} 16$$
$$2(x + 2) = 16$$
$$2x + 4 = 16$$
$$2x = 12$$
$$x = \mathbf{6}$$

10.
(40)
$$\log_5(x + 3) - \log_5(x - 6) = \log_5 3$$
$$\log_5 \frac{x + 3}{x - 6} = \log_5 3$$
$$\frac{x + 3}{x - 6} = 3$$
$$x + 3 = 3x - 18$$
$$2x = 21$$
$$x = \frac{\mathbf{21}}{\mathbf{2}}$$

11.
(36,41)
$$\csc 750° + \sin(-630°) + \tan 675°$$
$$= \csc 30° + \sin(-270°) + \tan 315°$$
$$= \frac{1}{\sin 30°} + \sin 90° + (-\tan 45°)$$
$$= 2 + 1 - 1 = \mathbf{2}$$

12.
(41,48)
$$\sec^2 \frac{5\pi}{4} + \cos^3 \frac{\pi}{2} + \cot^2 \frac{\pi}{6}$$
$$= \frac{1}{\left(-\cos \frac{\pi}{4}\right)^2} + \left(\cos \frac{\pi}{2}\right)^3 + \frac{1}{\left(\tan \frac{\pi}{6}\right)^2}$$
$$= \left(-\sqrt{2}\right)^2 + (0)^3 + \left(\sqrt{3}\right)^2$$
$$= 2 + 0 + 3 = \mathbf{5}$$

13.
(24)
$$f(x) = 5x^2, \quad g(x) = x - \frac{4}{x}$$

(a) $(f - g)(x) = 5x^2 - x + \frac{4}{x}$

$$(f - g)(4) = 5(4)^2 - 4 + \frac{4}{4} = \mathbf{77}$$

(b) $(f/g)(x) = \dfrac{5x^2}{x - \dfrac{4}{x}}$

$$(f/g)(4) = \frac{5(4)^2}{4 - \dfrac{4}{4}} = \frac{\mathbf{80}}{\mathbf{3}}$$

(c) $(f \circ g)(x) = 5\left(x - \dfrac{4}{x}\right)^2$

$$(f \circ g)(4) = 5\left(4 - \frac{4}{4}\right)^2 = 5(3)^2 = \mathbf{45}$$

14.
(42)
$$(x - h)^2 + (y - k)^2 = r^2$$
$$(x + 3)^2 + (y - 4)^2 = 5^2$$

15.
(42)
$$f(x) = \left(\frac{1}{5}\right)^{-x+1} = \left[\left(\frac{1}{5}\right)^{-1}\right]^x \left(\frac{1}{5}\right) = \frac{1}{5} \cdot 5^x$$

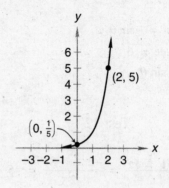

16. (a) $g(x) = |x - 3| - 4$
(22)

x	−1	0	3	7
y	0	−1	−4	0

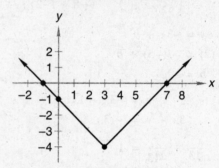

(b) $h(x) = \dfrac{1}{|x - 3| - 4}$

x	−2	3	8
y	1	$-\frac{1}{4}$	1

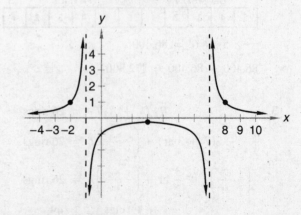

17.
(45)

2	5	5

$\rightarrow \quad 2 \times 5 \times 5 = \mathbf{50}$

18. $RWT = V$
(44)

$R(w)(5) = v$

$$R = \frac{v}{5w} \; \frac{\text{valves}}{\text{worker-day}}$$

$$RWT = V$$

$$\left(\frac{v}{5w}\right)(w + n)T = v$$

$$T = \frac{5wv}{v(w + n)}$$

$$T = \frac{5w}{w + n} \text{ days}$$

19. Function $= -\cos\theta$
(47)

Centerline $= 0$

Amplitude $= 4$

$$y = -4\cos\theta$$

20. Function $= -\sin x$
(47)

Centerline $= -2$

Amplitude $= 5$

$$y = -2 - 5\sin x$$

Test 13

1. $x_m = \dfrac{x_1 + x_2}{2} = \dfrac{-2 + 6}{2} = 2$
(39,48)

$$y_m = \frac{y_1 + y_2}{2} = \frac{2 + 4}{2} = 3$$

$(2, 3)$

$$m = \frac{-1}{\left(\dfrac{y_2 - y_1}{x_2 - x_1}\right)} = \frac{-1}{\left[\dfrac{4 - 2}{6 - (-2)}\right]} = \frac{-1}{\dfrac{2}{8}} = -4$$

$y = -4x + b$

$(3) = -4(2) + b$

$b = 11$

$$y = -4x + 11$$

$$4x + y - 11 = 0$$

2. $RCT = B$
(44)

$R(d)(11) = b$

$$R = \frac{b}{11d} \; \frac{\text{batteries}}{\text{circuit-day}}$$

$$RCT = B$$

$$\left(\frac{b}{11d}\right)(d + 8)T = r$$

$$T = \frac{11rd}{b(d + 8)} \text{ days}$$

3. $\sqrt{(x + 3)^2 + (y + 6)^2} = \sqrt{(x - 4)^2 + (y - 7)^2}$
(37)

$$(x + 3)^2 + (y + 6)^2 = (x - 4)^2 + (y - 7)^2$$

$$x^2 + 6x + 9 + y^2 + 12y + 36$$

$$= x^2 - 8x + 16 + y^2 - 14y + 49$$

$$26y = -14x + 20$$

$$y = -\frac{7}{13}x + \frac{10}{13}$$

4. $R_J T_J + R_S T_S = 107 \text{ jobs}$
(25)

$$\left(\frac{2}{4}\frac{\text{job}}{\text{day}}\right)(T + 6 \text{ days}) + \left(\frac{4}{5}\frac{\text{job}}{\text{day}}\right)T = 107 \text{ jobs}$$

$$\left(\frac{1}{2}\frac{\text{job}}{\text{day}}\right)T + 3 \text{ jobs} + \left(\frac{4}{5}\frac{\text{job}}{\text{day}}\right)T = 107 \text{ jobs}$$

$$\left(\frac{13}{10}\frac{\text{jobs}}{\text{day}}\right)T = 104 \text{ jobs}$$

$$T = \textbf{80 days}$$

5. $[x - (1 + 5i)][x - (1 - 5i)] = 0$
(46)

$$(x - 1 - 5i)(x - 1 + 5i) = 0$$

$$x^2 - x + 5xi - x + 1 - 5i - 5xi + 5i - 25i^2 = 0$$

$$x^2 - 2x + 26 = 0$$

6. Distance $= b$ mi, time $= h$ hr, rate $= \dfrac{b}{h}\dfrac{\text{mi}}{\text{hr}}$
(28)

New distance $= b$ mi

New time $= (h - 2)$ hr

New rate $= \dfrac{b}{h - 2}\dfrac{\text{mi}}{\text{hr}}$

7. $f(x) = |x|$
(31)

$g(x) - (-2) = |x - (-4)|$

$$g(x) = |x + 4| - 2$$

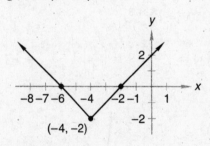

$(-4, -2)$

8.
(45)

| 3 | 5 | 5 | $\rightarrow 3 \times 5 \times 5 = 75$
|---|---|---|
| | 5 | 5 | $\rightarrow 5 \times 5 = 25$
| | | 5 | $\rightarrow 5$

$$75 + 25 + 5 = \textbf{105}$$

9.
(45)

5	1	6	5	6

$\longrightarrow \quad 5 \times 1 \times 6 \times 5 \times 6 = \textbf{900}$

10. (a) $\cos\theta = \dfrac{1}{\sqrt{2}}$
(50,52)

$\qquad \theta = \textbf{45}°, \textbf{315}°$

(b) $\tan\dfrac{\theta}{2} + \sqrt{3} = 0$

$\qquad\qquad \tan\dfrac{\theta}{2} = -\sqrt{3}$

$\qquad\qquad \dfrac{\theta}{2} = 120°$

$\qquad\qquad \theta = \textbf{240}°$

11. Function $= -\cos x$
(47)

Centerline $= 8$

Amplitude $= 12$

$y = \textbf{8} - \textbf{12}\cos x$

12. $B = mA + b$
(45)

$m = 0.1845$

$b = 6.0988$

$r = \textbf{0.9527}$

$\textbf{B} = \textbf{0.1845A} + \textbf{6.0988}$

This is a **good correlation** since $0.9 < |r| < 1.0$.

13. $\csc^2\left(-\dfrac{8\pi}{3}\right) + \tan^2\left(\dfrac{7\pi}{6}\right)$
(41,48)

$= \dfrac{1}{\left(-\sin\dfrac{\pi}{3}\right)^2} + \left(\tan\dfrac{\pi}{6}\right)^2$

$= \left(-\dfrac{2}{\sqrt{3}}\right)^2 + \left(\dfrac{1}{\sqrt{3}}\right)^2 = \dfrac{4}{3} + \dfrac{1}{3} = \dfrac{\textbf{5}}{\textbf{3}}$

14. $\ln 4200 = 8.3428$
(51)

$4200 = e^{8.3428}$

15. $f(x) = \left(\dfrac{1}{4}\right)^{x-2} = \left(\dfrac{1}{4}\right)^x\left(\dfrac{1}{4}\right)^{-2} = 16\left(\dfrac{1}{4}\right)^x$
(42)

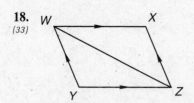

16.
(32,47)

$-90° \le \theta \le 90°$

$\text{Arcsin}\,(\tan 45°) = \text{Arcsin}\,(1) = \textbf{90}°$

17. Replace x with $x - 4$ and y with $-y$.
(31)

$-y = \sqrt{x - 4}$

$\textbf{y} = -\sqrt{\textbf{x} - \textbf{4}}$

18.
(33)

STATEMENTS	REASONS
1. $\overline{WY} \parallel \overline{XZ}$	1. Given
2. $\angle ZWY \cong \angle WZX$	2. If two parallel lines are cut by a transversal, then each pair of alternate interior angles is congruent.
3. $\overline{WX} \parallel \overline{YZ}$	3. Given
4. $\angle YZW \cong \angle XWZ$	4. If two parallel lines are cut by a transversal, then each pair of alternate interior angles is congruent.
5. $\angle Y \cong \angle X$	5. If two angles in one triangle are congruent to two angles in a second triangle, then the third angles are congruent.
6. $\overline{WZ} \cong \overline{WZ}$	6. Reflexive axiom
7. $\triangle WYZ \cong \triangle ZXW$	7. AAAS congruency postulate
8. $\overline{WY} \cong \overline{XZ}$	8. CPCTC

19. $\log 7.4 = \textbf{0.8692}$
(51)

20. $\ln 7.4 = \textbf{2.0015}$
(51)

Test 14

1. Distance $= d$ mi, rate $= n\,\dfrac{\text{mi}}{\text{hr}}$, time $= \dfrac{d}{n}$ hr
(28)

New distance $= d$ mi

New time $= \left(\dfrac{d}{n} - 3\right)$ hr $= \dfrac{d - 3n}{n}$ hr

New rate $= \dfrac{d}{\dfrac{d - 3n}{n}} = \dfrac{\textbf{dn}}{\textbf{d} - \textbf{3n}}\,\dfrac{\textbf{mi}}{\textbf{hr}}$

2. $(N - 1)! = (7 - 1)! = 6! = \textbf{720}$
(55)

3. (a) $\begin{cases} R_1 T_1 = 500 \text{ mi} \\ R_2 T_2 = 500 \text{ mi} \end{cases}$
(25)   (b)

$R_2 = 2R_1, \quad T_1 + T_2 = 5$ hr

$$T_1 + T_2 = 5$$

$$T_2 = 5 - T_1$$

(b) $\qquad R_2 T_2 = 500$

$$\left(2R_1\right)\left(5 - T_1\right) = 500$$

$$10R_1 - 2R_1 T_1 = 500$$

$$5R_1 - R_1 T_1 = 250$$

$$5R_1 - (500) = 250$$

$$5R_1 = 750$$

$$R_1 = 150 \frac{\text{mi}}{\text{hr}}$$

$$R_2 = 2R_1$$

$$R_2 = 2(150)$$

$$R_2 = \mathbf{300 \frac{\text{mi}}{\text{hr}}}$$

4. $\dfrac{N!}{a!b!} = \dfrac{9!}{4!3!} = \mathbf{2520}$
(55)

5. $y = x^2 - 4x + 3$
(54)

$$y = \left(x^2 - 4x \quad\right) + 3$$

$$y = \left(x^2 - 4x + 4\right) + 3 - 4$$

$$y = \mathbf{(x - 2)^2 - 1}$$

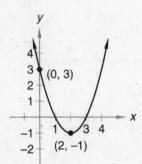

6. $2 \ln 1 + 2 \ln 5 = \ln (x + 3)$
(40,51)

$$\ln 1^2 + \ln 5^2 = \ln (x + 3)$$

$$\ln (1 \cdot 25) = \ln (x + 3)$$

$$x + 3 = 25$$

$$x = \mathbf{22}$$

7. $\log_6 18x - 3 \log_6 3 = 1$
(40)

$$\log_6 18x - \log_6 3^3 = 1$$

$$\log_6 \frac{18x}{3^3} = 1$$

$$\frac{18x}{27} = 6^1$$

$$18x = 162$$

$$x = \mathbf{9}$$

8. $v = r\omega$
(53)

$$v = 13 \text{ in.}\left(60 \frac{\text{rad}}{\text{min}}\right)\left(\frac{1 \text{ ft}}{12 \text{ in.}}\right)\left(\frac{60 \text{ min}}{1 \text{ hr}}\right)$$

$$v = \frac{13(60)(60)}{12} \frac{\text{ft}}{\text{hr}} = \mathbf{3900 \frac{\text{ft}}{\text{hr}}}$$

9. (a) $\log 6600 = 3.8195$
(51)
$$6600 = \mathbf{10^{3.8195}}$$

(b) $\ln 6600 = 8.7948$
$$6600 = \mathbf{e^{8.7948}}$$

10. D.
(31)

11. $\qquad RAT = C$
(44)
$$R(a)(h) = c$$

$$R = \frac{c}{ah} \frac{\text{crafts}}{\text{artisan-hr}}$$

$$RAT = C$$

$$\left(\frac{c}{ah}\right)(a - m)T = d$$

$$T = \frac{dah}{c(a - m)} \text{ hr}$$

12. $\text{Rate} = \dfrac{c}{p} \dfrac{\text{cents}}{\text{pear}}$
(44)

$$\text{New rate} = \frac{c}{p} - 5 = \frac{c - 5p}{p} \frac{\text{cents}}{\text{pear}}$$

$$\text{New rate} \times N = \text{price}$$

$$\left(\frac{c - 5p}{p}\right)N = 400$$

$$N = \mathbf{\frac{400p}{c - 5p} \text{ pears}}$$

13. $\text{Function} = \sin \theta$
(47)

$$\text{Centerline} = -6$$

$$\text{Amplitude} = 8$$

$$y = \mathbf{-6 + 8 \sin \theta}$$

14.
(56)

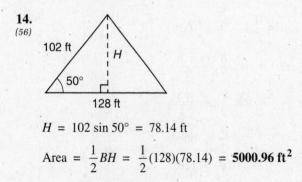

$$H = 102 \sin 50° = 78.14 \text{ ft}$$

$$\text{Area} = \frac{1}{2}BH = \frac{1}{2}(128)(78.14) = \mathbf{5000.96 \text{ ft}^2}$$

15.
(56)

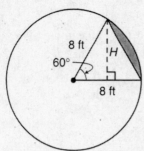

$H = 8 \sin 60° = 6.93$ ft

$A_{segment} = A_{sector} - A_{triangle}$

$$= \pi r^2 \left(\frac{60°}{360°} \right) - \frac{1}{2} rH$$

$$= \pi (8)^2 \left(\frac{60°}{360°} \right) - \frac{1}{2} (8)(6.93)$$

$$= 33.51 - 27.72 = \textbf{5.79 ft}^2$$

16. $48° \left(\dfrac{\pi}{180°} \right) \left(\dfrac{7920}{2} \right) = 1056\pi = \textbf{3317.52 mi}$
(39)

17. $x^2 - 7x + 13 = 0$
(46)

$$x = \frac{-(-7) \pm \sqrt{(-7)^2 - 4(1)(13)}}{2(1)}$$

$$x = \frac{7 \pm \sqrt{-3}}{2} = \frac{7}{2} \pm \frac{\sqrt{3}}{2} i$$

$$\left(x - \frac{7}{2} + \frac{\sqrt{3}}{2} i \right) \left(x - \frac{7}{2} - \frac{\sqrt{3}}{2} i \right)$$

18. $\sqrt{(x - 3)^2 + (y - 5)^2} = \sqrt{(x + 5)^2 + (y + 5)^2}$
(37,39)

$$(x - 3)^2 + (y - 5)^2 = (x + 5)^2 + (y + 5)^2$$

$$x^2 - 6x + 9 + y^2 - 10y + 25$$

$$= x^2 + 10x + 25 + y^2 + 10y + 25$$

$$16x + 20y = -16$$

$$\frac{x}{-1} + \frac{y}{-\dfrac{4}{5}} = 1$$

19. $3 \cot \dfrac{\theta}{2} - \sqrt{3} = 0$
(41,52)

$$\cot \frac{\theta}{2} = \frac{\sqrt{3}}{3}$$

$$\tan \frac{\theta}{2} = \frac{3}{\sqrt{3}}$$

$$\frac{\theta}{2} = 60°$$

$$\theta = \textbf{120}°$$

20. $2 \cos 3\theta - \sqrt{2} = 0$
(52)

$$\cos 3\theta = \frac{\sqrt{2}}{2}$$

$$3\theta = 45°, 315°, 405°, 675°, 765°, 1035°$$

$$\theta = \textbf{15}°, \textbf{105}°, \textbf{135}°, \textbf{225}°, \textbf{255}°, \textbf{345}°$$

Test 15

1. $v = r\omega$
(53)

$$v = 6\,\text{m} \left(30\,\frac{\text{rad}}{\text{s}} \right) \left(\frac{100\,\text{cm}}{1\,\text{m}} \right) \left(\frac{1\,\text{in.}}{2.54\,\text{cm}} \right) \left(\frac{1\,\text{ft}}{12\,\text{in.}} \right)$$

$$\times \left(\frac{1\,\text{mi}}{5280\,\text{ft}} \right) \left(\frac{60\,\text{s}}{1\,\text{min}} \right) \left(\frac{60\,\text{min}}{1\,\text{hr}} \right)$$

$$v = \frac{(6)(30)(100)(60)(60)}{(2.54)(12)(5280)} \frac{\text{mi}}{\text{hr}} = \textbf{402.65}\ \frac{\textbf{mi}}{\textbf{hr}}$$

2. $\dfrac{N!}{a!b!c!} = \dfrac{11!}{3!2!6!} = \textbf{4620}$
(55)

3. Function $= -\cos \theta$
(47)

Centerline $= 5$

Amplitude $= 3$

$y = \textbf{5} - \textbf{3} \cos \theta$

4.
(56)

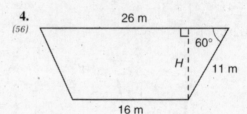

$H = 11 \sin 60° = 9.53$ m

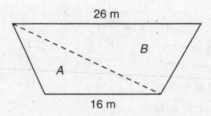

Total area $=$ Area A $+$ Area B

$$= \frac{1}{2}(16)(9.53) + \frac{1}{2}(26)(9.53)$$

$$= 76.24 + 123.89 = \textbf{200.13 m}^2$$

5.
(56)

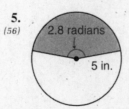

$A_{sector} = \pi r^2 \left(\dfrac{2.8}{2\pi} \right) = \pi (5)^2 \left(\dfrac{2.8}{2\pi} \right) = \textbf{35 in.}^2$

6. (a) $\log 36{,}000 = 4.5563$
(51) $\qquad 36{,}000 = 10^{4.5563}$

(b) $\ln 36{,}000 = 10.4913$
$\qquad 36{,}000 = e^{10.4913}$

7. $\begin{cases} y \geq x^2 + 6x + 4 & \text{(parabola)} \\ y \leq x + 3 & \text{(line)} \end{cases}$
(56)

$y \geq x^2 + 6x + 4$

$y \geq (x^2 + 6x + 9) + 4 - 9$

$y \geq (x + 3)^2 - 5$

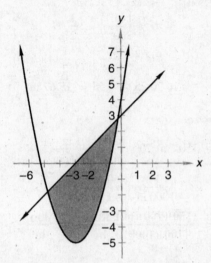

The region must be on or above the parabola and on or below the line.

Test point: $(-2, -1)$

Line: $-1 \leq -2 + 3$
$\qquad -1 \leq 1 \qquad$ True

Parabola: $-1 \geq (-2 + 3)^2 - 5$
$\qquad\qquad -1 \geq (1)^2 - 5$
$\qquad\qquad -1 \geq -4 \qquad$ True

8. $(x - h)^2 + (y - k)^2 = r^2$
(42)
$\mathbf{(x - 3)^2 + (y + 4)^2 = 8^2}$

9. $\qquad\qquad \sin^2 \theta = 1$
(60)
$\qquad\qquad \sin^2 \theta - 1 = 0$

$\qquad (\sin \theta - 1)(\sin \theta + 1) = 0$

$\sin \theta - 1 = 0 \qquad\qquad \sin \theta + 1 = 0$
$\quad \sin \theta = 1 \qquad\qquad\quad \sin \theta = -1$
$\qquad\quad \theta = 90° \qquad\qquad\qquad \theta = 270°$

$\boldsymbol{\theta = 90°, 270°}$

10. $\qquad\qquad \sqrt{3} \tan \theta \sin \theta = \sin \theta$
(60)
$\sqrt{3} \tan \theta \sin \theta - \sin \theta = 0$

$\sin \theta \left(\sqrt{3} \tan \theta - 1 \right) = 0$

$\sin \theta = 0 \qquad\qquad \sqrt{3} \tan \theta - 1 = 0$
$\quad \theta = 0°, 180° \qquad\qquad \sqrt{3} \tan \theta = 1$

$\qquad\qquad\qquad\qquad\qquad \tan \theta = \dfrac{1}{\sqrt{3}}$

$\qquad\qquad\qquad\qquad\qquad \theta = 30°, 210°$

$\boldsymbol{\theta = 0°, 30°, 180°, 210°}$

11. $\log_{20} (x + 2) + \log_{20} (x + 3) = 1$
(59)
$\qquad \log_{20} [(x + 2)(x + 3)] = 1$

$\qquad\qquad (x + 2)(x + 3) = 20^1$

$\qquad\qquad\qquad x^2 + 5x + 6 = 20$

$\qquad\qquad\qquad x^2 + 5x - 14 = 0$

$\qquad\qquad\qquad (x + 7)(x - 2) = 0$

$\qquad\qquad\qquad\qquad x = -7, 2 \quad (x \neq -7)$

$\qquad\qquad\qquad\qquad x = 2$

12. $\dfrac{5}{3} \log_6 8 - \log_6 (x + 4) = \log_6 2$
(40)
$\log_6 8^{5/3} - \log_6 (x + 4) = \log_6 2$

$\qquad\qquad \log_6 \dfrac{32}{(x + 4)} = \log_6 2$

$\qquad\qquad\qquad \dfrac{32}{(x + 4)} = 2$

$\qquad\qquad\qquad\qquad 32 = 2x + 8$

$\qquad\qquad\qquad\qquad 2x = 24$

$\qquad\qquad\qquad\qquad x = 12$

13. $7^{\log_7 \sqrt{3} + \log_7 \sqrt{6}} = 7^{\log_7 \sqrt{18}} = \sqrt{18} = \mathbf{3\sqrt{2}}$
(59)

14. $\sin^3 \dfrac{\pi}{2} + \cos^2 \dfrac{5\pi}{3} - \tan^2 \dfrac{7\pi}{4}$
(48)
$= \left(\sin \dfrac{\pi}{2} \right)^3 + \left(\cos \dfrac{\pi}{3} \right)^2 - \left(-\tan \dfrac{\pi}{4} \right)^2$

$= (1)^3 + \left(\dfrac{1}{2} \right)^2 - (-1)^2 = 1 + \dfrac{1}{4} - 1 = \dfrac{1}{4}$

15. $x^2 - 4x + 5 = 0$
(46)
$x = \dfrac{-(-4) \pm \sqrt{(-4)^2 - 4(1)(5)}}{2(1)}$

$x = \dfrac{4 \pm \sqrt{-4}}{2} = 2 \pm i$

$(x - 2 + i)(x - 2 - i)$

16. $y = x - 10$
(58)

Equation of the perpendicular line:

$y = -x + b$

$(5) = -(3) + b$

$b = 8$

$y = -x + 8$

Point of intersection:

$x - 10 = -x + 8$

$2x = 18$

$x = 9$

$y = -x + 8 = -(9) + 8 = -1$

$(9, -1)$ and $(3, 5)$

$D = \sqrt{(3 - 9)^2 + [5 - (-1)]^2}$

$\quad = \sqrt{(-6)^2 + (6)^2}$

$\quad = \sqrt{72} = \mathbf{6\sqrt{2}}$

17. $\qquad\qquad R_R T_R + R_W T_W = 30 \text{ x rays}$
(25)

$\left(\frac{8}{2} \frac{\text{x rays}}{\text{day}}\right)(T + 4 \text{ days}) + \left(\frac{9}{3} \frac{\text{x rays}}{\text{day}}\right)T = 30 \text{ x rays}$

$\left(4 \frac{\text{x rays}}{\text{day}}\right)T + 16 \text{ x rays} + \left(3 \frac{\text{x rays}}{\text{day}}\right)T = 30 \text{ x rays}$

$\qquad\qquad\qquad \left(7 \frac{\text{x rays}}{\text{day}}\right)T = 14 \text{ x rays}$

$\qquad\qquad\qquad\qquad T = \mathbf{2\ days}$

18. (a) $\begin{cases} (M + C)T_D = D_D \\ (M - C)T_U = D_U \end{cases}$
(36) (b)

$M = 3C, \quad T_D = T_U - 2$

(b) $(M - C)T_U = D_U$

$\quad (3C - C)T_U = 140$

$\qquad\quad 2CT_U = 140$

$\qquad\quad CT_U = 70$

(a) $\qquad (M + C)T_D = D_D$

$\quad (3C + C)(T_U - 2) = 160$

$\qquad 4CT_U - 8C = 160$

$\qquad 4(70) - 8C = 160$

$\qquad\qquad 8C = 120$

$\qquad\qquad C = 15$

$M = 3C = 3(15) = \mathbf{45\ mph}$

19. Domain $= \left\{x \in \mathbb{R} \mid -4 < x \leq 4\right\}$
(21)

Range $= \left\{y \in \mathbb{R} \mid -3 < y \leq 4\right\}$

20. Domain $= \left\{x \in \mathbb{R} \mid -\infty < x \leq 6\right\}$
(21)

Range $= \left\{y \in \mathbb{R} \mid -\infty < y \leq 5\right\}$

Test 16

1.
(56)

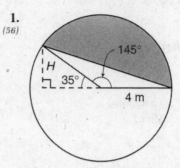

$H = 4 \sin 35° = 2.29 \text{ m}$

$A_{\text{segment}} = A_{\text{sector}} - A_{\text{triangle}}$

$\qquad = \pi r^2 \left(\frac{145°}{360°}\right) - \frac{1}{2}rH$

$\qquad = \pi(4)^2 \left(\frac{145°}{360°}\right) - \frac{1}{2}(4)(2.29)$

$\qquad = 20.25 - 4.58 = \mathbf{15.67\ m^2}$

2. $v = r\omega$
(53)

$v = 150 \text{ cm}\left(700 \frac{\text{rad}}{\text{min}}\right)\left(\frac{1 \text{ m}}{100 \text{ cm}}\right)$

$\qquad \times \left(\frac{1 \text{ km}}{1000 \text{ m}}\right)\left(\frac{60 \text{ min}}{1 \text{ hr}}\right)$

$v = \frac{(150)(700)(60)}{(100)(1000)} \frac{\text{km}}{\text{hr}} = \mathbf{63} \frac{\mathbf{km}}{\mathbf{hr}}$

3. $C = mN + b$
(62)

(a) $\begin{cases} 550 = m30 + b \\ 700 = m40 + b \end{cases}$
(b)

$\quad$ (b) $\quad 700 = \quad m40 + b$

-1(a) $\underline{-550 = -m30 - b}$

$\qquad\quad 150 = \quad m10$

$\qquad\qquad m = 15$

(b) $700 = m40 + b$

$\quad 700 = (15)40 + b$

$\qquad b = 100$

$\mathbf{C = 15N + 100}$

$C = 15(60) + 100 = \mathbf{\$1000}$

4. $\mu = 69, \ \sigma = 4$
(61)

About 68% of the data lie within one standard deviation of the mean.

$\mu \pm \sigma = 69 \pm 4 = 65, 73$

68% of the data lie between 65 and 73.

About 95% of the data lie within two standard deviations of the mean.

$\mu \pm 2\sigma = 69 \pm 2(4) = 61, 77$

95% of the data lie between 61 and 77.

About 99% of the data lie within three standard deviations of the mean.

$\mu \pm 3\sigma = 69 \pm 3(4) = 57, 81$

99% of the data lie between 57 and 81.

5. (a) $\begin{cases} dx + cy = f \\ rx + sy = t \end{cases}$
(62) (b)

s(a) $dsx + csy = sf$

$-c$(b) $\dfrac{-crx - csy = -ct}{(ds - cr)x = sf - ct}$

$$x = \frac{sf - ct}{ds - cr}$$

6. $(2 \text{ cis } 15°)(\sqrt{2} \text{ cis } 30°) = 2\sqrt{2} \text{ cis }(15° + 30°)$
(64)
$= 2\sqrt{2} \text{ cis } 45° = 2\sqrt{2}(\cos 45° + i \sin 45°)$

$= 2\sqrt{2}\left(\dfrac{1}{\sqrt{2}} + i\dfrac{1}{\sqrt{2}}\right) = \mathbf{2 + 2i}$

7. Overall average rate $= \dfrac{\text{overall distance}}{\text{overall time}}$
(38)
$= \dfrac{m + t}{h + s} \dfrac{\text{mi}}{\text{hr}}$

Time $= \dfrac{\text{distance}}{\text{rate}}$

$= \dfrac{200 \text{ mi}}{\dfrac{(m + \text{t}) \text{ mi}}{(h + s) \text{ hr}}} = \dfrac{\mathbf{200(h + s)}}{\mathbf{m + t}} \mathbf{hr}$

8. $x^2 + y^2 + 6x - 4y - 3 = 0$
(63)
$\left(x^2 + 6x \quad\right) + \left(y^2 - 4y \quad\right) = 3$

$\left(x^2 + 6x + 9\right) + \left(y^2 - 4y + 4\right) = 16$

$(x + 3)^2 + (y - 2)^2 = 4^2$

Center $= (-3, 2)$; radius $= 4$

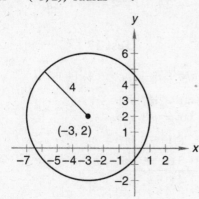

9. Range $= 15 - 7 = \mathbf{8}$
(61)
Mean $= \dfrac{15 + 12 + 11 + 8 + 13 + 11 + 7}{7} = \mathbf{11}$

Median $= \mathbf{11}$

Mode $= \mathbf{11}$

Variance

$= \dfrac{1}{7}\left[4^2 + 1^2 + 0^2 + (-3)^2 + 2^2 + 0^2 + (-4)^2\right]$

$= \mathbf{6.57}$

Standard deviation $= \sqrt{6.57} = \mathbf{2.56}$

10. $\tan \theta \cos 2\theta + \cos 2\theta = 0$
(60)
$\cos 2\theta(\tan \theta + 1) = 0$

$\cos 2\theta = 0$

$2\theta = 90°, 270°, 450°, 630°$

$\theta = 45°, 135°, 225°, 315°$

$\tan \theta + 1 = 0$

$\tan \theta = -1$

$\theta = 135°, 315°$

$\theta = \mathbf{45°, 135°, 225°, 315°}$

11.

STEM	LEAF
6	3, 5, 7
5	5, 6, 8, 9
4	3, 6, 8
3	4, 6

(61)

12. **Mean $= 568.71$**
(61)
Standard deviation $= 91.89$

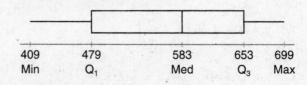

409	479	583	653	699
Min	Q_1	Med	Q_3	Max

13.
(32)

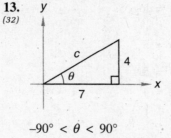

$-90° < \theta < 90°$

$c = \sqrt{7^2 + 4^2} = \sqrt{65}$

$\sin\left(\text{Arctan } \dfrac{4}{7}\right) = \dfrac{4}{\sqrt{65}} = \dfrac{\mathbf{4\sqrt{65}}}{\mathbf{65}}$

14. $\tan^2 315° - \sec^2 315° + \cos 720°$
(41,48)
$= (-\tan 45°)^2 - \left(\dfrac{1}{\cos 45°}\right)^2 + \cos 360°$

$= (-1)^2 - (\sqrt{2})^2 + 1 = 1 - 2 + 1 = \mathbf{0}$

15.
(56)

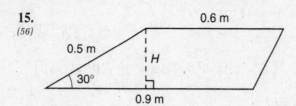

$H = 0.5 \sin 30° = 0.25$ m

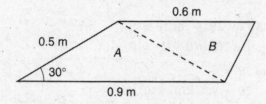

Total area = Area A + Area B

$$= \frac{1}{2}(0.9)(0.25) + \frac{1}{2}(0.6)(0.25)$$

$$= 0.113 + 0.075$$

$$= 0.188 \text{ m}^2$$

$$0.188 \text{ m}^2 \left[\frac{(100)^2 \text{ cm}^2}{1 \text{ m}^2} \right] = \mathbf{1880 \text{ cm}^2}$$

16. Function = $\sin x$
(47,57)

Centerline = 4

Amplitude = 4

Period = 2π

Phase angle = $\dfrac{\pi}{6}$

$$y = 4 + 4 \sin \left(x - \frac{\pi}{6} \right)$$

17. $\log_6 (x + 4) - \log_6 x = \log_6 5$
(40)

$$\log_6 \frac{x + 4}{x} = \log_6 5$$

$$\frac{x + 4}{x} = 5$$

$$x + 4 = 5x$$

$$4x = 4$$

$$x = \mathbf{1}$$

18. $\log x + \log (x - 9) = 1$
(59)

$$\log [x(x - 9)] = 1$$

$$x(x - 9) = 10^1$$

$$x^2 - 9x = 10$$

$$x^2 - 9x - 10 = 0$$

$$(x - 10)(x + 1) = 0$$

$$x = 10, -1 \quad (x \neq -1)$$

$$x = \mathbf{10}$$

19. $\begin{cases} y \le -(x - 2)^2 + 3 & \text{(parabola)} \\ y \le x - 4 & \text{(line)} \end{cases}$
(56)

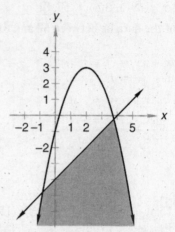

The region must be on or below the parabola and on or below the line.

Test point: $(2, -6)$

Line: $-6 \le 2 - 4$

$\qquad -6 \le -2 \qquad$ True

Parabola: $-6 \le -(2 - 2)^2 + 3$

$\qquad -6 \le 3 \qquad$ True

20. $f(x) = x(x + 3)$
(21)

$$f(x + h) = (x + h)[(x + h) + 3]$$

$$= x^2 + xh + 3x + xh + h^2 + 3h$$

$$= x^2 + h^2 + 3x + 3h + 2xh$$

$$f(x - h) = (x - h)[(x - h) + 3]$$

$$= x^2 - xh + 3x - xh + h^2 - 3h$$

$$= x^2 + h^2 + 3x - 3h - 2xh$$

$$\frac{f(x + h) - f(x - h)}{2h} = \frac{4xh + 6h}{2h} = \mathbf{2x + 3}$$

Test 17

1. $C = mN + b$
(62)

(a) $\begin{cases} 8.40 = m7 + b \\ (b) \ \ 3.60 = m3 + b \end{cases}$

$\qquad$ (a) $\quad 8.40 = m7 + b$

$-1(b) \ \ \underline{-3.60 = -m3 - b}$

$\qquad \quad 4.8 \ = \ m4$

$\qquad \qquad m = 1.2$

(a) $8.40 = m7 + b$

$\quad 8.40 = (1.2)7 + b$

$\quad\ b = 0$

$C = 1.2N = 1.2(10) = \mathbf{\$12.00}$

2. Overall average rate $= \dfrac{\text{overall distance}}{\text{overall time}}$
(38)

$$= \dfrac{n + f}{m + (2m - 5)} \dfrac{\text{ft}}{\text{min}}$$

$$= \dfrac{n + f}{3m - 5} \dfrac{\text{ft}}{\text{min}}$$

Time $= \dfrac{\text{distance}}{\text{rate}}$

$$= \dfrac{30 \text{ ft}}{\dfrac{(n + f) \text{ ft}}{(3m - 5) \text{ min}}} = \dfrac{30(3m - 5)}{n + f} \text{ min}$$

3. (a) $\text{antilog}_4\, 3 = 4^3 = \mathbf{64}$
(67)
  (b) $\text{antilog}_8\, 2 = 8^2 = \mathbf{64}$

4. (a) $\begin{cases} ax + dy = g \\ bx + cy = f \end{cases}$
(62) (b)

$b(a) \quad abx + bdy = \ bg$
$-a(b) \ \underline{-abx - acy = -af}$
$\qquad\quad (bd - ac)y = bg - af$

$$y = \dfrac{bg - af}{bd - ac}$$

5. $\begin{cases} 3x + 4y = 8 \\ 7x + 6y = 2 \end{cases}$
(62,66)

$a = 3,\ b = 7,\ c = 6,\ d = 4,\ f = 2,\ g = 8$

$$y = \dfrac{bg - af}{bd - ac} = \dfrac{(7)(8) - (3)(2)}{(7)(4) - (3)(6)} = \dfrac{56 - 6}{28 - 18} = \mathbf{5}$$

6. $y = \log_4 x$
(65) $4^y = x$

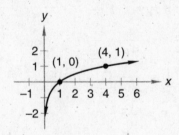

7. (a) $6 - 8i$
(64)

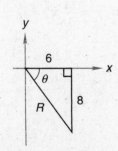

$R = \sqrt{6^2 + 8^2} = 10$

$\tan \theta = \dfrac{8}{6}$

$\theta = 53.13°$

The polar angle is $360° - 53.13° = 306.87°$.

10 cis 306.87°

(b) $6 \text{ cis } 300° = 6(\cos 300° + i \sin 300°)$

$$= 6\left[\dfrac{1}{2} + i\left(-\dfrac{\sqrt{3}}{2} \right) \right] = \mathbf{3 - 3\sqrt{3}i}$$

8. $\omega = \dfrac{v}{r} = \dfrac{34 \dfrac{\text{mi}}{\text{hr}}}{22 \text{ in.}} = \dfrac{34}{22} \dfrac{\text{mi}}{\text{in.-hr}}$
(53)

$$\omega = \left(\dfrac{34}{22} \dfrac{\text{mi}}{\text{in.-hr}} \right)\left(\dfrac{5280 \text{ ft}}{1 \text{ mi}} \right)\left(\dfrac{12 \text{ in.}}{1 \text{ ft}} \right)\left(\dfrac{1 \text{ hr}}{60 \text{ min}} \right)$$

$$\omega = \dfrac{(34)(5280)(12)}{(22)(60)} \dfrac{\text{rad}}{\text{min}} = \mathbf{1632 \dfrac{\text{rad}}{\text{min}}}$$

9. Range $= 14 - 3 = \mathbf{11}$
(61)

Mean $= \dfrac{6 + 5 + 7 + 14 + 7 + 3 + 7}{7} = \mathbf{7}$

Median $= \mathbf{7}$

Mode $= \mathbf{7}$

Variance

$$= \dfrac{1}{7}\left[(-1)^2 + (-2)^2 + 0^2 + 7^2 + 0^2 + (-4)^2 + 0^2 \right]$$

$$= \mathbf{10}$$

Standard deviation $= \sqrt{10} = \mathbf{3.16}$

10. (a) Function $= -\sin \theta$
(47,66)
  Centerline $= 8$
  Amplitude $= 4$
  Period $= 120°$

  Coefficient $= \dfrac{360°}{120°} = 3$

  $\mathbf{y = 8 - 4 \sin 3\theta}$

(b) Function $= -\cos \theta$
  Centerline $= -6$
  Amplitude $= 12$
  Period $= 80°$

  Coefficient $= \dfrac{360°}{80°} = \dfrac{9}{2}$

  $\mathbf{y = -6 - 12 \cos \dfrac{9}{2}\theta}$

11. $8 \ln e^3 + 6^{\log_6 8 - \log_6 2} - 5^{\log_5 30 + \log_5 1}$
(51,59)
$= 8(3) \ln e + 6^{\log_6 (8/2)} - 5^{\log_5 (30 \cdot 1)}$
$= 24 + 4 - 30 = \mathbf{-2}$

12. $[4 \operatorname{cis} (-60°)](3 \operatorname{cis} 300°) = 12 \operatorname{cis} (-60° + 300°)$
(64)
$= 12 \operatorname{cis} 240° = 12(\cos 240° + i \sin 240°)$
$= 12\left[\left(-\dfrac{1}{2}\right) + i\left(-\dfrac{\sqrt{3}}{2}\right)\right] = \mathbf{-6 - 6\sqrt{3}i}$

13. $\begin{cases} y \geq (x - 3)^2 - 5 & \text{(parabola)} \\ y \leq x - 4 & \text{(line)} \end{cases}$
(56)

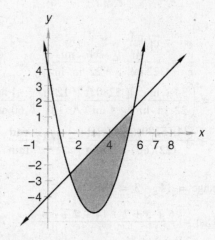

The region must be on or above the parabola and on or below the line.

Test point: $(3, -3)$

Line: $-3 \leq 3 - 4$
$\qquad -3 \leq -1 \qquad$ True

Parabola: $-3 \geq (3 - 3)^2 - 5$
$\qquad\qquad -3 \geq -5 \qquad$ True

14. $\qquad\qquad x^2 + y^2 - 10x - 6y + 18 = 0$
(63)
$\left(x^2 - 10x \qquad\right) + \left(y^2 - 6y \qquad\right) = -18$
$\left(x^2 - 10x + 25\right) + \left(y^2 - 6y + 9\right) = 16$
$\qquad\qquad (x - 5)^2 + (y - 3)^2 = 4^2$

Center = $(5, 3)$; radius = 4

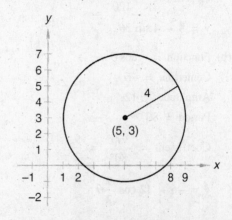

15. **Mean = 367.67**
(61)
Standard deviation = 67.36

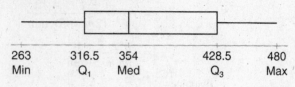

263	316.5	354	428.5	480
Min	Q_1	Med	Q_3	Max

16. $\mu = 87, \sigma = 5$
(61)
(a) $\mu \pm \sigma = 87 \pm 5 = 82, 92$

About **68%** of the data points lie within one standard deviation of the mean.

(b) $\mu + \sigma = 92$

About **34%** of the data points lie on one side of the mean within one standard deviation.

17. $\ln (x + 8) = \ln 5 + \ln (x - 4)$
(40,51)
$\ln (x + 8) = \ln [5(x - 4)]$
$\qquad x + 8 = 5(x - 4)$
$\qquad x + 8 = 5x - 20$
$\qquad\qquad 4x = 28$
$\qquad\qquad x = 7$

18. Directrix: $y = k - p = -4$
(68)
Focus: $(h, k + p) = (0, 4)$

$\qquad k + p = 4$
$\qquad \underline{k - p = -4}$
$\qquad 2k \qquad = 0$
$\qquad\quad k = 0$

Vertex: $(h, k) = (0, 0)$

$\qquad k + p = 4$
$\qquad (0) + p = 4$
$\qquad\qquad p = 4$

$\qquad y - k = \dfrac{1}{4p}(x - h)^2$

$\qquad y - (0) = \dfrac{1}{4(4)}[x - (0)]^2$

$\qquad\qquad y = \dfrac{1}{16}x^2$

Vertex: $(0, 0)$

Parabola: $y = \dfrac{1}{16}x^2$

19. (a) $\left(\tan x - \sqrt{3}\right)\left(2 \cos x + \sqrt{2}\right) = 0$
(52,60)
$\qquad \tan x - \sqrt{3} = 0$
$\qquad\qquad \tan x = \sqrt{3}$
$\qquad\qquad\qquad x = \dfrac{\pi}{3}, \dfrac{4\pi}{3}$

$$2 \cos x + \sqrt{2} = 0$$
$$2 \cos x = -\sqrt{2}$$
$$\cos x = -\frac{\sqrt{2}}{2}$$
$$x = \frac{3\pi}{4}, \frac{5\pi}{4}$$
$$x = \frac{\pi}{3}, \frac{3\pi}{4}, \frac{5\pi}{4}, \frac{4\pi}{3}$$

(b) $\tan 2x + \dfrac{\sqrt{3}}{3} = 0$

$$\tan 2x = -\frac{\sqrt{3}}{3}$$
$$2x = \frac{5\pi}{6}, \frac{11\pi}{6}, \frac{17\pi}{6}, \frac{23\pi}{6}$$
$$x = \frac{5\pi}{12}, \frac{11\pi}{12}, \frac{17\pi}{12}, \frac{23\pi}{12}$$

20.
(56)

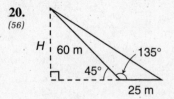

$$H = 60 \sin 45° = 42.43 \text{ m}$$
$$\text{Area} = \frac{1}{2}BH = \frac{1}{2}(25)(42.43) = \textbf{530.38 m}^2$$

Test 18

1. $y = ax^2$
(68)
$$y = \frac{1}{28}x^2$$
$$a = \frac{1}{4p}$$
$$\frac{1}{28} = \frac{1}{4p}$$
$$4p = 28$$
$$p = 7$$

The receiver should be placed **7 ft** above the vertex.

2. Vertex: $(h, k) = (-3, 2)$
(68)
Focus: $(h, k + p) = (-3, -2)$
$$k + p = -2$$
$$(2) + p = -2$$
$$p = -4$$
Directrix: $y = k - p = 2 - (-4) = 6$
Axis of symmetry: $x = h = -3$

$$y - k = \frac{1}{4p}(x - h)^2$$
$$y - (2) = \frac{1}{4(-4)}[x - (-3)]^2$$
$$y = -\frac{1}{16}(x + 3)^2 + 2$$

Parabola: $y = -\dfrac{1}{16}(x + 3)^2 + 2$

Directrix: $y = 6$

Axis of symmetry: $x = -3$

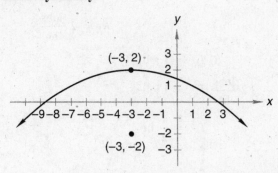

3. (a) $\text{antilog}_9 2 = 9^2 = \textbf{81}$
(67)

(b) $\text{antilog}_8 (-2) = 8^{-2} = \dfrac{1}{8^2} = \dfrac{\mathbf{1}}{\mathbf{64}}$

4.
(69)
$$\begin{vmatrix} x + 3 & 2 \\ -3 & x \end{vmatrix} = 10$$
$$x(x + 3) - (-3)(2) = 10$$
$$x^2 + 3x + 6 = 10$$
$$x^2 + 3x - 4 = 0$$
$$(x + 4)(x - 1) = 0$$
$$x = \textbf{-4, 1}$$

5. $n = \dfrac{p\sqrt{t}}{m^2}$
(18)
$$\frac{2p\sqrt{9t}}{(6m)^2} = \frac{2p(3)\sqrt{t}}{36m^2} = \frac{6p\sqrt{t}}{36m^2} = \frac{1}{6}n$$

n **is divided by 6.**

6. $(7 \text{ cis } 68°)(-2 \text{ cis } 82°) = -14 \text{ cis } (68° + 82°)$
(64)
$$= -14 \text{ cis } 150° = -14(\cos 150° + i \sin 150°)$$
$$= -14\left[\left(-\frac{\sqrt{3}}{2}\right) + i\left(\frac{1}{2}\right)\right] = \mathbf{7\sqrt{3} - 7i}$$

7. $3(180 - A) = 7(90 - A) + 130$
(1)
$$540 - 3A = 630 - 7A + 130$$
$$4A = 220$$
$$A = \textbf{55}°$$

8. $\dfrac{N!}{a!b!} = \dfrac{9!}{6!3!} = \mathbf{84}$
(55)

9.
(25)
$$R_J T_J + R_K T_K = 56 \text{ jobs}$$
$$\left(\dfrac{4}{5}\dfrac{\text{job}}{\text{hr}}\right)(20 \text{ hr}) + R_K(20 \text{ hr}) = 56 \text{ jobs}$$
$$16 \text{ jobs} + R_K(20 \text{ hr}) = 56 \text{ jobs}$$
$$R_K(20 \text{ hr}) = 40 \text{ jobs}$$
$$R_K = \dfrac{40}{20}\dfrac{\text{jobs}}{\text{hr}}$$
$$R_K = 2\dfrac{\text{jobs}}{\text{hr}}$$

$$R_K T_K = 1 \text{ job}$$
$$\left(2\dfrac{\text{jobs}}{\text{hr}}\right)T_K = 1 \text{ job}$$
$$T_K = \dfrac{1}{2}\ \mathbf{hr}$$

10. $\dfrac{x^2}{16} + \dfrac{y^2}{9} = 1$
(71)

Let $x = 0$ Let $y = 0$

$\dfrac{0}{16} + \dfrac{y^2}{9} = 1$ $\dfrac{x^2}{16} + \dfrac{0}{9} = 1$

$y = \pm 3$ $x = \pm 4$

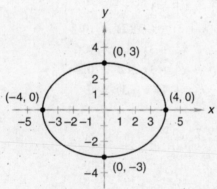

11. $\cos\theta + 2\cos^2\theta = 0$
(60)
$\cos\theta(1 + 2\cos\theta) = 0$

$\cos\theta = 0$ $1 + 2\cos\theta = 0$

$\theta = 90°, 270°$ $\cos\theta = -\dfrac{1}{2}$

                                $\theta = 120°, 240°$

$\theta = \mathbf{90°, 120°, 240°, 270°}$

12. Range $= 7 - 2 = \mathbf{5}$
(61)

Mean $= \dfrac{5 + 6 + 4 + 6 + 7 + 2}{6} = \mathbf{5}$

Median $= \dfrac{5 + 6}{2} = \mathbf{5.5}$

Mode $= \mathbf{6}$

Variance $= \dfrac{1}{6}\left[0^2 + 1^2 + (-1)^2 + 1^2 + 2^2 + (-3)^2\right]$

           $= \mathbf{2.67}$

Standard deviation $= \sqrt{2.67} = \mathbf{1.63}$

13. $A = 180° - 60° - 50°$
(72)
$A = \mathbf{70°}$

$\dfrac{b}{\sin 60°} = \dfrac{10}{\sin 50°}$

$b = \dfrac{10\sin 60°}{\sin 50°}$

$b = \mathbf{11.31}$

$\dfrac{a}{\sin 70°} = \dfrac{10}{\sin 50°}$

$a = \dfrac{10\sin 70°}{\sin 50°}$

$a = \mathbf{12.27}$

14.
(56)

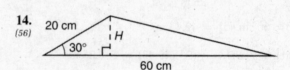

$H = 20\sin 30° = 10 \text{ cm}$

Area $= \dfrac{1}{2}BH = \dfrac{1}{2}(60)(10) = \mathbf{300\ cm^2}$

15. $\begin{cases} (x - 2)^2 + y^2 \le 5^2 & \text{(circle)} \\ y \ge (x - 2)^2 & \text{(parabola)} \end{cases}$
(56)

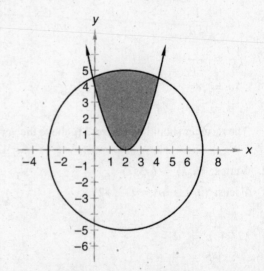

The region must be on or within the circle and on or above the parabola.

Test point: $(2, 3)$

Circle: $(2 - 2)^2 + 3^2 \leq 5^2$

$9 \leq 25$ True

Parabola: $3 \geq (2 - 2)^2$

$3 \geq 0$ True

16. (a) $\log_2 8 + 2^{\log_2 6} = \log_2 2^3 + 2^{\log_2 6}$
(51,59)
$= 3 + 6 = \mathbf{9}$

(b) $\ln e + \log 10 = 1 + 1 = \mathbf{2}$

(c) $\log 10^5 + \log 10^{1/5} = 5 + \dfrac{1}{5} = \dfrac{\mathbf{26}}{\mathbf{5}}$

17. $\dfrac{2}{3} \log_5 27 - \log_5 x = \log_5 3$
(40)

$\log_5 27^{2/3} - \log_5 x = \log_5 3$

$\log_5 \dfrac{9}{x} = \log_5 3$

$\dfrac{9}{x} = 3$

$3x = 9$

$x = \mathbf{3}$

18. $\ln x + \ln (x + 5) = \ln 6$
(51,59)

$\ln [x(x + 5)] = \ln 6$

$x(x + 5) = 6$

$x^2 + 5x = 6$

$x^2 + 5x - 6 = 0$

$(x + 6)(x - 1) = 0$

$x = -6, 1 \quad (x \neq -6)$

$x = \mathbf{1}$

19. $y = \log_5 x$
(65)
$5^y = x$

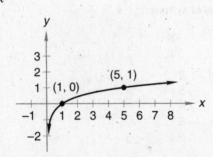

20. z score $= \dfrac{x - \mu}{\sigma} = \dfrac{5.4 - 6}{0.4} = -1.5$
(70)

Percentile $= 0.0668$

6.68%

Test 19

1. $R_C T_C + R_T T_T = 50$ pears
(25)

$\left(\dfrac{6}{9} \dfrac{\text{pear}}{\text{min}}\right)(T + 3 \text{ min}) + \left(\dfrac{4}{7} \dfrac{\text{pear}}{\text{min}}\right)T = 50$ pears

$\left(\dfrac{6}{9} \dfrac{\text{pear}}{\text{min}}\right)T + 2 \text{ pears} + \left(\dfrac{4}{7} \dfrac{\text{pear}}{\text{min}}\right)T = 50$ pears

$\left(\dfrac{26}{21} \dfrac{\text{pears}}{\text{min}}\right)T = 48$ pears

$T = \dfrac{\mathbf{504}}{\mathbf{13}}$ min

2. Members $= M$ members, fund $= 3000$ dollars
(44)

Rate $= \dfrac{3000}{M} \dfrac{\text{dollars}}{\text{member}}$

New Rate $= \dfrac{3000}{M - 50} \dfrac{\text{dollars}}{\text{member}}$

Increase $= \dfrac{3000}{M - 50} - \dfrac{3000}{M}$

$= \dfrac{3000M - 3000(M - 50)}{M(M - 50)}$

$= \dfrac{3000M - 3000M + 150,000}{M^2 - 50M}$

$= \dfrac{\mathbf{150,000}}{\mathbf{M^2 - 50M}} \dfrac{\textbf{dollars}}{\textbf{member}}$

3. $3x^2 + 3y^2 - 36x + 12y + 45 = 0$
(63)

$x^2 + y^2 - 12x + 4y + 15 = 0$

$\left(x^2 - 12x \quad\right) + \left(y^2 + 4y \quad\right) = -15$

$\left(x^2 - 12x + 36\right) + \left(y^2 + 4y + 4\right) = 25$

$(x - 6)^2 + (y + 2)^2 = 5^2$

Center $= (6, -2)$; radius $= 5$

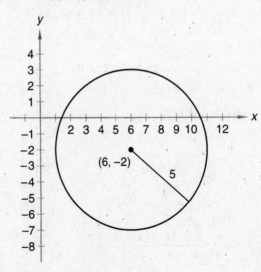

4.
(74)
$$y = \frac{\begin{vmatrix} 8 & 17 \\ 3 & 9 \end{vmatrix}}{\begin{vmatrix} 8 & 5 \\ 3 & -7 \end{vmatrix}} = \frac{72 - 51}{-56 - 15} = -\frac{21}{71}$$

5.
(73)

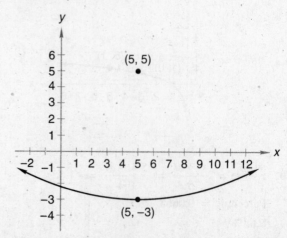

$$\theta = \frac{1}{2}\left(\frac{360°}{8}\right) = 22.5°$$

$$x = 16 \sin 22.5° = 6.123 \text{ ft}$$

$$A = 16 \cos 22.5° = 14.782 \text{ ft}$$

$$\text{Area}_\triangle = \frac{1}{2}(6.123)(14.782) = 45.255 \text{ ft}^2$$

$$\text{Area} = 16(45.255) = \textbf{724.08 ft}^2$$

6.
(70)
$$z \text{ score} = \frac{x - \mu}{\sigma} = \frac{69 - 90}{15} = -1.4$$

$$\text{Percentile} = 0.0808$$

$$1 - 0.0808 = 0.9192$$

$$\textbf{91.92\%}$$

7.
(75)
$${}_nC_r = \frac{n!}{(n - r)!\,r!}$$

$${}_{11}C_6 = \frac{11!}{(11 - 6)!6!} = \frac{11!}{5!6!} = \textbf{462}$$

8.
(64)
$(6 \text{ cis } 80°)(2 \text{ cis } 40°) = 12 \text{ cis } (80° + 40°)$

$= 12 \text{ cis } 120° = 12(\cos 120° + i \sin 120°)$

$$= 12\left[\left(-\frac{1}{2}\right) + i\left(\frac{\sqrt{3}}{2}\right)\right] = \textbf{-6} + \textbf{6}\sqrt{\textbf{3}}\,\textbf{i}$$

9.
(60)
$$\csc^2 x - 2 = 0$$

$$\left(\csc x + \sqrt{2}\right)\left(\csc x - \sqrt{2}\right) = 0$$

$\csc x + \sqrt{2} = 0 \qquad\qquad \csc x - \sqrt{2} = 0$

$\qquad \csc x = -\sqrt{2} \qquad\qquad\qquad \csc x = \sqrt{2}$

$\qquad \sin x = -\frac{1}{\sqrt{2}} \qquad\qquad\qquad \sin x = \frac{1}{\sqrt{2}}$

$\qquad\quad x = \frac{5\pi}{4}, \frac{7\pi}{4} \qquad\qquad\qquad x = \frac{\pi}{4}, \frac{3\pi}{4}$

$$x = \frac{\pi}{4}, \frac{3\pi}{4}, \frac{5\pi}{4}, \frac{7\pi}{4}$$

10.
(25)
(a) $\begin{cases} T_N = K_N + 5 \\ K_N + 5 = 2(T_N - 10) \end{cases}$

(b) $K_N + 5 = 2(T_N - 10)$

$\qquad K_N + 5 = 2T_N - 20$

$\qquad K_N + 5 = 2(K_N + 5) - 20$

$\qquad K_N + 5 = 2K_N + 10 - 20$

$\qquad\qquad K_N = 15$

$K_N + 7 = (15) + 7 = \textbf{22 yr}$

11.
(18)
$c + 1.5c = 75.00$

$\qquad 2.5c = 75.00$

$\qquad\quad c = 30.00$

$c + 0.9c = 30.00 + 0.9(30.00) = \textbf{\$57.00}$

12.
(68)
Vertex: $(h, k) = (5, -3)$

Focus: $(h, k + p) = (5, 5)$

$\qquad k + p = 5$

$\qquad (-3) + p = 5$

$\qquad\qquad p = 8$

Directrix: $y = k - p = (-3) - 8 = -11$

Axis of symmetry: $x = h = 5$

$$y - k = \frac{1}{4p}(x - h)^2$$

$$y - (-3) = \frac{1}{4(8)}(x - 5)^2$$

$$y = \frac{1}{32}(x - 5)^2 - 3$$

Parabola: $y = \dfrac{1}{32}(x - 5)^2 - 3$

Directrix: $y = -11$

Axis of symmetry: $x = 5$

13.
(56)
$$\begin{cases} 16 \leq x^2 + (y-4)^2 & \text{(circle)} \\ y > 4x + 4 & \text{(line)} \end{cases}$$

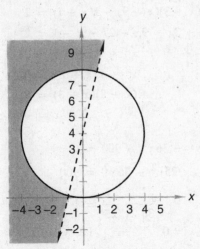

The region must be on or outside the circle and above the line.

Test point: $(-4, 1)$

Line: $1 > 4(-4) + 4$

$\qquad 1 > -12 \qquad$ True

Circle: $16 \leq (-4)^2 + (1-4)^2$

$\qquad 16 \leq 25 \qquad$ True

14.
(69)
$$\begin{vmatrix} b+4 & 5 \\ 1 & b+1 \end{vmatrix} = 5$$

$(b+4)(b+1) - (1)(5) = 5$

$b^2 + 4b + b + 4 - 5 = 5$

$b^2 + 5b - 1 = 5$

$b^2 + 5b - 6 = 0$

$(b+6)(b-1) = 0$

$b = \mathbf{-6, 1}$

15.
(47,66)
Function $= \sin \theta$

Centerline $= 5$

Amplitude $= 10$

Period $= 720°$

Coefficient $= \dfrac{360°}{720°} = \dfrac{1}{2}$

$y = 5 + 10 \sin \dfrac{1}{2}\theta$

16.
(72)
$A = 180° - 130° - 30°$

$A = \mathbf{20°}$

$\dfrac{a}{\sin 20°} = \dfrac{22}{\sin 130°}$

$a = \dfrac{22 \sin 20°}{\sin 130°}$

$a = \mathbf{9.82}$

$\dfrac{b}{\sin 30°} = \dfrac{22}{\sin 130°}$

$b = \dfrac{22 \sin 30°}{\sin 130°}$

$b = \mathbf{14.36}$

17.
(71)
$\dfrac{x^2}{25} + \dfrac{y^2}{16} = 1$

Let $x = 0$ $\qquad\qquad$ Let $y = 0$

$\dfrac{0}{25} + \dfrac{y^2}{16} = 1 \qquad\qquad \dfrac{x^2}{25} + \dfrac{0}{16} = 1$

$\qquad y = \pm 4 \qquad\qquad\qquad x = \pm 5$

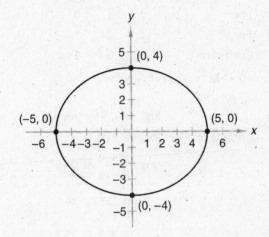

18.
(48)
$f\left(\dfrac{7\pi}{6}\right) + g\left(\dfrac{5\pi}{6}\right) f\left(\dfrac{7\pi}{4}\right)$

$= \sin^2\left(\dfrac{7\pi}{6}\right) + \cos^2\left(\dfrac{5\pi}{6}\right) \sin^2\left(\dfrac{7\pi}{4}\right)$

$= \left(-\sin\dfrac{\pi}{6}\right)^2 + \left(-\cos\dfrac{\pi}{6}\right)^2 \left(-\sin\dfrac{\pi}{4}\right)^2$

$= \left(-\dfrac{1}{2}\right)^2 + \left(-\dfrac{\sqrt{3}}{2}\right)^2 \left(-\dfrac{\sqrt{2}}{2}\right)^2$

$= \dfrac{1}{4} + \dfrac{3}{4} \cdot \dfrac{2}{4} = \dfrac{1}{4} + \dfrac{6}{16} = \dfrac{10}{16} = \dfrac{\mathbf{5}}{\mathbf{8}}$

19.
(40)
$3 \log_4 x - 2 \log_4 2 = 2$

$\log_4 x^3 - \log_4 2^2 = 2$

$\log_4 \dfrac{x^3}{4} = 2$

$\dfrac{x^3}{4} = 4^2$

$x^3 = 4^3$

$x = \mathbf{4}$

20.
(76)
$\dfrac{\csc x}{\sec x} = \dfrac{\dfrac{1}{\sin x}}{\dfrac{1}{\cos x}} = \dfrac{\cos x}{\sin x} = \dfrac{1}{\tan x} = \cot x$

Test 20

1. $(x + y)^5$
(77)

Term	①	②	③	④	⑤	⑥
For x	5	4	3	2	1	0
For y	0	1	2	3	4	5
Coefficient	1	5	10	10	5	1

$$10x^3y^2$$

2. $(x + y)^3$
(77)

Term	①	②	③	④
For x	3	2	1	0
For y	0	1	2	3
Coefficient	1	3	3	1

$$x^3 + 3x^2y + 3xy^2 + y^3$$

3.
(40)

$$\log_3 (x + 4) = \log_3 (6 - x) + 2$$
$$\log_3 (x + 4) - \log_3 (6 - x) = 2$$
$$\log_3 \frac{x + 4}{6 - x} = 2$$
$$\frac{x + 4}{6 - x} = 3^2$$
$$x + 4 = 54 - 9x$$
$$10x = 50$$
$$x = 5$$

4. $7x^2 + 63y^2 - 252 = 0$
(71)
$$7x^2 + 63y^2 = 252$$
$$\frac{x^2}{36} + \frac{y^2}{4} = 1$$

Let $x = 0$ Let $y = 0$

$$\frac{0}{36} + \frac{y^2}{4} = 1 \qquad \frac{x^2}{36} + \frac{0}{4} = 1$$
$$y = \pm 2 \qquad\qquad x = \pm 6$$

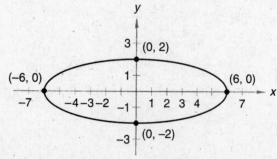

5. $\dfrac{\sin^2 \theta + \cos^2 \theta}{1 + \cot^2 \theta} = \dfrac{1}{\csc^2 \theta} = \sin^2 \theta$
(76,80)

6.
(69)
$$\begin{vmatrix} x + 3 & 1 \\ x + 1 & x + 9 \end{vmatrix} = 2$$
$$(x + 3)(x + 9) - 1(x + 1) = 2$$
$$x^2 + 3x + 9x + 27 - x - 1 = 2$$
$$x^2 + 11x + 26 = 2$$
$$x^2 + 11x + 24 = 0$$
$$(x + 8)(x + 3) = 0$$
$$x = -8, -3$$

7. $25y^2 - 36x^2 - 900 = 0$
(78)
$$25y^2 - 36x^2 = 900$$
$$\frac{y^2}{36} - \frac{x^2}{25} = 1$$

Let $x = 0$ Let $y = 0$

$$\frac{y^2}{36} - \frac{0}{25} = 1 \qquad \frac{0}{36} - \frac{x^2}{25} = 1$$
$$y = \pm 6 \qquad\qquad x = \pm 5i$$

Vertices: $(0, 6), (0, -6)$

Asymptotes: $y = \dfrac{6}{5}x$; $y = -\dfrac{6}{5}x$

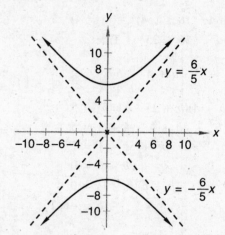

8. $_nC_r = \dfrac{n!}{(n - r)!r!}$
(75)

$$_{16}C_{11} = \frac{16!}{(16 - 11)!11!} = \frac{16!}{5!11!} = 4368$$

9. $\left(\sqrt{3} + i\right)^4$
(79)
$$r = \sqrt{\left(\sqrt{3}\right)^2 + 1^2} = 2$$
$$\tan \theta = \frac{1}{\sqrt{3}}$$
$$\theta = 30°$$
$$\left(\sqrt{3} + i\right)^4 = (2 \text{ cis } 30°)^4 = 2^4 \text{ cis } (4 \cdot 30°)$$
$$= 16 \text{ cis } 120° = 16(\cos 120° + i \sin 120°)$$
$$= 16\left[\left(-\frac{1}{2}\right) + i\left(\frac{\sqrt{3}}{2}\right)\right] = -8 + 8\sqrt{3}i$$

10. $A = 180° - 60° - 40°$
(72)
$A = 80°$

$$\frac{a}{\sin 80°} = \frac{8}{\sin 40°}$$

$$a = \frac{8 \sin 80°}{\sin 40°}$$

$$a = 12.26 \text{ in.}$$

$$\frac{c}{\sin 60°} = \frac{8}{\sin 40°}$$

$$c = \frac{8 \sin 60°}{\sin 40°}$$

$$c = 10.78 \text{ in.}$$

11. Function $= \cos x$
(47,66)
Centerline $= -5$

Amplitude $= 4$

Period $= 2\pi$

Phase angle $= \dfrac{\pi}{4}$

$$y = -5 + 4 \cos\left(x - \frac{\pi}{4}\right)$$

12. $[-5 \operatorname{cis}(-30°)](3 \operatorname{cis} 180°) = -15 \operatorname{cis}(-30° + 180°)$
(64)
$= -15 \operatorname{cis} 150° = -15(\cos 150° + i \sin 150°)$

$$= -15\left[\left(-\frac{\sqrt{3}}{2}\right) + i\left(\frac{1}{2}\right)\right] = \frac{15\sqrt{3}}{2} - \frac{15}{2}i$$

13. Side $= \dfrac{96}{8}$
(73)
Side = 12 cm

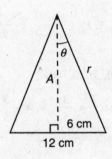

6 cm

12 cm

$$\theta = \frac{1}{2}\left(\frac{360°}{8}\right) = 22.5°$$

$$r = \frac{6}{\sin 22.5°}$$

Radius = 15.68 cm

14. $\dfrac{\text{Side}_S}{\text{Side}_L} = \dfrac{5}{6}$
(5)

$$\frac{\text{Area}_S}{\text{Area}_L} = \left(\frac{\text{Side}_S}{\text{Side}_L}\right)^2 = \left(\frac{5}{6}\right)^2 = \frac{25}{36}$$

15. $C = mN + b$
(62)
(a) $\begin{cases} 6000 = m18 + b \\ (b) \ 3800 = m10 + b \end{cases}$

(a)$\quad 6000 = m18 + b$

-1(b)$\ \ \underline{-3800 = -m10 - b}$

$2200 = m8$

$m = 275$

(b) $3800 = m10 + b$

$3800 = (275)10 + b$

$b = 1050$

$C = 275N + 1050 = 275(8) + 1050 = \textbf{\$3250}$

16. (a) $\begin{cases} (B + C)T_D = D_D \\ (b)\ (B - C)T_U = D_U \end{cases}$
(36)
$B = 5C,\ T_D = T_U - 4$

(b) $\quad (B - C)T_U = D_U$

$(5C - C)T_U = 84$

$4CT_U = 84$

$CT_U = 21$

(a) $\qquad\quad (B + C)T_D = D_D$

$(5C + C)\left(T_U - 4\right) = 54$

$6C\left(T_U - 4\right) = 54$

$6CT_U - 24C = 54$

$6(21) - 24C = 54$

$24C = 72$

$C = 3$

$B = 5C = 5(3) = \textbf{15 mph}$

17. $(343 \operatorname{cis} 90°)^{1/3} = \sqrt[3]{343}\ \operatorname{cis}\left(\dfrac{90°}{3} + n\dfrac{360°}{3}\right)$
(79)

$7 \operatorname{cis}\left(\dfrac{90°}{3}\right) = \textbf{7 cis 30°}$

$7 \operatorname{cis}\left(\dfrac{90°}{3} + 120°\right) = \textbf{7 cis 150°}$

$7 \operatorname{cis}\left(\dfrac{90°}{3} + 240°\right) = \textbf{7 cis 270°}$

18. $(27i)^{1/3} = (27 \operatorname{cis} 90°)^{1/3}$
(79)

$\phantom{(27i)^{1/3}} = \sqrt[3]{27}\ \operatorname{cis}\left(\dfrac{90°}{3} + n\dfrac{360°}{3}\right)$

$3 \operatorname{cis}\left(\dfrac{90°}{3}\right) = 3 \operatorname{cis} 30° = \dfrac{3\sqrt{3}}{2} + \dfrac{3}{2}i$

$3 \operatorname{cis}\left(\dfrac{90°}{3} + 120°\right) = 3 \operatorname{cis} 150° = -\dfrac{3\sqrt{3}}{2} + \dfrac{3}{2}i$

$3 \operatorname{cis}\left(\dfrac{90°}{3} + 240°\right) = 3 \operatorname{cis} 270° = \textbf{-3i}$

19. $y = -\log_4 x$
(65)
$y = \log_4 x^{-1}$

$x^{-1} = 4^y$

$x = \dfrac{1}{4^y}$

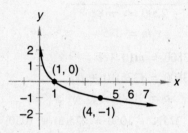

20. Vertex: $(h, k) = (-5, 4)$
(68)
Focus: $(h, k + p) = (-5, 2)$

$k + p = 2$

$(4) + p = 2$

$p = -2$

Directrix: $y = k - p = 4 - (-2) = 6$

Axis of symmetry: $x = h = -5$

$y - k = \dfrac{1}{4p}(x - h)^2$

$y - (4) = \dfrac{1}{4(-2)}[x - (-5)]^2$

$y = -\dfrac{1}{8}(x + 5)^2 + 4$

Parabola: $y = -\dfrac{1}{8}(x + 5)^2 + 4$

Directrix: $y = 6$

Axis of symmetry: $x = -5$

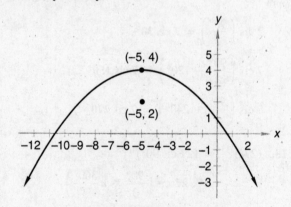

Test 21

1. $(-216i)^{1/3} = (216 \text{ cis } 270°)^{1/3}$
(79)
$= \sqrt[3]{216} \text{ cis } \left(\dfrac{270°}{3} + n\dfrac{360°}{3} \right)$

$6 \text{ cis } \left(\dfrac{270°}{3} \right) = 6 \text{ cis } 90° = \boldsymbol{6i}$

$6 \text{ cis } \left(\dfrac{270°}{3} + 120° \right) = 6 \text{ cis } 210° = \boldsymbol{-3\sqrt{3} - 3i}$

$6 \text{ cis } \left(\dfrac{270°}{3} + 240° \right) = 6 \text{ cis } 330° = \boldsymbol{3\sqrt{3} - 3i}$

2. $D = mF + b$
(62)

(a) $\begin{cases} 250 = m400 + b \\ (b) \ 200 = m300 + b \end{cases}$

$\quad$ (a) $\quad 250 = \quad m400 + b$

$-1(b) \ \dfrac{-200 = -m300 - b}{50 = \quad m100}$

$m = \dfrac{1}{2}$

(a) $250 = m400 + b$

$250 = \left(\dfrac{1}{2} \right)400 + b$

$b = 50$

$D = \dfrac{1}{2}F + 50 = \dfrac{1}{2}(250) + 50 = \boldsymbol{175}$

3. $25y^2 - 9x^2 = 225$
(78)
$\dfrac{y^2}{9} - \dfrac{x^2}{25} = 1$

Let $x = 0$ $\qquad$ Let $y = 0$

$\dfrac{y^2}{9} - \dfrac{0}{25} = 1$ $\qquad$ $\dfrac{0}{9} - \dfrac{x^2}{25} = 1$

$\qquad y = \pm 3$ $\qquad\qquad x = \pm 5i$

Vertices: $(0, 3), (0, -3)$

Asymptotes: $y = \dfrac{3}{5}x, \ y = -\dfrac{3}{5}x$

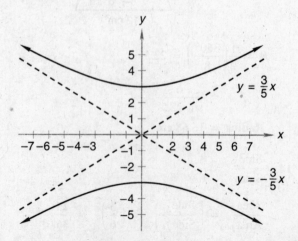

4. $RCT = F$
(44) $R(c)(10) = 8$

$$R = \frac{8}{10c} \frac{\text{flowers}}{\text{child-min}}$$

$$RCT = F$$

$$\left(\frac{8}{10c}\right)(c + 4)T = y$$

$$T = \frac{10cy}{8(c + 4)} \text{ min}$$

5. $\begin{cases} x^2 + y^2 + 2x - 6y - 26 \leq 0 & \text{(circle)} \\ y \geq x^2 + 2 & \text{(parabola)} \end{cases}$
(56)

$$x^2 + y^2 + 2x - 6y - 26 \leq 0$$

$$\left(x^2 + 2x \quad\right) + \left(y^2 - 6y \quad\right) \leq 26$$

$$\left(x^2 + 2x + 1\right) + \left(y^2 - 6y + 9\right) \leq 36$$

$$(x + 1)^2 + (y - 3)^2 \leq 6^2$$

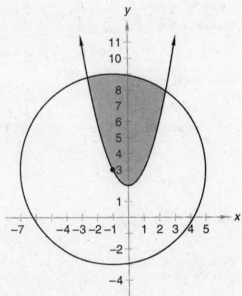

The region must be on or inside the circle and on or above the parabola.

Test point: $(0, 4)$

Circle: $(0 + 1)^2 + (4 - 3)^2 \leq 6^2$

$$2 \leq 36 \qquad \text{True}$$

Parabola: $4 \geq (0)^2 + 2$

$$4 \geq 2 \qquad \text{True}$$

6. $16y^2 + 25x^2 = 400$
(71)

$$\frac{y^2}{25} + \frac{x^2}{16} = 1$$

Let $x = 0$ Let $y = 0$

$$\frac{y^2}{25} + \frac{0}{16} = 1 \qquad \frac{0}{25} + \frac{x^2}{16} = 1$$

$$y = \pm 5 \qquad\qquad x = \pm 4$$

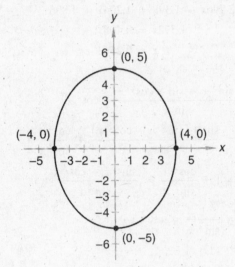

7. Side $= \dfrac{120}{10} = 12$ m
(73)

$$\theta = \frac{1}{2}\left(\frac{360°}{10}\right) = 18°$$

$$A = \frac{6}{\tan 18°} = 18.466 \text{ m}$$

$$\text{Area}_\Delta = \frac{1}{2}(6)(18.466) = 55.40 \text{ m}^2$$

$$\text{Area} = 20(55.40) = \mathbf{1108 \ m^2}$$

8.
(32)

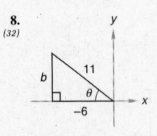

$$0° \leq \theta \leq 180°$$

$$b = \sqrt{11^2 - (-6)^2} = \sqrt{85}$$

$$\sin\left[\text{Arccos}\left(-\frac{6}{11}\right)\right] = \frac{\sqrt{85}}{11}$$

9.
(82)

$$5^{4x+2} = 4^{2x+3}$$

$$\log 5^{4x+2} = \log 4^{2x+3}$$

$$(4x + 2)\log 5 = (2x + 3)\log 4$$

$$(4x + 2)(0.699) = (2x + 3)(0.602)$$

$$2.796x + 1.398 = 1.204x + 1.806$$

$$1.592x = 0.408$$

$$x = \mathbf{0.256}$$

10.
(76,80)

$$\frac{\sin^3 x + \sin x \cos^2 x}{\sin x} + \cot^2 x$$

$$= \frac{\sin x \left(\sin^2 x + \cos^2 x\right)}{\sin x} + \frac{\cos^2 x}{\sin^2 x}$$

$$= 1 + \frac{\cos^2 x}{\sin^2 x} = \frac{\sin^2 x + \cos^2 x}{\sin^2 x}$$

$$= \frac{1}{\sin^2 x} = \csc^2 x$$

11. $(c + d)^6$
(77)

Term	①	②	③	④	⑤	⑥	⑦
For c	6	5	4	3	2	1	0
For d	0	1	2	3	4	5	6
Coefficient	1	6	15	20	15	6	1

$$c^6 + 6c^5 d + 15c^4 d^2 + 20c^3 d^3 + 15c^2 d^4 + 6cd^5 + d^6$$

12.
(79)

$$\left(\frac{1}{2} \text{ cis } 30°\right)^5 = \left(\frac{1}{2}\right)^5 \text{ cis } (5 \cdot 30°)$$

$$= \frac{1}{32} \text{ cis } 150° = \frac{1}{32}(\cos 150° + i \sin 150°)$$

$$= \frac{1}{32}\left[-\frac{\sqrt{3}}{2} + i\left(\frac{1}{2}\right)\right] = -\frac{\sqrt{3}}{64} + \frac{1}{64}i$$

13. (a) $P(\text{both green}) = \frac{5}{12} \cdot \frac{5}{12} = \frac{25}{144}$
(83)

    (b) $P(\text{both green}) = \frac{5}{12} \cdot \frac{4}{11} = \frac{5}{33}$

14. $P(\text{five heads}) = \frac{1}{2} \cdot \frac{1}{2} \cdot \frac{1}{2} \cdot \frac{1}{2} \cdot \frac{1}{2} = \frac{1}{32}$
(83)

15.
(81)

108 m   **60 m** L A $32°$ l

$$\frac{108}{\sin A} = \frac{60}{\sin 32°}$$

$$\sin A = \frac{108 \sin 32°}{60}$$

$$A = 107.47°$$

$$L = 180° - 32° - 107.47° = 40.53°$$

$$\frac{l}{\sin 40.53°} = \frac{60}{\sin 32°}$$

$$l = \frac{60 \sin 40.53°}{\sin 32°}$$

$$l = \mathbf{73.58 \text{ m}}$$

16. z score $= \dfrac{x - \mu}{\sigma} = \dfrac{560 - 500}{75} = 0.8$
(70)

Percentile $= 0.7881$

$1 - 0.7881 = 0.2119$

21.19%

17.
(60)

$$2\csc^2 \theta - 3\csc \theta - 2 = 0$$

$$(2\csc \theta + 1)(\csc \theta - 2) = 0$$

$$2\csc \theta + 1 = 0 \qquad \csc \theta - 2 = 0$$

$$\csc \theta = -\frac{1}{2} \qquad\qquad \csc \theta = 2$$

$$\sin \theta = -2 \qquad\qquad \sin \theta = \frac{1}{2}$$

no answer $\qquad\qquad \theta = \mathbf{30°, 150°}$

18. $y = 3 + 5 \sin \frac{1}{2}(\theta + 45°)$
(84)

Period $= \dfrac{360°}{\frac{1}{2}} = 720°$

Phase angle $= -45°$

19. (a) $\log_2 x + \dfrac{1}{3} \log_2 27 = \dfrac{1}{2} \log_2 81$
(40,59)

$$\log_2 x + \log_2 27^{1/3} = \log_2 81^{1/2}$$

$$\log_2 [(x)(3)] = \log_2 9$$

$$3x = 9$$

$$x = \mathbf{3}$$

(b) $\log_4 (5x + 4) - \dfrac{2}{3} \log_4 64 = 1$

$\log_4 (5x + 4) - \log_4 64^{2/3} = 1$

$\log_4 \dfrac{5x + 4}{16} = 1$

$\dfrac{5x + 4}{16} = 4^1$

$5x + 4 = 64$

$5x = 60$

$x = \mathbf{12}$

20. $a^2 = b^2 + c^2 - 2bc \cos A$
(81)

$a = \sqrt{17^2 + 13^2 - 2(17)(13) \cos 70°}$

$a = \mathbf{17.52\ cm}$

$\dfrac{17}{\sin B} = \dfrac{a}{\sin 70°}$

$\sin B = \dfrac{17 \sin 70°}{17.52}$

$B = \mathbf{65.76°}$

$C = 180° - 70° - 65.76°$

$C = \mathbf{44.24°}$

Test 22

1. (a) $P(\text{both blue}) = \dfrac{5}{15} \cdot \dfrac{5}{15} = \dfrac{1}{9}$
(83)

(b) $P(\text{both blue}) = \dfrac{5}{15} \cdot \dfrac{4}{14} = \dfrac{2}{21}$

2.
(83)

	1	2	3	4	5	6
1	②	③	④	⑤	6	7
2	③	④	⑤	6	7	8
3	④	⑤	6	7	8	9
4	⑤	6	7	8	9	10
5	6	7	8	9	10	11
6	7	8	9	10	11	12

$P(\text{sum} < 6) = \dfrac{10}{36} = \dfrac{\mathbf{5}}{\mathbf{18}}$

3. $R_B = 1,\ R_L = \dfrac{1}{12},\ T_L = T_B$
(85)

Big hand:

$R_B T_B = S + 20$

$(1)T = S + 20$

$S = T - 20$

Little hand:

$R_L T_L = S$

$\left(\dfrac{1}{12}\right) T = S$

$S = \dfrac{T}{12}$

$\dfrac{T}{12} = T - 20$

$\dfrac{11}{12} T = 20$

$T = \dfrac{240}{11}$

$T = \mathbf{21\dfrac{9}{11}\ min}$

4. $y = -3 + 4 \cos (x + 60°)$
(84)

Period $= 360°$

Phase angle $= -60°$

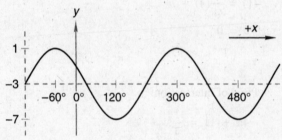

5.
(60,85)

$2 \sin^2 3\theta = 11 \cos 3\theta + 7$

$2(1 - \cos^2 3\theta) = 11 \cos 3\theta + 7$

$2 \cos^2 3\theta + 11 \cos 3\theta + 5 = 0$

$(2 \cos 3\theta + 1)(\cos 3\theta + 5) = 0$

$2 \cos 3\theta + 1 = 0 \qquad\qquad \cos 3\theta + 5 = 0$

$\cos 3\theta = -\dfrac{1}{2} \qquad\qquad \cos 3\theta = -5$

$\qquad\qquad\qquad\qquad\qquad\qquad$ no answer

$3\theta = 120°, 240°,$
$\qquad 480°, 600°,$
$\qquad 840°, 960°$

$\theta = \mathbf{40°, 80°, 160°,}$
$\qquad \mathbf{200°, 280°,}$
$\qquad \mathbf{320°}$

6. $b^2 = a^2 + c^2 - 2ac \cos B$
(81)

$\cos B = \dfrac{a^2 + c^2 - b^2}{2ac}$

$\cos B = \dfrac{13^2 + 6^2 - 18^2}{2(13)(6)}$

$B = \mathbf{139.71°}$

7.
(74)
$$y = \dfrac{\begin{vmatrix} 3 & -2 \\ -4 & 7 \end{vmatrix}}{\begin{vmatrix} 3 & -8 \\ -4 & 5 \end{vmatrix}} = \dfrac{21 - 8}{15 - 32} = -\dfrac{13}{17}$$

8.
(82)
$$4^{9x-2} = 9^{4x+3}$$
$$\log 4^{9x-2} = \log 9^{4x+3}$$
$$(9x - 2)\log 4 = (4x + 3)\log 9$$
$$(9x - 2)(0.602) = (4x + 3)(0.954)$$
$$5.418x - 1.204 = 3.816x + 2.862$$
$$1.602x = 4.066$$
$$x = \mathbf{2.538}$$

9.
(58)
$$4x = 11 - y$$
$$y = -4x + 11$$

Equation of the perpendicular line:

$$y = \dfrac{1}{4}x + b$$
$$(1) = \dfrac{1}{4}(4) + b$$
$$b = 0$$
$$y = \dfrac{1}{4}x$$

Point of intersection:

$$-4x + 11 = \dfrac{1}{4}x$$
$$\dfrac{17}{4}x = 11$$
$$x = \dfrac{44}{17}$$
$$y = \dfrac{1}{4}x = \dfrac{1}{4}\left(\dfrac{44}{17}\right) = \dfrac{11}{17}$$
$$\left(\dfrac{44}{17}, \dfrac{11}{17}\right) \text{ and } (4, 1)$$

$$D = \sqrt{\left(4 - \dfrac{44}{17}\right)^2 + \left(1 - \dfrac{11}{17}\right)^2}$$
$$= \sqrt{\left(\dfrac{24}{17}\right)^2 + \left(\dfrac{6}{17}\right)^2}$$
$$= \sqrt{\dfrac{612}{289}} = \sqrt{\dfrac{36}{17}} = \dfrac{6}{\sqrt{17}} = \dfrac{\mathbf{6\sqrt{17}}}{\mathbf{17}}$$

10.
(87)
$$\cos\left(\theta + \dfrac{\pi}{4}\right) = \cos\theta\cos\dfrac{\pi}{4} - \sin\theta\sin\dfrac{\pi}{4}$$
$$= \cos\theta\left(\dfrac{\sqrt{2}}{2}\right) - \sin\theta\left(\dfrac{\sqrt{2}}{2}\right)$$
$$= \dfrac{\sqrt{2}}{2}(\cos\theta - \sin\theta)$$

11.
(79)
$$(625 \text{ cis } 120°)^{1/4} = \sqrt[4]{625}\text{ cis}\left(\dfrac{120°}{4} + n\dfrac{360°}{4}\right)$$
$$5 \text{ cis}\left(\dfrac{120°}{4}\right) = 5 \text{ cis } 30° = \dfrac{5\sqrt{3}}{2} + \dfrac{5}{2}i$$
$$5 \text{ cis}\left(\dfrac{120°}{4} + 90°\right) = 5 \text{ cis } 120° = -\dfrac{5}{2} + \dfrac{5\sqrt{3}}{2}i$$
$$5 \text{ cis}\left(\dfrac{120°}{4} + 180°\right) = 5 \text{ cis } 210° = -\dfrac{5\sqrt{3}}{2} - \dfrac{5}{2}i$$
$$5 \text{ cis}\left(\dfrac{120°}{4} + 270°\right) = 5 \text{ cis } 300° = \dfrac{5}{2} - \dfrac{5\sqrt{3}}{2}i$$

12.
(87)
$$\tan(A + B) = \dfrac{\sin(A + B)}{\cos(A + B)}$$
$$= \dfrac{\sin A\cos B + \cos A\sin B}{\cos A\cos B - \sin A\sin B}$$
$$= \dfrac{\dfrac{\sin A\cos B}{\cos A\cos B} + \dfrac{\cos A\sin B}{\cos A\cos B}}{\dfrac{\cos A\cos B}{\cos A\cos B} - \dfrac{\sin A\sin B}{\cos A\cos B}}$$
$$= \dfrac{\tan A + \tan B}{1 - \tan A\tan B}$$

13.
(40)
$$\dfrac{1}{3}\log_4 27 - \log_4(x - 8) + \log_4(x - 1) = \log_4 24$$
$$\log_4 27^{1/3} - \log_4(x - 8) + \log_4(x - 1) = \log_4 24$$
$$\log_4 \dfrac{3(x - 1)}{x - 8} = \log_4 24$$
$$\dfrac{3(x - 1)}{x - 8} = 24$$
$$3x - 3 = 24x - 192$$
$$21x = 189$$
$$x = \mathbf{9}$$

14.
(80)
$$\dfrac{\sec x}{1 - \cos x} - \dfrac{\sec x}{1 + \cos x}$$
$$= \dfrac{\sec x\left[(1 + \cos x) - (1 - \cos x)\right]}{1 - \cos^2 x} = \dfrac{2\sec x\cos x}{\sin^2 x}$$
$$= \dfrac{2 \cdot \dfrac{1}{\cos x} \cdot \cos x}{\sin^2 x} = \dfrac{2}{\sin^2 x} = 2\csc^2 x$$

15.
(81)

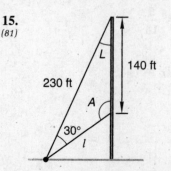

$$\frac{230}{\sin A} = \frac{140}{\sin 30°}$$

$$\sin A = \frac{230 \sin 30°}{140}$$

$$A = 124.77°$$

$$L = 180° - 124.77° - 30° = 25.23°$$

$$\frac{l}{\sin 25.23} = \frac{140}{\sin 30°}$$

$$l = \frac{140 \sin 25.23}{\sin 30°}$$

$$l = \mathbf{119.35 \ ft}$$

16.
(71)

$$49x^2 + 4y^2 = 196$$

$$\frac{x^2}{4} + \frac{y^2}{49} = 1$$

Let $x = 0$ Let $y = 0$

$$\frac{0}{4} + \frac{y^2}{49} = 1 \qquad \frac{x^2}{4} + \frac{0}{49} = 1$$

$$y = \pm 7 \qquad\qquad x = \pm 2$$

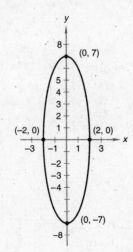

17. $A_0 = 600$, $A_{35} = 350$
(88)

$$A_t = A_0 e^{kt}$$

$$350 = 600 e^{k35}$$

$$e^{k35} = 0.58333$$

$$35k = \ln 0.58333$$

$$k = -0.015400$$

$$A_t = \mathbf{600} e^{\mathbf{-0.015400}t}$$

$$\frac{1}{2}(600) = 600 e^{-0.015400t}$$

$$-0.015400t = \ln \frac{1}{2}$$

$$t = \mathbf{45.01 \ hr}$$

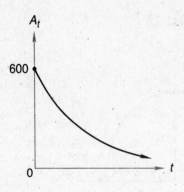

18. $a_1 = 8$, $d = -5$, $n = 23$
(86)

$$a_n = a_1 + (n - 1)d$$

$$a_{23} = 8 + (23 - 1)(-5) = 8 + 22(-5) = \mathbf{-102}$$

19. $a_{31} = a_1 + 30d = 34$
(86) $\quad a_{49} = a_1 + 48d = -56$

(a) $\begin{cases} a_1 + 30d = 34 \\ a_1 + 48d = -56 \end{cases}$
(b)

$$\begin{array}{r} \text{(a)} \quad a_1 + 30d = 34 \\ -1\text{(b)} \quad \underline{-a_1 - 48d = 56} \\ -18d = 90 \\ d = -5 \end{array}$$

(a) $\quad a_1 + 30d = 34$

$$a_1 + 30(-5) = 34$$

$$a_1 = 184$$

184, 179, 174

20. $x^2 - 9y^2 = 81$
(78)

$$\frac{x^2}{81} - \frac{y^2}{9} = 1$$

Let $x = 0$ Let $y = 0$

$$\frac{0}{81} - \frac{y^2}{9} = 1 \qquad \frac{x^2}{81} - \frac{0}{9} = 1$$

$$y = \pm 3i \qquad\qquad x = \pm 9$$

Vertices: $(9, 0)$, $(-9, 0)$

Asymptotes: $y = \frac{1}{3}x$, $y = -\frac{1}{3}x$

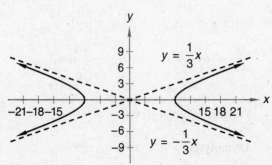

Test 23

1.
(89)

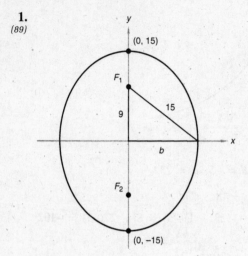

$$9^2 + b^2 = 15^2$$
$$b^2 = 144$$
$$b = 12$$

$$\frac{x^2}{b^2} + \frac{y^2}{a^2} = 1$$

$$\frac{x^2}{144} + \frac{y^2}{225} = 1$$

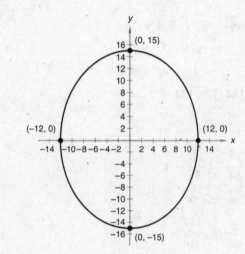

2. $x^2 - 49y^2 = 49$
(78)

$$\frac{x^2}{49} - \frac{y^2}{1} = 1$$

Let $x = 0$ Let $y = 0$

$$\frac{0}{49} - \frac{y^2}{1} = 1 \qquad \frac{x^2}{49} - \frac{0}{1} = 1$$
$$y = \pm i \qquad\qquad x = \pm 7$$

Vertices: $(7, 0), (-7, 0)$

Asymptotes: $y = \frac{1}{7}x;\ y = -\frac{1}{7}x$

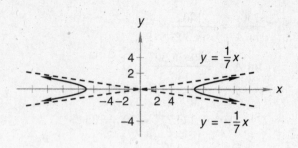

3. $A_0 = 2000,\ A_{20} = 1600$
(88)

$$A_t = A_0 e^{kt}$$
$$1600 = 2000 e^{k20}$$
$$e^{k20} = 0.80$$
$$20k = \ln 0.80$$
$$k = -0.011157$$

$$A_t = 2000 e^{-0.011157t}$$
$$400 = 2000 e^{-0.011157t}$$
$$e^{-0.011157t} = 0.2$$
$$-0.011157t = \ln 0.2$$
$$t = \textbf{144.25 min}$$

4. $N,\ N + 2,\ N + 4$
(7)

$$N(N + 4) = 8(N + 2) - 4$$
$$N^2 + 4N = 8N + 16 - 4$$
$$N^2 - 4N - 12 = 0$$
$$(N - 6)(N + 2) = 0$$
$$N = 6, -2$$

6, 8, 10

5. (a) $a_1 = 2,\ r = -2,\ n = 6$
(91)
$$a_n = a_1 r^{(n-1)}$$
$$a_6 = (2)(-2)^{(6-1)} = 2(-2)^5 = \textbf{-64}$$

(b) ①   ②   ③   ④
$$4, \quad \underline{\quad}, \quad \underline{\quad}, \quad -32$$
$$a_1, \quad a_1 r, \quad a_1 r^2, \quad a_1 r^3$$

$$a_1 r^3 = -32$$
$$(4)r^3 = -32$$
$$r^3 = -8$$
$$r = -2$$

$$a_1 r = 4(-2) = -8$$

$$a_1 r^2 = 4(-2)^2 = 16$$

-8, 16

6. $y = 3 + \cos 2\left(x - \dfrac{\pi}{6}\right)$
(84)

Period $= \dfrac{2\pi}{2} = \pi$

Phase angle $= \dfrac{\pi}{6}$

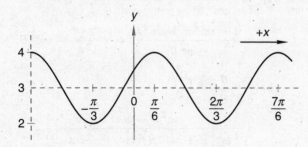

7. $32^{(4-x)} = 128^{(x+4)}$
(82)

$2^{5(4-x)} = 2^{7(x+4)}$

$5(4 - x) = 7(x + 4)$

$20 - 5x = 7x + 28$

$12x = -8$

$x = -\dfrac{2}{3}$

8. $(-81)^{1/4} = (81 \text{ cis } 180°)^{1/4}$
(79)

$= \sqrt[4]{81} \text{ cis}\left(\dfrac{180°}{4} + n\dfrac{360°}{4}\right)$

$3 \text{ cis}\left(\dfrac{180°}{4}\right) = 3 \text{ cis } 45° = \dfrac{3\sqrt{2}}{2} + \dfrac{3\sqrt{2}}{2}i$

$3 \text{ cis}\left(\dfrac{180°}{4} + 90°\right) = 3 \text{ cis } 135° = -\dfrac{3\sqrt{2}}{2} + \dfrac{3\sqrt{2}}{2}i$

$3 \text{ cis}\left(\dfrac{180°}{4} + 180°\right) = 3 \text{ cis } 225° = -\dfrac{3\sqrt{2}}{2} - \dfrac{3\sqrt{2}}{2}i$

$3 \text{ cis}\left(\dfrac{180°}{4} + 270°\right) = 3 \text{ cis } 315° = \dfrac{3\sqrt{2}}{2} - \dfrac{3\sqrt{2}}{2}i$

9. $\cos(A + B) = \cos A \cos B - \sin A \sin B$
(87,90)

$\cos(A + A) = \cos A \cos A - \sin A \sin A$

$\cos 2A = \cos^2 A - \sin^2 A$

10. $a_1 = 16$, $d = 6$, $n = 29$
(86)

$a_n = a_1 + (n - 1)d$

$a_{29} = 16 + (29 - 1)(6) = 16 + (28)(6) = \mathbf{184}$

11. $a_{10} = a_1 + 9d = 18$
(86)

$a_{14} = a_1 + 13d = 34$

(a) $\begin{cases} a_1 + 9d = 18 \\ a_1 + 13d = 34 \end{cases}$

(a) $a_1 + 9d = 18$

-1(b) $\underline{-a_1 - 13d = -34}$

$-4d = -16$

$d = 4$

(a) $a_1 + 9d = 18$

$a_1 + 9(4) = 18$

$a_1 = -18$

$\mathbf{-18, -14, -10, -6, -2}$

12. (a) $P(\text{green, then purple}) = \dfrac{5}{15} \cdot \dfrac{4}{15} = \dfrac{4}{45}$
(83)

(b) $P(\text{green, then purple}) = \dfrac{5}{14} \cdot \dfrac{4}{13} = \dfrac{10}{91}$

13. $R_B = 1$, $R_L = \dfrac{1}{12}$, $T_L = T_B$
(85)

Big hand:

$R_B T_B = S + 10$

$(1)T = S + 10$

$S = T - 10$

Little hand:

$R_L T_L = S$

$\left(\dfrac{1}{12}\right)T = S$

$S = \dfrac{T}{12}$

$\dfrac{T}{12} = T - 10$

$\dfrac{11}{12}T = 10$

$T = 10\dfrac{10}{11} \text{ min}$

$5{:}10\dfrac{10}{11}$

14. $P(J \cup B) = P(J) + P(B) - P(J \cap B)$
(92)

$= \dfrac{4}{52} + \dfrac{26}{52} - \dfrac{2}{52} = \dfrac{28}{52} = \dfrac{7}{13}$

15. $4^{\log_4 6 - 3\log_4 2 + 2\log_4 \sqrt{5} - 4\log_4 1}$
(59)

$= 4^{\log_4 6 - \log_4 2^3 + \log_4 \sqrt{5}^2 - \log_4 1^4}$

$= 4^{\log_4 \frac{(6)(5)}{(8)(1)}} = \dfrac{(6)(5)}{(8)(1)} = \dfrac{15}{4}$

16. (a) $\qquad\qquad 3\cot^2 3\theta + 1 = 5\csc 3\theta$
(85)

$$3\left(\csc^2 3\theta - 1\right) + 1 = 5\csc 3\theta$$

$$3\csc^2 3\theta - 5\csc 3\theta - 2 = 0$$

$$(3\csc 3\theta + 1)(\csc 3\theta - 2) = 0$$

$$3\csc 3\theta + 1 = 0$$

$$\csc 3\theta = -\frac{1}{3}$$

$$\sin 3\theta = -3$$

no answer

$$\csc 3\theta - 2 = 0$$

$$\csc 3\theta = 2$$

$$\sin 3\theta = \frac{1}{2}$$

$$3\theta = 30°, 150°, 390°, 510°, 750°, 870°$$

$$\boldsymbol{\theta = 10°, 50°, 130°, 170°, 250°, 290°}$$

(b) $\qquad\qquad\qquad \tan^2\theta = \frac{1}{3}$

$$\tan^2\theta - \frac{1}{3} = 0$$

$$\left(\tan\theta + \frac{1}{\sqrt{3}}\right)\left(\tan\theta - \frac{1}{\sqrt{3}}\right) = 0$$

$$\tan\theta + \frac{1}{\sqrt{3}} = 0$$

$$\tan\theta = -\frac{1}{\sqrt{3}}$$

$$\theta = 150°, 330°$$

$$\tan\theta - \frac{1}{\sqrt{3}} = 0$$

$$\tan\theta = \frac{1}{\sqrt{3}}$$

$$\theta = 30°, 210°$$

$$\boldsymbol{\theta = 30°, 150°, 210°, 330°}$$

17. $2\log(x + 2) - \log(x + 5) = \log 2 + \log(x - 2)$
(59)

$$\log\frac{(x + 2)^2}{x + 5} = \log 2(x - 2)$$

$$\frac{(x + 2)^2}{x + 5} = 2(x - 2)$$

$$x^2 + 4x + 4 = 2\left(x^2 + 3x - 10\right)$$

$$x^2 + 4x + 4 = 2x^2 + 6x - 20$$

$$x^2 + 2x - 24 = 0$$

$$(x + 6)(x - 4) = 0$$

$$x = -6, 4 \quad (x \neq -6)$$

$$\boldsymbol{x = 4}$$

18. (a) $\operatorname{antilog}_4(-1) = 4^{-1} = \boldsymbol{\dfrac{1}{4}}$
(67)

(b) $\operatorname{antilog}_{1/4}(-1) = \left(\dfrac{1}{4}\right)^{-1} = \boldsymbol{4}$

19. (a) $\dfrac{\cos^2\theta}{1 - \cos^2\theta} + 1 = \dfrac{1 - \sin^2\theta}{\sin^2\theta} + 1$
(80)

$$= \frac{1 - \sin^2\theta + \sin^2\theta}{\sin^2\theta} = \frac{1}{\sin^2\theta} = \csc^2\theta$$

(b) $\dfrac{\csc^2\theta + \cot^2\theta}{\csc^4\theta - \cot^4\theta}$

$$= \frac{\csc^2\theta + \cot^2\theta}{\left(\csc^2\theta + \cot^2\theta\right)\left(\csc^2\theta - \cot^2\theta\right)}$$

$$= \frac{1}{\csc^2\theta - \cot^2\theta} = \frac{1}{1} = 1$$

20. $\qquad a^2 = b^2 + c^2 - 2bc\cos A$
(81)

$$\cos A = \frac{b^2 + c^2 - a^2}{2bc}$$

$$\cos A = \frac{16^2 + 11^2 - 14^2}{2(16)(11)}$$

$$\boldsymbol{A = 59.06°}$$

$$\frac{14}{\sin 59.06°} = \frac{16}{\sin B}$$

$$\sin B = \frac{16\sin 59.06°}{14}$$

$$\boldsymbol{B = 78.59°}$$

Test 24

1. $\tan 2A = \dfrac{\sin 2A}{\cos 2A} = \dfrac{2\sin A\cos A}{\cos^2 A - \sin^2 A}$
(90)

$$= \frac{\dfrac{2\sin A\cos A}{\cos^2 A}}{\dfrac{\cos^2 A - \sin^2 A}{\cos^2 A}} = \frac{2\dfrac{\sin A}{\cos A}}{\dfrac{\cos^2 A}{\cos^2 A} - \dfrac{\sin^2 A}{\cos^2 A}}$$

$$= \frac{2\tan A}{1 - \tan^2 A}$$

2. $x^2 + 8x + 20 = 0$
(46)

$$x = \frac{-8 \pm \sqrt{8^2 - (4)(1)(20)}}{2(1)}$$

$$x = \frac{-8 \pm \sqrt{-16}}{2}$$

$$x = \frac{-8 \pm 4i}{2} = -4 \pm 2i$$

$$(x + 4 - 2i)(x + 4 + 2i)$$

3. $RWT = J$
(44)
$R(w)(40) = j$

Rate $= \dfrac{j}{40w} \dfrac{\text{jobs}}{\text{woman-min}}$

$RWT = J$

$\left(\dfrac{j}{40w}\right)(w + n)T = j + 15$

$T = \dfrac{40w(j + 15)}{j(w + n)} \text{ min}$

4. $\dfrac{x^2}{64} + \dfrac{y^2}{9} = 1$
(89)

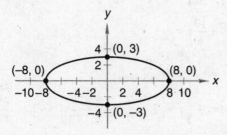

5. $a_7 = a_1 + 6d = 22$
(86)
$a_{11} = a_1 + 10d = 6$

(a) $\begin{cases} a_1 + 6d = 22 \\ a_1 + 10d = 6 \end{cases}$
(b)

(a) $a_1 + 6d = 22$
−1(b) $\underline{-a_1 - 10d = -6}$
         $-4d = 16$
         $d = -4$

(a) $a_1 + 6d = 22$
         $a_1 + 6(-4) = 22$
         $a_1 = 46$

46, 42, 38, 34, 30

6. $6 + 4i$
(95)

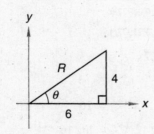

$R = \sqrt{6^2 + 4^2} = \sqrt{52}$

$\tan \theta = \dfrac{4}{6}$

$\theta = 33.69°$

$6 + 4i = \sqrt{52} \text{ cis } 33.69°$

$\left(\sqrt{52} \text{ cis } 33.69°\right)^{1/5}$

$= \left(52^{1/2}\right)^{1/5} \text{cis} \left(\dfrac{33.69°}{5} + n\dfrac{360°}{5}\right)$

$= \textbf{1.48 cis 6.74°, 1.48 cis 78.74°, 1.48 cis 150.74°,}$
   1.48 cis 222.74°, 1.48 cis 294.74°

7. (a) $y = 6 + 4 \csc x$
(94)
   (b) $y = \cot \theta$

8. $y = \sec x$
(94)

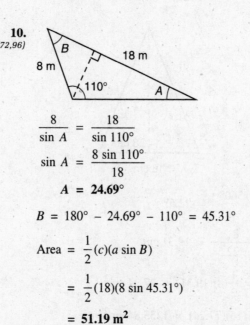

9. $y = \tan x$
(94)

10.
(72,96)

$\dfrac{8}{\sin A} = \dfrac{18}{\sin 110°}$

$\sin A = \dfrac{8 \sin 110°}{18}$

$A = \textbf{24.69°}$

$B = 180° - 24.69° - 110° = 45.31°$

$\text{Area} = \dfrac{1}{2}(c)(a \sin B)$

$= \dfrac{1}{2}(18)(8 \sin 45.31°)$

$= \textbf{51.19 m}^2$

11.
(81,96)

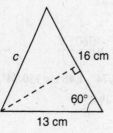

$c^2 = 16^2 + 13^2 - 2(16)(13)\cos 60°$

$c^2 = 217$

$c = \textbf{14.73 cm}$

Area $= \dfrac{1}{2}(a)(b \sin C)$

$= \dfrac{1}{2}(16)(13 \sin 60°)$

$= \textbf{90.07 cm}^2$

12. $P(O \cup S) = P(O) + P(S) - P(O \cap S)$
(92)

$= \dfrac{7}{12} + \dfrac{5}{12} - \dfrac{3}{12} = \dfrac{9}{12} = \dfrac{\textbf{3}}{\textbf{4}}$

13. $\csc \theta - \cot^2 \theta = 1$
(85)

$\csc \theta - \left(\csc^2 \theta - 1\right) = 1$

$\csc^2 \theta - \csc \theta = 0$

$\csc \theta(\csc \theta - 1) = 0$

$\csc \theta = 0 \qquad\qquad \csc \theta - 1 = 0$

no answer $\qquad\qquad\quad \csc \theta = 1$

$\qquad\qquad\qquad\qquad\quad \sin \theta = 1$

$\qquad\qquad\qquad\qquad\qquad \theta = \textbf{90}°$

14. Side $= \dfrac{128}{8} = 16$ cm
(73)

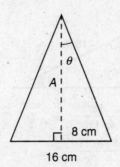

$\theta = \dfrac{1}{2}\left(\dfrac{360°}{8}\right) = 22.5°$

$A = \dfrac{8}{\tan 22.5°} = 19.31$ cm

$\text{Area}_\Delta = \dfrac{1}{2}(8)(19.31) = 77.24$ cm^2

Area $= (16)(77.24) = \textbf{1235.84 cm}^2$

15. $y = \dfrac{2}{3}x + 3$
(58)

Equation of the perpendicular line:

$y = -\dfrac{3}{2}x + b$

$(2) = -\dfrac{3}{2}(0) + b$

$b = 2$

$y = -\dfrac{3}{2}x + 2$

Point of intersection:

$\dfrac{2}{3}x + 3 = -\dfrac{3}{2}x + 2$

$\dfrac{13}{6}x = -1$

$x = -\dfrac{6}{13}$

$y = -\dfrac{3}{2}x + 2 = \left(-\dfrac{3}{2}\right)\left(-\dfrac{6}{13}\right) + 2 = \dfrac{35}{13}$

$\left(-\dfrac{6}{13}, \dfrac{35}{13}\right)$ and $(0, 2)$

$D = \sqrt{\left[0 - \left(-\dfrac{6}{13}\right)\right]^2 + \left(2 - \dfrac{35}{13}\right)^2}$

$= \sqrt{\left(\dfrac{6}{13}\right)^2 + \left(-\dfrac{9}{13}\right)^2}$

$= \sqrt{\dfrac{117}{169}} = \sqrt{\dfrac{9}{13}} = \dfrac{3}{\sqrt{13}} = \dfrac{\textbf{3}\sqrt{\textbf{13}}}{\textbf{13}}$

16. $A_0 = 1, A_5 = 3$
(88)

$A_t = A_0 e^{kt}$

$3 = e^{k5}$

$5k = \ln 3$

$k = 0.21972$

$A_t = e^{0.21972t}$

$A_{15} = e^{0.21972(15)}$

$A_{15} = \textbf{27}$

17. $12^{3x+1} = 16^{2x+1}$
(82)

$\log 12^{3x+1} = \log 16^{2x+1}$

$(3x + 1)\log 12 = (2x + 1)\log 16$

$(3x + 1)(1.079) = (2x + 1)(1.204)$

$3.237x + 1.079 = 2.408x + 1.204$

$0.829x = 0.125$

$x = \textbf{0.151}$

18. $\log_4 (4x + 4) - \log_4 (x - 5) = \dfrac{2}{3} \log_4 64$
(40)

$$\log_4 (4x + 4) - \log_4 (x - 5) = \log_4 64^{2/3}$$

$$\log_4 \frac{4x + 4}{x - 5} = \log_4 16$$

$$\frac{4x + 4}{x - 5} = 16$$

$$4x + 4 = 16x - 80$$

$$12x = 84$$

$$x = \mathbf{7}$$

19. $y = -3 + 4 \sin \dfrac{1}{3}(x - 45°)$
(84)

$$\text{Period} = \frac{360°}{\dfrac{1}{3}} = 1080°$$

$$\text{Phase angle} = 45°$$

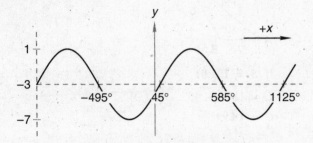

20. $\dfrac{\sin \theta}{1 + \cos \theta} \cdot \dfrac{\sin \theta}{\sin \theta} = \dfrac{\sin^2 \theta}{(1 + \cos \theta) \sin \theta}$
(93)

$$= \frac{1 - \cos^2 \theta}{(1 + \cos \theta) \sin \theta} = \frac{(1 + \cos \theta)(1 - \cos \theta)}{(1 + \cos \theta) \sin \theta}$$

$$= \frac{1 - \cos \theta}{\sin \theta}$$

Test 25

1. Distance = m mi, rate = $w \dfrac{\text{mi}}{\text{hr}}$, time = $\dfrac{m}{w}$ hr
(28)

New distance = $(m + 6)$ mi

New rate = $\dfrac{(m + 6) \text{ mi}}{\left(\dfrac{m}{w}\right) \text{hr}} = \dfrac{w(m + 6)}{m} \dfrac{\text{mi}}{\text{hr}}$

2. Rate = $\dfrac{c}{h} \dfrac{\text{dollars}}{\text{glove}}$
(44)

New rate = $\dfrac{c}{h} - d = \dfrac{c - dh}{h} \dfrac{\text{dollars}}{\text{glove}}$

New rate $\times N$ = price

$$\left(\frac{c - dh}{h}\right) \times N = 40$$

$$N = \frac{40h}{c - dh} \text{ gloves}$$

3. (a)　　　　$y = \log_5 23$
(98)

$$5^y = 23$$

$$\log 5^y = \log 23$$

$$y \log 5 = \log 23$$

$$y = \frac{\log 23}{\log 5}$$

$$y = \mathbf{1.95}$$

(b)　　　　$y = \log_9 35$

$$9^y = 35$$

$$\log 9^y = \log 35$$

$$y \log 9 = \log 35$$

$$y = \frac{\log 35}{\log 9}$$

$$y = \mathbf{1.62}$$

4. $\left(\dfrac{1}{x + 7}\right) 5^{\log_5 (x^2 + 11x + 28) - \log_5 (x + 4)}$
(59,98)

$$= \left(\frac{1}{x + 7}\right) 5^{\log_5 \frac{x^2 + 11x + 28}{x + 4}}$$

$$= \left(\frac{1}{x + 7}\right)\left(\frac{x^2 + 11x + 28}{x + 4}\right)$$

$$= \left(\frac{1}{x + 7}\right)\left[\frac{(x + 7)(x + 4)}{(x + 4)}\right] = \frac{x + 7}{x + 7} = \mathbf{1}$$

5. Radius = 10 m
(73)

Side of square = 2(radius) = 2(10) = 20 m

Perimeter = 4(side) = 4(20) = **80 m**

6. Arithmetic mean = $\dfrac{x + y}{2} = \dfrac{32 + 16}{2} = \dfrac{48}{2} = \mathbf{24}$
(99)

Geometric mean = $\pm\sqrt{xy} = \pm\sqrt{32 \cdot 16} = \pm\mathbf{16\sqrt{2}}$

7. $a_1 = 375$, $r = \dfrac{2}{5}$, $n = 4$
(99)

$$D = a_1 r^{(n-1)} = 375\left(\frac{2}{5}\right)^{(4-1)} = 375\left(\frac{2}{5}\right)^3 = \mathbf{24 \ ft}$$

8.　　　　　　$R_T T_T + R_B T_B = 1 \text{ clock}$
(44)

$$\left(\frac{3}{n} \frac{\text{clocks}}{\text{hr}}\right)T + \left(\frac{4}{s} \frac{\text{clocks}}{\text{hr}}\right)T = 1 \text{ clock}$$

$$\left(\frac{3}{n} + \frac{4}{s}\right)\frac{\text{clocks}}{\text{hr}} \, T = 1 \text{ clock}$$

$$\left(\frac{3s + 4n}{ns}\right)\frac{\text{clocks}}{\text{hr}} \, T = 1 \text{ clock}$$

$$T = \frac{ns}{3s + 4n} \text{ hr}$$

9. $-8 + 5i$
(95)

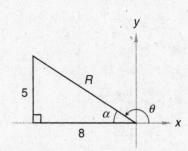

$$R = \sqrt{8^2 + 5^2} = \sqrt{89}$$

$$\tan \alpha = \frac{5}{8}$$

$$\alpha = 32.01°$$

$$\theta = 180° - \alpha = 180° - 32.01° = 147.99°$$

$$-8 + 5i = \sqrt{89} \text{ cis } 147.99°$$

$$\left(\sqrt{89} \text{ cis } 147.99°\right)^{1/3}$$

$$= \left(89^{1/2}\right)^{1/3} \text{ cis } \left(\frac{147.99°}{3} + n\frac{360°}{3}\right)$$

$$= \textbf{2.11 cis 49.33°, 2.11 cis 169.33°, 2.11 cis 289.33°}$$

10. $y = 3 + \csc \theta$
(94)

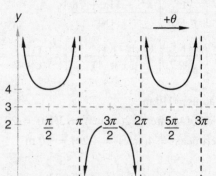

11. $a_1 = 5$, $r = -4$, $n = 6$
(91)

$$a_n = a_1 r^{n-1}$$

$$a_6 = 5(-4)^{(6-1)} = 5(-4)^5 = \textbf{-5120}$$

12.
(97)

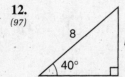

$$H = 8 \sin 40° = 5.14$$

$H < 6 < 8$, therefore two triangles are possible.

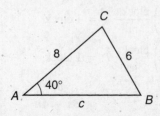

$$\frac{6}{\sin 40°} = \frac{8}{\sin B}$$

$$\sin B = \frac{8 \sin 40°}{6}$$

$$B = 58.99° \text{ or } 121.01°$$

If $B = \textbf{58.99°}$,

$$C = 180° - 40° - 58.99°$$

$$C = \textbf{81.01°}$$

$$\frac{6}{\sin 40°} = \frac{c}{\sin 81.01°}$$

$$c = \frac{6 \sin 81.01°}{\sin 40°}$$

$$c = \textbf{9.22}$$

If $B = \textbf{121.01°}$,

$$C = 180° - 40° - 121.01°$$

$$C = \textbf{18.99°}$$

$$\frac{6}{\sin 40°} = \frac{c}{\sin 18.99°}$$

$$c = \frac{6 \sin 18.99°}{\sin 40°}$$

$$c = \textbf{3.04}$$

13. $A_0 = 700{,}000$, $A_{20} = 25{,}000$
(88)

$$A_t = A_0 e^{kt}$$

$$25{,}000 = 700{,}000 e^{k20}$$

$$20k = \ln \frac{25{,}000}{700{,}000}$$

$$k = -0.16661$$

$$A_t = 700{,}000 e^{-0.16661t}$$

$$10 = 700{,}000 e^{-0.16661t}$$

$$-0.16661t = \ln \frac{10}{700{,}000}$$

$$t = \textbf{66.96 yr}$$

14. (a) $\begin{cases} L - S = 24 \\ \sqrt{LS} = 9 \end{cases}$
(99)

(b) $\sqrt{LS} = 9$

$$LS = 81$$

$$S = \frac{81}{L}$$

(a)
$$L - S = 24$$
$$L - \frac{81}{L} = 24$$
$$L^2 - 81 = 24L$$
$$L^2 - 24L - 81 = 0$$
$$(L - 27)(L + 3) = 0$$
$$L = 27, -3$$

If $L = 27$,
$$S = \frac{81}{L} = \frac{81}{27} = 3$$

If $L = -3$,
$$S = \frac{81}{L} = \frac{81}{-3} = -27$$

$$(L, S) = \textbf{(27, 3)} \text{ and } \textbf{(-3, -27)}$$

15.
(85)
$$2 \cos^2 x = 11 \sin x + 7$$
$$2(1 - \sin^2 x) = 11 \sin x + 7$$
$$2 \sin^2 x + 11 \sin x + 5 = 0$$
$$(2 \sin x + 1)(\sin x + 5) = 0$$

$$2 \sin x + 1 = 0 \qquad\qquad \sin x + 5 = 0$$
$$\sin x = -\frac{1}{2} \qquad\qquad \sin x = -5$$
$$\qquad\qquad\qquad\qquad \text{no answer}$$
$$x = \frac{7\pi}{6}, \frac{11\pi}{6}$$

16. $_{12}P_6 = \dfrac{12!}{(12 - 6)!} = \dfrac{12!}{6!}$
(92)
$$_{12}P_6 = \textbf{665,280}$$

$$_{12}C_6 = \frac{12!}{(12 - 6)!6!} = \frac{12!}{6!6!}$$
$$_{12}C_6 = \textbf{924}$$

17. $\log_4 (\log_4 x) = 1$
(98)
$$\log_4 x = 4^1$$
$$x = 4^4$$
$$x = \textbf{256}$$

18. $\dfrac{2 \sin^2 x + \cos 2x}{\sin x}$
(93)
$$= \frac{2(1 - \cos^2 x) + (2 \cos^2 x - 1)}{\sin x}$$
$$= \frac{2 - 2 \cos^2 x + 2 \cos^2 x - 1}{\sin x}$$
$$= \frac{1}{\sin x} = \csc x$$

19.
(89)

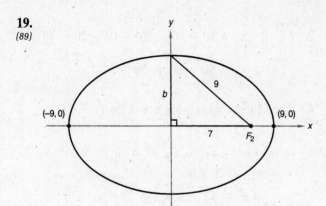

$$7^2 + b^2 = 9^2$$
$$b^2 = 32$$
$$b = \sqrt{32}$$
$$b = 4\sqrt{2}$$

$$\frac{x^2}{a^2} + \frac{y^2}{b^2} = 1$$
$$\frac{x^2}{81} + \frac{y^2}{32} = 1$$

Length of major axis = 18

Length of minor axis = $8\sqrt{2}$

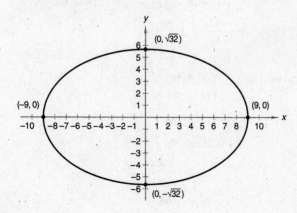

20. D.
(21)

Test 26

1. $a_1 = 200$, $r = \dfrac{1}{2}$, $n = 3$
(99)

$$D = a_1 r^{(n-1)} = 200\left(\frac{1}{2}\right)^{(3-1)} = 200\left(\frac{1}{2}\right)^2 = \textbf{50 ft}$$

2. $_{11}P_5 = \dfrac{11!}{(11 - 5)!} = \dfrac{11!}{6!}$
(92)
$$_{11}P_5 = \textbf{55,440}$$

$$_{11}C_5 = \frac{11!}{(11 - 5)!5!} = \frac{11!}{6!5!}$$
$$_{11}C_5 = \textbf{462}$$

3.
(101)
$$\begin{vmatrix} 4 & 2 & 6 \\ 5 & 0 & 5 \\ 6 & 1 & 4 \end{vmatrix} = (0 + 60 + 30) - (0 + 20 + 40)$$
$$= 90 - 60 = \mathbf{30}$$

4.
(98)
$2 \log (x^2 - 4) - 3 \log y - 4 \log (x + 2)$
$\quad + \log (xy + 2y)$

$= \log (x^2 - 4)^2 - \log y^3 - \log (x + 2)^4$
$\quad + \log (xy + 2y)$

$= \log \dfrac{(x^2 - 4)^2 (xy + 2y)}{y^3 (x + 2)^4}$

$= \log \dfrac{(x + 2)(x - 2)(x + 2)(x - 2)y(x + 2)}{y^3 (x + 2)(x + 2)(x + 2)(x + 2)}$

$= \log \dfrac{(x - 2)^2}{y^2 (x + 2)}$

5.
(101)
$$x = \dfrac{\begin{vmatrix} 3 & 6 & 3 \\ -10 & 2 & -2 \\ 1 & 1 & 0 \end{vmatrix}}{\begin{vmatrix} 9 & 6 & 3 \\ 4 & 2 & -2 \\ 4 & 1 & 0 \end{vmatrix}}$$

$= \dfrac{(0 - 12 - 30) - (6 - 6 + 0)}{(0 - 48 + 12) - (24 - 18 + 0)}$

$= \dfrac{-42}{-42} = \mathbf{1}$

6. (a)
(98)
$\qquad y = \log_{17} 7$
$\qquad 17^y = 7$
$\qquad \log 17^y = \log 7$
$\qquad y \log 17 = \log 7$
$\qquad\qquad y = \dfrac{\log 7}{\log 17}$
$\qquad\qquad y = \mathbf{0.687}$

(b)
$\qquad y = \log_7 17$
$\qquad 7^y = 17$
$\qquad \log 7^y = \log 17$
$\qquad y \log 7 = \log 17$
$\qquad\qquad y = \dfrac{\log 17}{\log 7}$
$\qquad\qquad y = \mathbf{1.456}$

7. $\sin 330° = \sin (120° + 210°)$
(87)
$\qquad = \sin 120° \cos 210° + \cos 120° \sin 210°$

$\qquad = \left(\dfrac{\sqrt{3}}{2}\right)\left(-\dfrac{\sqrt{3}}{2}\right) + \left(-\dfrac{1}{2}\right)\left(-\dfrac{1}{2}\right)$

$\qquad = -\dfrac{3}{4} + \dfrac{1}{4} = -\dfrac{1}{2}$

8.
(98)
$$\log_8 y = \sqrt{\log_8 y}$$
$$(\log_8 y)^2 = \log_8 y$$
$$(\log_8 y)^2 - \log_8 y = 0$$
$$(\log_8 y)(\log_8 y - 1) = 0$$

$\log_8 y = 0 \qquad\qquad \log_8 y - 1 = 0$
$\quad y = 8^0 \qquad\qquad\quad \log_8 y = 1$
$\quad y = 1 \qquad\qquad\qquad\quad y = 8^1$
$\qquad\qquad\qquad\qquad\qquad\quad y = 8$

$y = \mathbf{1, 8}$

9. $(-512)^{1/3} = (512 \operatorname{cis} 180°)^{1/3}$
(79)
$\qquad\qquad\quad = \sqrt[3]{512} \operatorname{cis} \left(\dfrac{180°}{3} + n\dfrac{360°}{3}\right)$

$8 \operatorname{cis} \dfrac{180°}{3} = 8 \operatorname{cis} 60° = \mathbf{4 + 4\sqrt{3}i}$

$8 \operatorname{cis} \left(\dfrac{180°}{3} + 120°\right) = 8 \operatorname{cis} 180° = \mathbf{-8}$

$8 \operatorname{cis} \left(\dfrac{180°}{3} + 240°\right) = 8 \operatorname{cis} 300° = \mathbf{4 - 4\sqrt{3}i}$

10. (a) $H^+ = 6.90 \times 10^{-9}$
(103)
$\qquad pH = -\log H^+ = -\log (6.90 \times 10^{-9}) = \mathbf{8.16}$

(b) $pH = 3.6$
$\qquad H^+ = 10^{-pH} = 10^{-3.6} = \mathbf{2.51 \times 10^{-4}} \dfrac{\textbf{mole}}{\textbf{liter}}$

11. $y = -3 + 2 \sin \dfrac{2}{3}(\theta - 80°)$
(84)

Period $= \dfrac{360°}{\dfrac{2}{3}} = 540°$

Phase angle $= 80°$

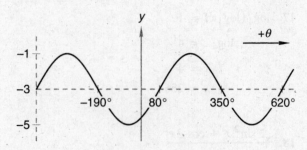

12. $\quad \sin (x + y) = \quad \sin x \cos y + \cos x \sin y$
(100)
$\dfrac{-\sin (x - y) = -\sin x \cos y + \cos x \sin y}{\sin (x + y) - \sin (x - y) = 2 \cos x \sin y}$

$\cos x \sin y = \dfrac{1}{2} \big[\sin (x + y) - \sin (x - y)\big]$

13. $(4x - 5y^2)^5$
(102)

$F = 4x, \ S = -5y^2$

Term	①	②	③	④	⑤	⑥
Exp. of F	5	4	3	2	1	0
Exp. of S	0	1	2	3	4	5
Coefficient	1	5	10	10	5	1

$10F^2S^3 = 10(4x)^2(-5y^2)^3 = \mathbf{-20{,}000x^2y^6}$

14.
(97)

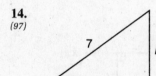

$H = 7 \sin 35° = 4.02$

$H < 5 < 7$, therefore two triangles are possible.

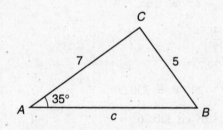

$\dfrac{5}{\sin 35°} = \dfrac{7}{\sin B}$

$\sin B = \dfrac{7 \sin 35°}{5}$

$B = 53.42°$ or $126.58°$

If $B = 53.42°$,

$C = 180° - 35° - 53.42°$

$C = \mathbf{91.58°}$

$\dfrac{5}{\sin 35°} = \dfrac{c}{\sin 91.58°}$

$c = \dfrac{5 \sin 91.58°}{\sin 35°}$

$c = \mathbf{8.71}$

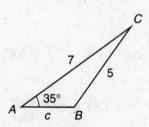

If $B = 126.58°$,

$C = 180° - 35° - 126.58°$

$C = \mathbf{18.42°}$

$\dfrac{5}{\sin 35°} = \dfrac{c}{\sin 18.42°}$

$c = \dfrac{5 \sin 18.42°}{\sin 35°}$

$c = \mathbf{2.75}$

15. $\sin 2x = \cos x$
(90)

$2 \sin x \cos x = \cos x$

$2 \sin x \cos x - \cos x = 0$

$\cos x(2 \sin x - 1) = 0$

$\cos x = 0 \qquad\qquad 2 \sin x - 1 = 0$

$x = \dfrac{\pi}{2}, \dfrac{3\pi}{2} \qquad\qquad \sin x = \dfrac{1}{2}$

$\qquad\qquad\qquad\qquad x = \dfrac{\pi}{6}, \dfrac{5\pi}{6}$

$x = \dfrac{\pi}{6}, \dfrac{\pi}{2}, \dfrac{5\pi}{6}, \dfrac{3\pi}{2}$

16. $\dfrac{3 + 5 \sec x + 2 \sec^2 x}{\tan^2 x}$
(93)

$= \dfrac{(2 \sec x + 3)(\sec x + 1)}{(\sec^2 x - 1)}$

$= \dfrac{(2 \sec x + 3)(\sec x + 1)}{(\sec x + 1)(\sec x - 1)}$

$= \dfrac{2 \sec x + 3}{\sec x - 1}$

17. $\log\left(\dfrac{x^3 z^2}{y^4}\right)$
(103)

$= \log x^3 + \log z^2 - \log y^4$

$= \mathbf{3 \log x + 2 \log z - 4 \log y}$

18. (a) $a_1 = 4, \ r = -3, \ n = 9$
(104)

$S_n = \dfrac{a_1(1 - r^n)}{1 - r}$

$S_9 = \dfrac{4[1 - (-3)^9]}{1 - (-3)}$

$= \dfrac{4(1 + 19{,}683)}{1 + 3}$

$= \dfrac{78{,}736}{4} = \mathbf{19{,}684}$

(b) $a_1 = 4, \ d = -3, \ n = 9$

$a_n = a_1 + (n - 1)d$

$a_9 = 4 + (9 - 1)(-3) = 4 + 8(-3) = -20$

$S_n = \dfrac{n}{2}(a_1 + a_n)$

$S_9 = \dfrac{9}{2}(a_1 + a_9) = \dfrac{9}{2}[4 + (-20)] = \mathbf{-72}$

19. $A_0 = 74$, $A_{45} = 36$
(88)

$$A_t = A_0 e^{kt}$$

$$36 = 74 e^{k45}$$

$$45k = \ln \frac{36}{74}$$

$$k = -0.016012$$

$$A_t = 74 e^{-0.016012t}$$

$$12 = 74 e^{-0.016012t}$$

$$-0.016012t = \ln \frac{12}{74}$$

$$t = \textbf{113.61 min}$$

20. (a) $y = \cot\theta$
(94)
　　(b) $y = 3 + 7\sec x$

Test 27

1.
(44)
$$R_E T_E + R_J T_J = 100 \text{ tomatoes}$$

$$\left(\frac{9}{40}\frac{\text{tomato}}{\text{min}}\right)T + \left(\frac{t}{x}\frac{\text{tomatoes}}{\text{min}}\right)T = 100 \text{ tomatoes}$$

$$\left(\frac{9}{40} + \frac{t}{x}\right)\frac{\text{tomatoes}}{\text{min}}T = 100 \text{ tomatoes}$$

$$\left(\frac{9x + 40t}{40x}\right)\frac{\text{tomatoes}}{\text{min}}T = 100 \text{ tomatoes}$$

$$T = \frac{\textbf{4000}x}{\textbf{9}x + \textbf{40}t}\ \textbf{min}$$

2.
(105)
$$\begin{vmatrix} -3 & 4 & -1 \\ 4 & 2 & 3 \\ 1 & -2 & 0 \end{vmatrix}$$

$$= (-3)(+)\begin{vmatrix} 2 & 3 \\ -2 & 0 \end{vmatrix} + (4)(-)\begin{vmatrix} 4 & 3 \\ 1 & 0 \end{vmatrix}$$

$$+ (-1)(+)\begin{vmatrix} 4 & 2 \\ 1 & -2 \end{vmatrix}$$

$$= (-3)(+)(0 + 6) + (4)(-)(0 - 3)$$

$$+ (-1)(+)(-8 - 2)$$

$$= (-18) + 12 + 10 = \textbf{4}$$

3.
(96)

$$\frac{16}{\sin 100°} = \frac{9}{\sin C}$$

$$\sin C = \frac{9\sin 100°}{16}$$

$$C = 33.64°$$

$$A = 180° - 100° - 33.64° = 46.36°$$

$$\text{Area} = \frac{1}{2}(b)(c\sin A)$$

$$= \frac{1}{2}(16)(9\sin 46.36°)$$

$$= \textbf{52.11 ft}^2$$

4. $7 - 4i$
(95)

$$R = \sqrt{7^2 + 4^2} = \sqrt{65}$$

$$\tan\alpha = \frac{4}{7}$$

$$\alpha = 29.74°$$

$$\theta = 360° - 29.74° = 330.26°$$

$$7 - 4i = \sqrt{65}\ \text{cis}\ 330.26°$$

$$\left(\sqrt{65}\ \text{cis}\ 330.26°\right)^{1/4}$$

$$= \left(65^{1/2}\right)^{1/4}\ \text{cis}\left(\frac{330.26°}{4} + n\frac{360°}{4}\right)$$

$$= \textbf{1.69 cis 82.57°, 1.69 cis 172.57°, 1.69 cis 262.57°,}$$
$$\textbf{1.69 cis 352.57°}$$

5.
(98)
$$y = \log_8 3$$

$$8^y = 3$$

$$\ln 8^y = \ln 3$$

$$y\ln 8 = \ln 3$$

$$y = \frac{\textbf{ln 3}}{\textbf{ln 8}}$$

6. (a) $H^+ = 3.4 \times 10^{-3}$
(103)
$$pH = -\log H^+ = -\log\left(3.4 \times 10^{-3}\right) = \textbf{2.47}$$

　　(b) $pH = 7.8$
$$H^+ = 10^{-pH} = 10^{-7.8} = \textbf{1.58} \times \textbf{10}^{-8}\ \frac{\textbf{mole}}{\textbf{liter}}$$

7. $\dfrac{\sqrt[4]{4500}\ \sqrt[9]{6800}}{\sqrt[3]{3200}} = \textbf{1.48}$
(103)

8. $(4x^2 - 7y)^4$
(102)

$F = 4x^2, \ S = -7y$

Term	①	②	③	④	⑤
Exp. of F	4	3	2	1	0
Exp. of S	0	1	2	3	4
Coefficient	1	4	6	4	1

$6F^2S^2 = 6(4x^2)^2(-7y)^2 = \mathbf{4704x^4y^2}$

9. (a) $\quad 2\sin^2 x + \sin x - 1 = 0$
(52,60)

$(2\sin x - 1)(\sin x + 1) = 0$

$2\sin x - 1 = 0 \qquad\qquad \sin x + 1 = 0$

$\sin x = \dfrac{1}{2} \qquad\qquad\quad \sin x = -1$

$x = \dfrac{\pi}{6}, \dfrac{5\pi}{6} \qquad\qquad x = \dfrac{3\pi}{2}$

$x = \dfrac{\pi}{6}, \dfrac{5\pi}{6}, \dfrac{3\pi}{2}$

(b) $\sqrt{3} - \tan 2x = 0$

$\tan 2x = \sqrt{3}$

$2x = \dfrac{\pi}{3}, \dfrac{4\pi}{3}, \dfrac{7\pi}{3}, \dfrac{10\pi}{3}$

$x = \dfrac{\pi}{6}, \dfrac{2\pi}{3}, \dfrac{7\pi}{6}, \dfrac{5\pi}{3}$

10. $\quad 9x^2 + 16y^2 + 162x - 128y + 841 = 0$
(106)

$9(x^2 + 18x \quad) + 16(y^2 - 8y \quad) = -841$

$9(x^2 + 18x + 81) + 16(y^2 - 8y + 16) = 144$

$9(x + 9)^2 + 16(y - 4)^2 = 144$

$\dfrac{(x + 9)^2}{16} + \dfrac{(y - 4)^2}{9} = 1$

Center = (–9, 4)

$a = 4, \ b = 3$

Length of major axis = 8

Length of minor axis = 6

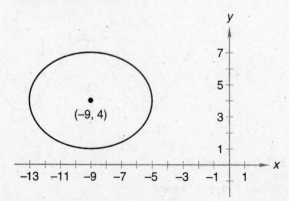

11. $\quad -9y^2 + x^2 - 36y + 4x + 4 = 0$
(106)

$-9(y^2 + 4y \quad) + (x^2 + 4x \quad) = -4$

$-9(y^2 + 4y + 4) + (x^2 + 4x + 4) = -36$

$-9(y + 2)^2 + (x + 2)^2 = -36$

$\dfrac{(y + 2)^2}{4} - \dfrac{(x + 2)^2}{36} = 1$

From the equation we obtain:

$h = -2, \ k = -2, \ a = 6, \ b = 2$

Center: $(h, k) = \mathbf{(-2, -2)}$

Vertices: $(h, k \pm b) = \mathbf{(-2, 0), (-2, -4)}$

Asymptotes:

$m = \pm\dfrac{b}{a} = \pm\dfrac{2}{6} = \pm\dfrac{1}{3}$

$y = mx + b \qquad\qquad y = mx + b$

$y = \dfrac{1}{3}x + b \qquad\qquad y = -\dfrac{1}{3}x + b$

$(-2) = \dfrac{1}{3}(-2) + b \qquad (-2) = -\dfrac{1}{3}(-2) + b$

$b = -\dfrac{4}{3} \qquad\qquad b = -\dfrac{8}{3}$

$y = \dfrac{1}{3}x - \dfrac{4}{3} \qquad\qquad y = -\dfrac{1}{3}x - \dfrac{8}{3}$

Asymptotes: $y = \dfrac{1}{3}x - \dfrac{4}{3}; \ y = -\dfrac{1}{3}x - \dfrac{8}{3}$

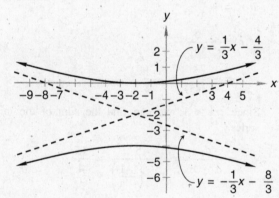

12. Rate $= \dfrac{c}{n} \dfrac{\text{dollars}}{\text{ticket}}$
(44)

New Rate $= \dfrac{c}{n} - y = \dfrac{c - ny}{n} \dfrac{\text{dollars}}{\text{ticket}}$

New rate $\times N =$ price

$\left(\dfrac{c - ny}{n}\right) \times N = 200$

$N = \dfrac{200n}{c - ny} \text{ tickets}$

13.
(108)
$A = \begin{bmatrix} 1 & -7 \\ 5 & 3 \end{bmatrix}$, $B = \begin{bmatrix} 2 & 4 \\ 8 & -6 \end{bmatrix}$

$A + B = \begin{bmatrix} 1+2 & -7+4 \\ 5+8 & 3-6 \end{bmatrix}$

$A + B = \begin{bmatrix} 3 & -3 \\ 13 & -3 \end{bmatrix}$

$A - B = \begin{bmatrix} 1-2 & -7-4 \\ 5-8 & 3+6 \end{bmatrix}$

$A - B = \begin{bmatrix} -1 & -11 \\ -3 & 9 \end{bmatrix}$

$2A = \begin{bmatrix} 2\cdot 1 & 2\cdot -7 \\ 2\cdot 5 & 2\cdot 3 \end{bmatrix}$

$2A = \begin{bmatrix} 2 & -14 \\ 10 & 6 \end{bmatrix}$

14.
(103)
$\log_7 \left(\dfrac{49\sqrt[5]{x^2 y^4}}{z^{-4}} \right)$

$= \log_7 49 + \log_7 x^{2/5} y^{4/5} - \log_7 z^{-4}$

$= \log_7 7^2 + \log_7 x^{2/5} + \log_7 y^{4/5} - \log_7 z^{-4}$

$= 2 + \dfrac{2}{5}\log_7 x + \dfrac{4}{5}\log_7 y + 4\log_7 z$

15.
(107)
$a_1 + a_1 r + a_1 r^2 + a_1 r^3 + \ldots$

$5 - \dfrac{5}{3} + \dfrac{5}{9} - \dfrac{5}{27} + \ldots$

$a_1 = 5$

$a_1 r = -\dfrac{5}{3}$

$r = -\dfrac{5}{3a_1}$

$r = -\dfrac{5}{3(5)} = -\dfrac{1}{3}$

Since $|r| < 1$, we can find the sum of the infinite series.

$S_n = \dfrac{a_1}{1-r} = \dfrac{5}{1 - \left(-\dfrac{1}{3}\right)} = \dfrac{15}{4}$

16.
(40)
$\log (x+3) - \log (x-2) = 8 \log \sqrt[4]{6}$

$\log (x+3) - \log (x-2) = \log \left(6^{1/4}\right)^8$

$\log \dfrac{x+3}{x-2} = \log 36$

$\dfrac{x+3}{x-2} = 36$

$x + 3 = 36x - 72$

$35x = 75$

$x = \dfrac{15}{7}$

17.
(90,93)
$\dfrac{\cos 2x + 1}{\sin 2x} = \dfrac{\cos^2 x - \sin^2 x + 1}{2 \sin x \cos x}$

$= \dfrac{\cos^2 x + \cos^2 x}{2 \sin x \cos x} = \dfrac{2\cos^2 x}{2 \sin x \cos x} = \cot x$

18. (a) $y = 3 + 2\sec\theta$
(94)

Centerline = 3

Amplitude = 2

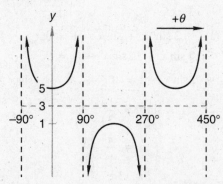

(b) $y = \cot\theta - 1$

Centerline = -1

Amplitude = 1

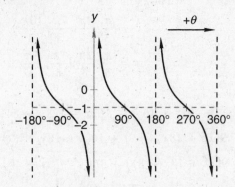

19. $y = 3 + 4\cos\dfrac{1}{2}(x + 2\pi)$
(84)

Period = $\dfrac{2\pi}{\dfrac{1}{2}} = 4\pi$

Phase angle = -2π

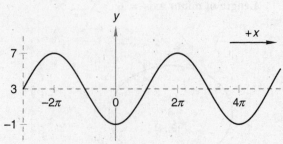

20. (a) $y = \tan\theta$
(94)
(b) $y = 6 + 8\csc x$

Test 28

1. $P(\text{both orange}) = \dfrac{5}{13} \cdot \dfrac{4}{12} = \dfrac{5}{39}$
(83)

2.
(101)
$$y = \frac{\begin{vmatrix} 3 & 2 & 5 \\ -1 & 1 & -2 \\ 1 & 1 & 0 \end{vmatrix}}{\begin{vmatrix} 3 & 3 & 5 \\ -1 & 0 & -2 \\ 1 & 2 & 0 \end{vmatrix}}$$

$$= \frac{(0 - 4 - 5) - (5 - 6 + 0)}{(0 - 6 - 10) - (0 - 12 + 0)}$$

$$= \frac{-8}{-4} = 2$$

3. $0.0\overline{287}$
(109)

$= 287 \times 10^{-4} + 287 \times 10^{-7} + 287 \times 10^{-10} + \dots$

$= 287 \times 10^{-4} + (287 \times 10^{-4})(10^{-3})$

$\qquad + (287 \times 10^{-4})(10^{-3})^2 + \dots$

$a_1 = 287 \times 10^{-4}, \; r = 10^{-3}$

Since $|r| < 1$, we can find the sum of the infinite series.

$$S = \frac{a_1}{1 - r}$$

$$= \frac{287 \times 10^{-4}}{1 - 10^{-3}} = \frac{287 \times 10^{-4}}{0.999} \cdot \frac{10^4}{10^4} = \frac{287}{9990}$$

4. Sum of distances the ball falls:
(107)

$a_1 = 156, \; r = \dfrac{1}{5}$

$$S = \frac{a_1}{1 - r} = \frac{156}{1 - \dfrac{1}{5}} = 195$$

Distance rebounded:

$S - a_1 = 195 - 156 = 39$

Sum of ups and downs:

$195 + 39 = \textbf{234 ft}$

5. $a_1 = -5, \; r = -3, \; n = 8$
(91,104)

(a) $a_n = a_1 r^{n-1}$

$\qquad a_8 = (-5)(-3)^{(8-1)} = (-5)(-3)^7 = \textbf{10,935}$

(b) $S_n = \dfrac{a_1(1 - r^n)}{1 - r}$

$\qquad S_8 = \dfrac{-5\left[1 - (-3)^8\right]}{1 - (-3)}$

$\qquad\quad = \dfrac{-5(1 - 6561)}{1 + 3} = \dfrac{32{,}800}{4} = \textbf{8200}$

6. (a) pH $= 12.6$
(103)

$\quad$ H$^+ = 10^{-\text{pH}} = 10^{-12.6} = \mathbf{2.51 \times 10^{-13}} \dfrac{\textbf{mole}}{\textbf{liter}}$

(b) H$^+ = 8.53 \times 10^{-10}$

$\quad$ pH $= -\log \text{H}^+ = -\log\left(8.53 \times 10^{-10}\right) = \textbf{9.07}$

7.
(106)
$\qquad -16x^2 + 4y^2 - 64x + 24y + 36 = 0$

$-16(x^2 + 4x \qquad) + 4(y^2 + 6y \qquad) = -36$

$-16(x^2 + 4x + 4) + 4(y^2 + 6y + 9) = -64$

$\qquad -16(x + 2)^2 + 4(y + 3)^2 = -64$

$$\frac{(x + 2)^2}{4} - \frac{(y + 3)^2}{16} = 1$$

From the equation of the line we obtain:

$h = -2, \; k = -3, \; a = 2, \; b = 4$

Center: $(h, k) = \textbf{(-2, -3)}$

Vertices: $(h \pm a, k) = \textbf{(0, -3), (-4, -3)}$

Asymptotes:

$$m = \pm\frac{b}{a} = \pm\frac{4}{2} = \pm 2$$

$y = mx + b$	$y = mx + b$
$y = 2x + b$	$y = -2x + b$
$(-3) = 2(-2) + b$	$(-3) = -2(-2) + b$
$b = 1$	$b = -7$
$y = 2x + 1$	$y = -2x - 7$

Asymptotes: $y = 2x + 1$; $y = -2x - 7$

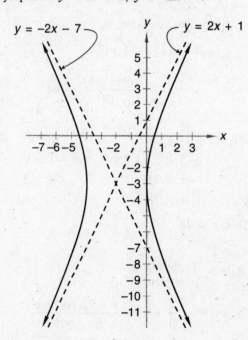

8.
(106)
$$4x^2 + y^2 + 24x + 8y + 16 = 0$$
$$4(x^2 + 6x \qquad) + (y^2 + 8y \qquad) = -16$$
$$4(x^2 + 6x + 9) + (y^2 + 8y + 16) = 36$$
$$4(x + 3)^2 + (y + 4)^2 = 36$$
$$\frac{(x + 3)^2}{9} + \frac{(y + 4)^2}{36} = 1$$

Center = $(-3, -4)$
$a = 6$, $b = 3$
Length of major axis = 12
Length of minor axis = 6
Vertical

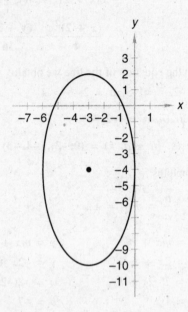

9.
(59)
$$16^{\log_4 16 + 2\log_4 2 - \log_4 8}$$
$$= 16^{\log_4 16 + \log_4 2^2 - \log_4 8}$$
$$= 4^{2(\log_4 16 + \log_4 4 - \log_4 8)}$$
$$= 4^{\log_4 16^2 + \log_4 4^2 - \log_4 8^2}$$
$$= 4^{\log_4 \frac{(256)(16)}{64}} = \frac{(256)(16)}{64} = \mathbf{64}$$

10.
(111)
$$\log_5 (x - 3) < 2$$
$$x - 3 < 5^2 \quad \text{and} \quad x - 3 > 0$$
$$x - 3 < 25 \qquad\qquad x > 3$$
$$x < 28$$
$$\mathbf{3 < x < 28}$$

11. Rate = $\dfrac{s}{p} \dfrac{\text{dollars}}{\text{airplane}}$
(44)

New rate = $\dfrac{s}{p} + 7 = \dfrac{s + 7p}{p} \dfrac{\text{dollars}}{\text{airplane}}$

New rate $\times N$ = price
$$\left(\frac{s + 7p}{p}\right) \times N = 100$$
$$N = \frac{100p}{s + 7p} \text{ airplanes}$$

12. $A_7 = 400$, $A_{10} = 650$
(88)
$$A_t = A_0 e^{kt}$$
$$A_{10} = A_7 e^{k(10-7)}$$
$$650 = 400 e^{k3}$$
$$3k = \ln \frac{650}{400}$$
$$k = 0.16184$$
$$A_{15} = A_7 e^{k(15-7)}$$
$$A_{15} = 400 e^{0.16184(8)}$$
$$A_{15} = \mathbf{1459.99}$$

13.
(98)
$$\log \sqrt[5]{x^7} + \log \sqrt[5]{x^8} = \frac{3}{4} \log 16$$
$$\log x^{7/5} + \log x^{8/5} = \log 16^{3/4}$$
$$\log \left(x^{7/5} x^{8/5}\right) = \log 8$$
$$x^3 = 8$$
$$x^3 = 2^3$$
$$x = \mathbf{2}$$

14.
(103)
$$\frac{\left(\sqrt[5]{512 \times 10^5}\right)^2}{\sqrt{708 \times 10^{16}}} = \mathbf{4.56 \times 10^{-7}}$$

15.
(52,60)
$$\cos^2 2\theta = 1$$
$$\cos^2 2\theta - 1 = 0$$
$$(\cos 2\theta + 1)(\cos 2\theta - 1) = 0$$

$\cos 2\theta + 1 = 0$ $\qquad\qquad$ $\cos 2\theta - 1 = 0$
$\cos 2\theta = -1$ $\qquad\qquad$ $\cos 2\theta = 1$
$2\theta = 180°, 540°$ $\qquad\qquad$ $2\theta = 0°, 360°$
$\theta = 90°, 270°$ $\qquad\qquad$ $\theta = 0°, 180°$

$\theta = \mathbf{0°, 90°, 180°, 270°}$

16.
(90)
$$\frac{2(1 - \cos^2 x)}{\tan x} = \frac{2\sin^2 x}{\tan x} = \frac{2\sin^2 x \cos x}{\sin x}$$
$$= 2\sin x \cos x = \sin 2x$$

17. $-\log_3 (n - 3) + 3 \log_3 n + \log_3 (n^2 - 9)$
(103)
$$- \log_3 (n^3 - 3n^2)$$

$$= \log_3 \frac{n^3 (n^2 - 9)}{(n^3 - 3n^2)(n - 3)}$$

$$= \log_3 \frac{n^3 (n + 3)(n - 3)}{n^2 (n - 3)(n - 3)}$$

$$= \log_3 \frac{n(n + 3)}{n - 3}$$

18. $(2x - 3y^2)^9$
(112)
$F = 2x, \; S = -3y^2, \; n = 9, \; k = 5$

$$\frac{n!}{(n - k + 1)!\,(k - 1)!} F^{n-k+1} S^{k-1}$$

$$= \frac{9!}{(9 - 5 + 1)!(5 - 1)!} F^{9-5+1} S^{5-1}$$

$$= \frac{9!}{5!4!} F^5 S^4$$

$$= \frac{9!}{5!4!} (2x)^5 (-3y^2)^4$$

$$= 126(32x^5)(81y^8) = \mathbf{326{,}592 x^5 y^8}$$

19. $(-i)^{1/3} = (1 \operatorname{cis} 270°)^{1/3}$
(79)
$$= \sqrt[3]{1} \operatorname{cis}\left(\frac{270°}{3} + n\frac{360°}{3}\right)$$

$1 \operatorname{cis} \dfrac{270°}{3} = 1 \operatorname{cis} 90° = i$

$1 \operatorname{cis}\left(\dfrac{270°}{3} + 120°\right) = 1 \operatorname{cis} 210° = -\dfrac{\sqrt{3}}{2} - \dfrac{1}{2}i$

$1 \operatorname{cis}\left(\dfrac{270°}{3} + 240°\right) = 1 \operatorname{cis} 330° = \dfrac{\sqrt{3}}{2} - \dfrac{1}{2}i$

20. $\theta = \arcsin x$
(110)

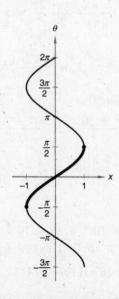

Domain $= \left\{ x \in \mathbb{R} \mid -1 \le x \le 1 \right\}$

Range $= \left\{ \theta \in \mathbb{R} \mid -\dfrac{\pi}{2} \le \theta \le \dfrac{\pi}{2} \right\}$

$\operatorname{Arcsin}\left(-\dfrac{\sqrt{3}}{2}\right) = -\dfrac{\pi}{3}$

$\operatorname{Arcsin} \dfrac{\sqrt{3}}{2} = \dfrac{\pi}{3}$

$\operatorname{Arcsin}\left(-\dfrac{1}{2}\right) = -\dfrac{\pi}{6}$

Test 29

1. $P(5 \cup D) = P(5) + P(D) - P(5 \cap D)$
(92)
$$= \frac{4}{52} + \frac{13}{52} - \frac{1}{52} = \frac{4}{13}$$

2. $x = \dfrac{\begin{vmatrix} 4 & 2 & 3 \\ -3 & 1 & 0 \\ 0 & 1 & 2 \end{vmatrix}}{\begin{vmatrix} 5 & 2 & 3 \\ -2 & 1 & 0 \\ 0 & 1 & 2 \end{vmatrix}}$
(101)

$$= \frac{(8 + 0 - 9) - (0 + 0 - 12)}{(10 + 0 - 6) - (0 + 0 - 8)}$$

$$= \frac{11}{12}$$

3. $A = \begin{bmatrix} 4 & 1 \\ 4 & -3 \\ 6 & 0 \end{bmatrix}, \; B = \begin{bmatrix} 1 & 7 \\ 2 & -5 \end{bmatrix}$
(108)

$$A \cdot B = \begin{bmatrix} 4 & 1 \\ 4 & -3 \\ 6 & 0 \end{bmatrix} \cdot \begin{bmatrix} 1 & 7 \\ 2 & -5 \end{bmatrix}$$

$$= \begin{bmatrix} 4 + 2 & 28 - 5 \\ 4 - 6 & 28 + 15 \\ 6 + 0 & 42 + 0 \end{bmatrix}$$

$$= \begin{bmatrix} 6 & 23 \\ -2 & 43 \\ 6 & 42 \end{bmatrix}$$

4. $f(x) = (x + 1)(x - 2)^2 = x^3 - 3x^2 + 4$
(114)

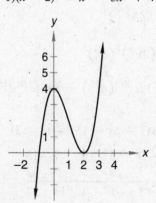

5. $\theta = \arccos x$
(110)

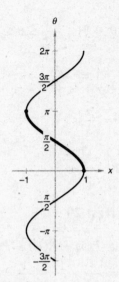

Domain $= \left\{ x \in \mathbb{R} \mid -1 \le x \le 1 \right\}$

Range $= \left\{ \theta \in \mathbb{R} \mid 0 \le \theta \le \pi \right\}$

$\text{Arccos } \dfrac{\sqrt{2}}{2} = \dfrac{\pi}{4}$

$\text{Arccos }\left(-\dfrac{\sqrt{2}}{2} \right) = \dfrac{3\pi}{4}$

$\text{Arccos } (-1) = \pi$

6. $\log_3 (x + 2) > 4$
(111)

$\qquad x + 2 > 3^4 \qquad$ and $\qquad x + 2 > 0$

$\qquad x + 2 > 81 \qquad\qquad\qquad\qquad x > -2$

$\qquad\qquad x > 79$

$x > 79$

7. $\left(2c^4 + d^3 \right)^{10}$
(112)

$F = 2c^4,\ S = d^3,\ n = 10,\ k = 6$

$\dfrac{n!}{(n - k + 1)!\,(k - 1)!}\, F^{n-k+1} S^{k-1}$

$= \dfrac{10!}{(10 - 6 + 1)!\,(6 - 1)!}\, F^{10-6+1} S^{6-1}$

$= \dfrac{10!}{5!\,5!}\, F^5 S^5$

$= \dfrac{10!}{5!\,5!}\, \left(2c^4 \right)^5 \left(d^3 \right)^5$

$= 252 \left(32c^{20} \right)\left(d^{15} \right) = \mathbf{8064 c^{20} d^{15}}$

8. $\left(x^5 - 8x^3 + 5x - 15 \right) \div (x - 3)$
(113)

$$
\underline{3}\ \begin{array}{rrrrrr}
1 & 0 & -8 & 0 & 5 & -15 \\
  & 3 & 9 & 3 & 9 & 42 \\
\hline
1 & 3 & 1 & 3 & 14 & 27
\end{array}
$$

$\dfrac{x^5 - 8x^3 + 5x - 15}{x - 3}$

$= x^4 + 3x^3 + x^2 + 3x + 14 + \dfrac{27}{x - 3}$

9. $y = \tan (x + \pi)$
(94)

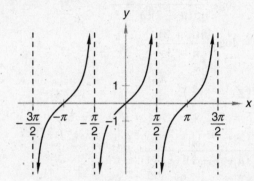

10. $\dfrac{\tan^2 x}{\sec x - 1} = \dfrac{\sec^2 x - 1}{\sec x - 1} = \dfrac{(\sec x - 1)(\sec x + 1)}{\sec x - 1}$
(93)

$= \sec x + 1 = \dfrac{1}{\cos x} + 1 = \dfrac{1 + \cos x}{\cos x}$

11. $x^5 - 3x^4 - 5x^2 - 44$
(113)

$$
\underline{2}\ \begin{array}{rrrrrr}
1 & -3 & 0 & -5 & 0 & -44 \\
  & 2 & -2 & -4 & -18 & -36 \\
\hline
1 & -1 & -2 & -9 & -18 & -80
\end{array}
$$

The remainder is not zero, so 2 is not a zero of the polynomial.

12. $(x + 2) 9^{\log_9 \left(x^2 + 4x - 12 \right) - \log_9 \left(x^2 - 4 \right)}$
(59)

$= (x + 2) 9^{\log_9 \frac{x^2 + 4x - 12}{x^2 - 4}}$

$= (x + 2)\left(\dfrac{x^2 + 4x - 12}{x^2 - 4} \right)$

$= \dfrac{(x + 2)(x + 6)(x - 2)}{(x + 2)(x - 2)} = \mathbf{x + 6}$

13. $\sin x + \sin y = 2 \sin \dfrac{x + y}{2} \cos \dfrac{x - y}{2}$
(100)

$\sin 90° + \sin 30°$

$= 2 \sin \dfrac{90° + 30°}{2} \cos \dfrac{90° - 30°}{2}$

$= 2 \sin 60° \cos 30° = 2\left(\dfrac{\sqrt{3}}{2} \right)\left(\dfrac{\sqrt{3}}{2} \right) = \dfrac{3}{2}$

14. $4.\overline{35}$
(109)

$= 4 + 35 \times 10^{-2} + 35 \times 10^{-4} + 35 \times 10^{-6} + \ldots$

$= 4 + \left(35 \times 10^{-2} \right) + \left(35 \times 10^{-2} \right)\left(10^{-2} \right)$

$\qquad + \left(35 \times 10^{-2} \right)\left(10^{-2} \right)^2 + \ldots$

$a_1 = 35 \times 10^{-2}$, $r = 10^{-2}$

Since $|r| < 1$, we can find the sum of the infinite series.

$$4 + \frac{a_1}{1-r} = 4 + \frac{35 \times 10^{-2}}{1 - 10^{-2}}$$

$$= 4 + \frac{35 \times 10^{-2}}{0.99} \cdot \frac{10^2}{10^2}$$

$$= 4 + \frac{35}{99}$$

$$= \frac{396}{99} + \frac{35}{99} = \frac{\mathbf{431}}{\mathbf{99}}$$

15.
(85,90)
$$\cos 2A + \sin^2 A - 1 = 0$$
$$\cos^2 A - \sin^2 A + \sin^2 A - 1 = 0$$
$$\cos^2 A - 1 = 0$$
$$(\cos A + 1)(\cos A - 1) = 0$$

$\cos A + 1 = 0 \qquad \cos A - 1 = 0$
$\quad\ \cos A = -1 \qquad\quad \cos A = 1$
$\qquad\quad A = 180° \qquad\qquad A = 0°$

$A = \mathbf{0°, 180°}$

16. $\log(a^2 c - b^2 c) - \log(a+b) - 2\log c$
(103)
$$= \log(a^2 c - b^2 c) - \log(a+b) - \log c^2$$

$$= \log \frac{(a^2 c - b^2 c)}{(a+b)c^2}$$

$$= \log \frac{c(a^2 - b^2)}{(a+b)c^2}$$

$$= \log \frac{c(a+b)(a-b)}{(a+b)c^2}$$

$$= \log \frac{a-b}{c}$$

17. $4x^3 - 3x^2 + 2x - 3$
(115)
$x = 2$

$$\begin{array}{r|rrrr} 2 & 4 & -3 & 2 & -3 \\ & & 8 & 10 & 24 \\ \hline & 4 & 5 & 12 & 21 \end{array}$$

$P(2) = \mathbf{21}$

18.
(106)
$$4x^2 + 9y^2 - 40x + 36y + 100 = 0$$

$$4(x^2 - 10x \quad\ ) + 9(y^2 + 4y \quad\ ) = -100$$

$$4(x^2 - 10x + 25) + 9(y^2 + 4y + 4) = 36$$

$$4(x-5)^2 + 9(y+2)^2 = 36$$

$$\frac{(x-5)^2}{9} + \frac{(y+2)^2}{4} = 1$$

Center = (5, –2)

$a = 3$, $b = 2$

Length of major axis = 6

Length of minor axis = 4

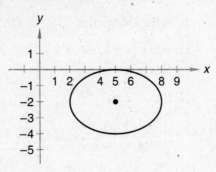

19. $y = x^3 - 3x + 2$
(116)
Radius $= |-3| + 1 = \mathbf{4}$

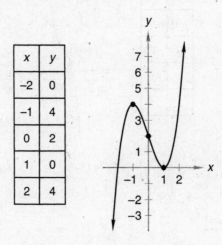

x	y
–2	0
–1	4
0	2
1	0
2	4

20. **E.**
(114)

Test 30

1. $138 = 2 \cdot 3 \cdot 23$
(117)
$40 = 2 \cdot 2 \cdot 2 \cdot 5$

No, they have a factor of 2 in common.

2. $x^3 - 5x^2 - 9x + 45 = 0$
(118)
$x = 5$

$$\begin{array}{r|rrrr} 5 & 1 & -5 & -9 & 45 \\ & & 5 & 0 & -45 \\ \hline & 1 & 0 & -9 & 0 \end{array}$$

$$(x-5)(x^2 - 9) = 0$$

$$(x-5)(x+3)(x-3) = 0$$

The other roots are: **3, –3**

3. $8x^8 + 4x^6 + 3x^2 + 2 = 0$
(117)

INTEGRAL FACTORS

$$\frac{\{1, -1, 2, -2\}}{\{1, -1, 2, -2, 4, -4, 8, -8\}}$$

POSSIBLE QUOTIENTS

$$\rightarrow \quad \pm 1, \pm 2, \pm \frac{1}{2}, \pm \frac{1}{4}, \pm \frac{1}{8}$$

4. $y = 3x^3 - 4x^2 + 3x + 1$
(116)

$$\text{Radius} = \left| -\frac{4}{3} \right| + 1 = \frac{7}{3}$$

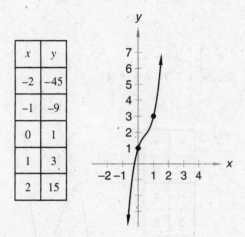

x	y
-2	-45
-1	-9
0	1
1	3
2	15

5. $4x^3 + 3x^2 - 2x + 1$
(115)

$x = -4$

$$\begin{array}{r|rrrr} -4 & 4 & 3 & -2 & 1 \\ & & -16 & 52 & -200 \\ \hline & 4 & -13 & 50 & -199 \end{array}$$

$P(-4) = \mathbf{-199}$

6. $f(x) = x(x - 2)(x + 3) = x^3 + x^2 - 6x$
(114)

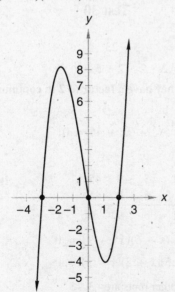

7. $A_0 = 400$, half-life $= 12$ days
(88)

$$A_t = A_0 e^{kt}$$

$$\frac{1}{2}(400) = 400e^{k12}$$

$$12k = \ln \frac{1}{2}$$

$$k = -0.057762$$

$$A_t = 400e^{-0.057762t}$$

$$150 = 400e^{-0.057762t}$$

$$-0.057762t = \ln \frac{150}{400}$$

$$t = \mathbf{16.98 \text{ days}}$$

8. $A = \begin{bmatrix} 2 & 0 \\ 3 & 1 \\ 2 & 1 \end{bmatrix}$, $B = \begin{bmatrix} 7 & -3 & 1 \\ 2 & 0 & 3 \end{bmatrix}$
(108)

$$A \cdot B = \begin{bmatrix} 2 & 0 \\ 3 & 1 \\ 2 & 1 \end{bmatrix} \cdot \begin{bmatrix} 7 & -3 & 1 \\ 2 & 0 & 3 \end{bmatrix}$$

$$= \begin{bmatrix} 14 + 0 & -6 + 0 & 2 + 0 \\ 21 + 2 & -9 + 0 & 3 + 3 \\ 14 + 2 & -6 + 0 & 2 + 3 \end{bmatrix}$$

$$= \begin{bmatrix} \mathbf{14} & \mathbf{-6} & \mathbf{2} \\ \mathbf{23} & \mathbf{-9} & \mathbf{6} \\ \mathbf{16} & \mathbf{-6} & \mathbf{5} \end{bmatrix}$$

9. ORIGINAL MATRIX   INVERSE MATRIX
(120)

$$\begin{bmatrix} a & b \\ c & d \end{bmatrix} \quad \begin{bmatrix} \dfrac{d}{ad - cb} & \dfrac{-b}{ad - cb} \\ \dfrac{-c}{ad - cb} & \dfrac{a}{ad - cb} \end{bmatrix}$$

$$\begin{bmatrix} 3 & 5 \\ 4 & 6 \end{bmatrix} \quad \begin{bmatrix} \dfrac{6}{(3)(6) - (4)(5)} & \dfrac{-5}{(3)(6) - (4)(5)} \\ \dfrac{-4}{(3)(6) - (4)(5)} & \dfrac{3}{(3)(6) - (4)(5)} \end{bmatrix}$$

$$= \begin{bmatrix} -3 & \dfrac{5}{2} \\ 2 & -\dfrac{3}{2} \end{bmatrix}$$

10. $\log_5 \left[\dfrac{\sqrt[3]{z}(x + 2)^3}{(x + 2)^4 \sqrt[4]{z + 1}} \right]$
(103)

$$= \log_5 \left[\frac{\sqrt[3]{z}}{(x + 2) \sqrt[4]{z + 1}} \right]$$

$$= \log_5 z^{1/3} - \log_5 (x + 2) - \log_5 (z + 1)^{1/4}$$

$$= \frac{1}{3} \log_5 z - \log_5 (x + 2) - \frac{1}{4} \log_5 (z + 1)$$

11. $\theta = \text{Arctan } x$
(110)

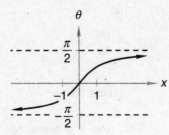

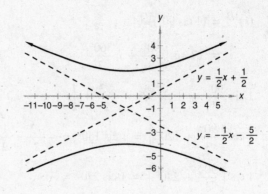

Domain $= \{x \in \mathbb{R}\}$

Range $= \left\{\theta \in \mathbb{R} \mid -\dfrac{\pi}{2} < \theta < \dfrac{\pi}{2}\right\}$

$\text{Arctan } 1 = \dfrac{\pi}{4}$

$\text{Arctan}\left(-\dfrac{1}{\sqrt{3}}\right) = -\dfrac{\pi}{6}$

$\text{Arctan } \sqrt{3} = \dfrac{\pi}{3}$

13. $27^{2x+3} = 81^{4x-1}$
(82)

$3^{3(2x+3)} = 3^{4(4x-1)}$

$3^{6x+9} = 3^{16x-4}$

$6x + 9 = 16x - 4$

$10x = 13$

$x = \dfrac{13}{10}$

12.
(106)

$$4y^2 - x^2 + 8y - 6x - 41 = 0$$

$$4\left(y^2 + 2y \quad\right) - \left(x^2 + 6x \quad\right) = 41$$

$$4\left(y^2 + 2y + 1\right) - \left(x^2 + 6x + 9\right) = 36$$

$$4(y + 1)^2 - (x + 3)^2 = 36$$

$$\dfrac{(y + 1)^2}{9} - \dfrac{(x + 3)^2}{36} = 1$$

From the equation we obtain:

$h = -3, \; k = -1, \; a = 6, \; b = 3$

Center: $(h, k) = (-3, -1)$

Vertices: $(h, k \pm b) = (-3, 2), (-3, -4)$

Asymptotes:

$m = \pm\dfrac{b}{a} = \pm\dfrac{3}{6} = \pm\dfrac{1}{2}$

$y = mx + b \qquad\qquad y = mx + b$

$y = \dfrac{1}{2}x + b \qquad\quad y = -\dfrac{1}{2}x + b$

$(-1) = \dfrac{1}{2}(-3) + b \qquad (-1) = -\dfrac{1}{2}(-3) + b$

$b = \dfrac{1}{2} \qquad\qquad\quad b = -\dfrac{5}{2}$

$y = \dfrac{1}{2}x + \dfrac{1}{2} \qquad\quad y = -\dfrac{1}{2}x - \dfrac{5}{2}$

Asymptotes: $y = \dfrac{1}{2}x + \dfrac{1}{2}$; $y = -\dfrac{1}{2}x - \dfrac{5}{2}$

14.
(90)

$$\dfrac{\tan 2x(1 - \tan^2 x)}{\sin 2x} = \dfrac{\left(\dfrac{2 \tan x}{1 - \tan^2 x}\right)(1 - \tan^2 x)}{2 \sin x \cos x}$$

$$= \dfrac{2 \tan x}{2 \sin x \cos x} = \dfrac{\dfrac{\sin x}{\cos x}}{\sin x \cos x} = \dfrac{1}{\cos^2 x} = \sec^2 x$$

15.
(85)

$$2\tan^2 x + 3 \sec x = 0$$

$$2\left(\sec^2 x - 1\right) + 3 \sec x = 0$$

$$2\sec^2 x + 3 \sec x - 2 = 0$$

$$(2 \sec x - 1)(\sec x + 2) = 0$$

$2 \sec x - 1 = 0 \qquad\qquad \sec x + 2 = 0$

$\sec x = \dfrac{1}{2} \qquad\qquad\quad \sec x = -2$

$\cos x = 2 \qquad\qquad\quad \cos x = -\dfrac{1}{2}$

no answer $\qquad\qquad\quad x = \dfrac{2\pi}{3}, \dfrac{4\pi}{3}$

16. $y = 2x^3 - x^2 + x - 3$
(119)

1	2	−1	1	−3		2	2	−1	1	−3
		2	1	2				4	6	14
	2	1	2	−1			2	3	7	11

Upper bound $= 2$

−1	2	−1	1	−3
		−2	3	−4
	2	−3	4	−7

Lower bound $= -1$

17. $(i)^{1/3} = (1 \text{ cis } 90°)^{1/3}$
(79)

$$= \sqrt[3]{1} \text{ cis}\left(\frac{90°}{3} + n\frac{360°}{3}\right)$$

$$1 \text{ cis } \frac{90°}{3} = 1 \text{ cis } 30° = \frac{\sqrt{3}}{2} + \frac{1}{2}i$$

$$1 \text{ cis}\left(\frac{90°}{3} + 120°\right) = 1 \text{ cis } 150° = -\frac{\sqrt{3}}{2} + \frac{1}{2}i$$

$$1 \text{ cis}\left(\frac{90°}{3} + 240°\right) = 1 \text{ cis } 270° = -i$$

18. $\left(5x^3 - \frac{1}{x}\right)^9$
(112)

$$F = 5x^3, \; S = -\frac{1}{x}, \; n = 9, \; k = 7$$

$$\frac{n!}{(n - k + 1)!(k - 1)!}F^{n-k+1}S^{k-1}$$

$$= \frac{9!}{(9 - 7 + 1)!(7 - 1)!}F^{9-7+1}S^{7-1}$$

$$= \frac{9!}{3!6!}F^3 S^6$$

$$= \frac{9!}{3!6!}\left(5x^3\right)^3\left(-\frac{1}{x}\right)^6$$

$$= 84\left(125x^9\right)\left(\frac{1}{x^6}\right) = \mathbf{10{,}500x^3}$$

19. (a) $p(x) = x^4 + x^3 - 3x^2 + x + 2$
(119)
$\qquad + \qquad + \; © \; - \; © \; + \qquad +$

There are **0 or 2** positive real roots.

(b) $p(x) = x^4 + x^3 - 3x^2 + x + 2$

$\quad p(-x) = x^4 - x^3 - 3x^2 - x + 2$
$\qquad + \; © \; - \qquad - \qquad - \; © \; +$

There are **0 or 2** negative real roots.

20. (a) $\begin{cases} R_E T_E = 60 \\ R_J T_J = 160 \end{cases}$
(25) (b)

$$R_E = R_J - 5, \; T_E = \frac{T_J}{2}$$

(a) $\qquad R_E T_E = 60$

$$\left(R_J - 5\right)\left(\frac{1}{2}T_J\right) = 60$$

$$\frac{1}{2}R_J T_J - \frac{5}{2}T_J = 60$$

$$\frac{1}{2}(160) - \frac{5}{2}T_J = 60$$

$$\frac{5}{2}T_J = 20$$

$$T_J = \mathbf{8 \text{ hr}}$$

(b) $R_J T_J = 160$

$\quad R_J(8) = 160$

$$R_J = \mathbf{20 \; \frac{mi}{hr}}$$

Test 31

1. Tests $= t$ tests, time $= h$ hours, rate $= \dfrac{t}{h} \dfrac{\text{tests}}{\text{hr}}$
(44)

New number of tests $= (t + 4)$ tests

New time $= (h - 2)$ hr

New rate $= \dfrac{t + 4}{h - 2} \dfrac{\text{tests}}{\text{hr}}$

2. $\begin{cases} y = 2 & \text{if } -\infty < x \le 0 \\ y = x & \text{if } 0 < x \le 3 \\ y = 3 - x & \text{if } 3 < x < \infty \end{cases}$
(121)

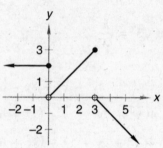

3. $xy = 8$
(123)

$$y = \frac{8}{x}, \; x \ne 0$$

$$x = \frac{8}{y}, \; y \ne 0$$

Asymptotes: $y = 0, \; x = 0$

x	y
−4	−2
−2	−4
−1	−8
1	8
2	4
4	2

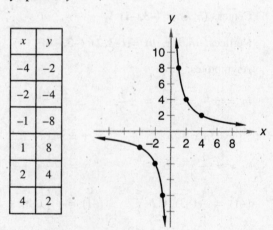

4. $x^3 + x^2 + 3x + 10 = 0$
(118)

Possible rational roots: $\pm 1, \pm 2, \pm 5, \pm 10$

$$\begin{array}{r|rrrr} -2 & 1 & 1 & 3 & 10 \\ & & -2 & 2 & -10 \\ \hline & 1 & -1 & 5 & 0 \end{array}$$

$(x + 2)(x^2 - x + 5) = 0$

For $x^2 - x + 5$ use the quadratic formula:

$$x = \frac{-(-1) \pm \sqrt{(-1)^2 - 4(1)(5)}}{2(1)}$$

$$x = \frac{1 \pm \sqrt{-19}}{2} = \frac{1}{2} \pm \frac{\sqrt{19}}{2}i$$

Roots: -2, $\dfrac{1}{2} + \dfrac{\sqrt{19}}{2}i$, $\dfrac{1}{2} - \dfrac{\sqrt{19}}{2}i$

5. $f(x) = [x] + 2$
(121)

This is the graph of $y = [x]$ translated 2 units up.

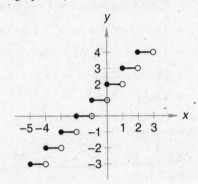

6. Side $= \dfrac{36}{6} = 6$ in.
(73)

$$\theta = \frac{1}{2}\left(\frac{360°}{6}\right) = 30°$$

$$r = \frac{3}{\sin 30°}$$

Radius = 6 in.

7. (a) $p(x) = 5x^3 + 4x^2 - 3x + 2$
(119)
$\qquad\quad + \qquad + \;\;ⓒ\;\; - \;\;ⓒ\;\; +$

There are **0 or 2** positive real roots.

(b) $p(x) = 5x^3 + 4x^2 - 3x + 2$

$p(-x) = -5x^3 + 4x^2 + 3x + 2$
$\qquad\quad -ⓒ \quad + \qquad + \qquad +$

There is **1** negative real root.

8.
(121)
$$\begin{cases} y = -x - 2 & \text{if } -\infty < x \le -2 \\ y = x & \text{if } -2 < x < 2 \\ y = -2x + 4 & \text{if } 2 \le x < \infty \end{cases}$$

9. $y = \dfrac{x^2 - 4x}{(x + 3)(x - 2)(x - 4)}$
(122)

$\qquad = \dfrac{x(x - 4)}{(x + 3)(x - 2)(x - 4)}$

x intercepts: $x = 0$

Asymptotes: $x = -3, 2$

Hole: $x = 4$

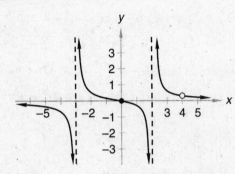

10. $P(\text{both green}) = \dfrac{9}{16} \cdot \dfrac{8}{15} = \dfrac{3}{10}$
(83)

11.
(72,96)

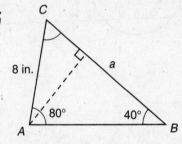

(a) $C = 180° - 80° - 40° = \mathbf{60°}$

(b) $\dfrac{8}{\sin 40°} = \dfrac{a}{\sin 80°}$

$\qquad a = \dfrac{8 \sin 80°}{\sin 40°}$

$\qquad a = \mathbf{12.26 \text{ in.}}$

(c) Area $= \dfrac{1}{2}(a)(b \sin C)$

$\qquad\quad = \dfrac{1}{2}(12.26)(8 \sin 60°)$

$\qquad\quad = \mathbf{42.47 \text{ in.}^2}$

12. $ax^2 + bxy + cy^2 + dx + ey + f = 0$
(123)

(a) $x^2 + y^2 - 12x - 4y + 4 = 0$

This is a **circle** since $b = 0$ and $a = c \ne 0$.

(b) $-y^2 + 9x^2 - 90x + 4y + 302 = 0$

This is a **hyperbola** since $b = 0$ and a and c have opposite signs.

(c) $x^2 + 2x - 8y - 3 = 0$

This is a **parabola** since $b = c = 0$, $a \ne 0$, and $e \ne 0$.

(d) $9x^2 + 4y^2 = 36$

This is an **ellipse** since $b = 0$, a and c have the same sign, and $a \neq c$.

(e) $x^2 - 4y^2 = 4$

This is a **hyperbola** since $b = 0$ and a and c have opposite signs.

13.
(63)
$$x^2 + y^2 - 12x - 4y + 4 = 0$$
$$\left(x^2 - 12x \quad\right) + \left(y^2 - 4y \quad\right) = -4$$
$$\left(x^2 - 12x + 36\right) + \left(y^2 - 4y + 4\right) = 36$$
$$(x - 6)^2 + (y - 2)^2 = 6^2$$

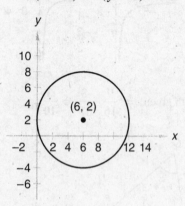

14. $P_1 = (1, 4)$, $P_2 = (6, 9)$
(124)
$$x_F = x_1 + \Delta x$$
$$= 1 + \frac{2}{5}(6 - 1)$$
$$= 1 + \frac{2}{5}(5) = 3$$
$$y_F = y_1 + \Delta y$$
$$= 4 + \frac{2}{5}(9 - 4)$$
$$= 4 + \frac{2}{5}(5) = 6$$

(3, 6)

15.
(76,90)
$$\cos 2x - \cos x = 0$$
$$2\cos^2 x - 1 - \cos x = 0$$
$$2\cos^2 x - \cos x - 1 = 0$$
$$(2\cos x + 1)(\cos x - 1) = 0$$

$2\cos x + 1 = 0$ $\cos x - 1 = 0$

                            $\cos x = 1$

$\cos x = -\dfrac{1}{2}$ $x = 0$

$x = \dfrac{2\pi}{3}, \dfrac{4\pi}{3}$

$x = \mathbf{0}, \dfrac{\mathbf{2\pi}}{\mathbf{3}}, \dfrac{\mathbf{4\pi}}{\mathbf{3}}$

16. $\log_{1/4}(x - 4) > 2$
(111)

$$x - 4 < \left(\frac{1}{4}\right)^2 \quad \text{and} \quad x - 4 > 0$$
$$\qquad\qquad\qquad\qquad\qquad\qquad x > 4$$
$$x - 4 < \frac{1}{16}$$
$$x < 4\frac{1}{16}$$

$$\mathbf{4 < x < 4\frac{1}{16}}$$

17. $\sin 3x = \sin(2x + x)$
(100)
$$= \sin 2x \cos x + \cos 2x \sin x$$
$$= (2\sin x \cos x)\cos x + \left(1 - 2\sin^2 x\right)\sin x$$
$$= 2\sin x \cos^2 x + \sin x - 2\sin^3 x$$
$$= 2\sin x\left(1 - \sin^2 x\right) + \sin x - 2\sin^3 x$$
$$= 2\sin x - 2\sin^3 x + \sin x - 2\sin^3 x$$
$$= 3\sin x - 4\sin^3 x$$

18. If $3i$ is a root, then $-3i$ is a root.
(118)
$$\frac{x^4 + 5x^2 - 36}{(x - 3i)(x + 3i)} = \frac{x^4 + 5x^2 - 36}{x^2 + 9}$$
$$= \frac{\left(x^2 + 9\right)\left(x^2 - 4\right)}{x^2 + 9} = x^2 - 4$$
$$x^2 - 4 = 0$$
$$x^2 = 4$$
$$x = \pm 2$$

The other roots are: **$-3i$, 2, -2**

19. $y = 4x^4 - 12x^2$
(116)
Radius $= |-3| + 1 = \mathbf{4}$

x	y
-2	16
-1	-8
0	0
1	-8
2	16

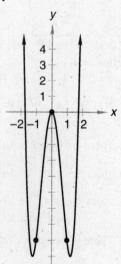

20. C.
(114)

problem set 8

1. $N_G = 50$; $N_P = 40$ **2.** 56   **3.** $N_N = 160$; $N_Q = 13$ **4.** $A = 74°$; $B = 84°$

5. Invalid.   **6.** Valid.   **7.** If it is blue, then it is a dog. Valid.   **8.** 5, 7, 9

9. $\triangle XYZ \sim \triangle XMY$ so $\dfrac{XY}{XM} = \dfrac{YZ}{MY}$ **10.** 3   **11.** $\dfrac{16}{3}$ **12.** $x = 3$; $y = 2$; $z = \dfrac{1}{2}$

13. $x = 3$; $y = 2$; $z = 1$ **14.** $x = 5$; $y = 3$ **15.** $-\dfrac{31}{7}$ **16.** 5   **17.** $\dfrac{73\sqrt{10}}{10}$

18. $6x^a - 2x^{\frac{a}{2}}y^{\frac{b}{3}} - 4y^{\frac{2b}{3}}$ **19.** $x^{\frac{a-8b+4}{4}}y^{\frac{3c+1}{2}}$ **20.** $2 + (10 + \sqrt{3})i$

21. $-10 - i$ **22.** Refer to Lesson 4.   **23.** Refer to Lesson 4.   **24.** Refer to Lesson 4.

25. $a = 7$; $b = 10$ **26.** $x = 20$; $y = 10$

27. $V = \dfrac{256\pi}{3}$ cm^3 = 268.08 cm^3; $A_{surface} = 64\pi$ cm^2 = 201.06 cm^2

28. $\left(\dfrac{220 + 20\pi}{3}\right)$ cm^3 = 94.28 cm^3 **29.** 5   **30.** 100

problem set 9

1. $N_G = 80$; $N_B = 200$ **2.** $N_B = 100$; $N_G = 200$

3. If two angles of a triangle are congruent, then the sides opposite these angles are congruent.

4. Invalid.   **5.** If the light is on, then the switch is not on. Invalid.   **6.** $-8, -7, -6, -5$

7. $\dfrac{9}{16}$ **8.** Obtuse triangle

9. (a) *AAAS* congruency postulate   (b) *SAS* congruency postulate
     (c) *SSS* congruency postulate   (d) *HL* congruency postulate

10. $\triangle ABD \cong \triangle CBD$ by *SAS* congruency postulate

11. $\triangle ABC \cong \triangle ADC$ by *SSS* congruency postulate; $\angle ABC \cong \angle ADC$ by *CPCTC*

12. $\dfrac{29\sqrt{6}}{6}$ **13.** $(2 - \sqrt{2})i$ **14.** $4x^a - y^b$ **15.** $x^{\frac{-5a-6}{2}}y^{\frac{-b-9}{6}}$ **16.** 3   **17.** $\dfrac{-19}{4}$

18. $x = 2$; $y = -1$; $z = 3$ **19.** $x = 4$; $y = 2$; $z = -2$

20. $a = 3\sqrt{7}$; $b = 3\sqrt{42}$; $h = 3\sqrt{6}$ **21.** $\triangle ABC \sim \triangle BDC$ so $\dfrac{AB}{BD} = \dfrac{AC}{BC}$ **22.** 12

23. Refer to Lesson 4.   **24.** Refer to Lesson 4.   **25.** $x = 20$; $y = 10$

26. $a = \dfrac{5}{2}$; $b = \dfrac{24}{5}$ **27.** $a = 3\sqrt{5}$; $b = 2\sqrt{5}$; $c = 5$ **28.** 200 cm^3 **29.** -28 **30.** A

problem set 10

1. $N_B = 680$; $N_S = 240$ **2.** $N_D = 42$; $N_Q = 100$ **3.** $\dfrac{1}{8}$ **4.** $-8, -6, -4$

5. $y = -x + 1$ **6.** $y = 2x - 7$ **7.** $3 - 5i$ **8.** $16i$ **9.** $\dfrac{4}{13} + \dfrac{7}{13}i$

10. $\dfrac{1}{10} + \dfrac{4}{5}i$ **11.** $-4 - 2\sqrt{3}$ **12.** $6, -2$ **13.** $-\dfrac{1}{6} \pm \dfrac{\sqrt{59}}{6}i$ **14.** Valid.

15. (a) *SSS* congruency postulate   (b) *SAS* congruency postulate
     (c) *AAAS* congruency postulate   (d) *SAS* congruency postulate

16. $\triangle BCD \cong \triangle AED$ by *AAAS* congruency postulate

17. $\triangle ADC \cong \triangle BDC$ by *SAS* congruency postulate; $\angle A \cong \angle B$ by *CPCTC*

18. $\triangle QSR \sim \triangle PSQ$ so $\dfrac{SR}{SQ} = \dfrac{QR}{PQ}$ **19.** $a = 2$; $b = \sqrt{5}$; $c = \sqrt{5}$ **20.** 2   **21.** 8

22. $x = 4$; $y = 2$; $z = 1$ **23.** $\dfrac{x^3y^6 + x^6}{y^8}$ **24.** $x^{\frac{27-2a}{6}}y^{\frac{-5a}{3}}$ **25.** Refer to Lesson 4.

26. Refer to Lesson 4.   **27.** 378 m^2 **28.** $V = 36\pi$ in.^{3}; $A_{surface} = 36\pi$ in.^{2}

29. A   **30.** C

problem set 11

1. $N_I = 8$; $N_E = 14$　**2.** $N_B = 135$; $N_S = 45$　**3.** 52, 54, 56, 58　**4.** Invalid.

5. $x = 38$; $y = 25$　**6.** 5　**7.** $x = 4$; $y = 15$

8. $x = \dfrac{-b \pm \sqrt{b^2 - 4ac}}{2a}$ (See Lesson 11.)　**9.** $-\dfrac{1}{3} \pm \dfrac{\sqrt{14}}{3}i$　**10.** $\dfrac{4}{3}, -1$

11. $y = \dfrac{1}{3}x - 3$　**12.** $-\dfrac{9}{17} + \dfrac{2}{17}i$　**13.** $\dfrac{-24 - 13\sqrt{3}}{23}$　**14.** $-\dfrac{1}{4} \pm \dfrac{\sqrt{39}}{4}i$

15. $\dfrac{1}{3} \pm \dfrac{\sqrt{22}}{3}$　**16.** $x = 2$; $y = 4$; $z = 1$　**17.** 8　**18.** -1

19. (a) *HL* congruency postulate　(b) *AAAS* congruency postulate
(c) *AAAS* congruency postulate　(d) *SSS* congruency postulate

20. $\Delta PQR \cong \Delta PSR$ by *HL* congruency postulate

21. $\Delta ABC \cong \Delta EDC$ by *AAAS* congruency postulate; $\overline{BC} \cong \overline{DC}$ by *CPCTC*

22. $\dfrac{26}{3}$　**23.** $\dfrac{5}{2}$　**24.** $x = \dfrac{13}{4}$; $y = \dfrac{39}{4}$　**25.** Refer to Lesson 4.　**26.** $\dfrac{b^5 + a^7b^2}{a^{11}}$

27. $x^{\frac{10a+3}{2}} y^{4-2a}$　**28.** $36x^3 - 4y$　**29.** B　**30.** C

problem set 12

1. 119　**2.** $N_B = 14$; $N_G = 38$　**3.** 305 grams　**4.** Interior: 720°; Exterior: 360°

5. 27　**6.** $x = 4$; $y = \dfrac{4}{3}$　**7.** $x = 160$; $y = 60$; $z = 140$　**8.** 36

9. $x = \dfrac{-b \pm \sqrt{b^2 - 4ac}}{2a}$ (See Lesson 11.)　**10.** $\dfrac{1}{4} \pm \dfrac{\sqrt{39}}{4}i$　**11.** $-\dfrac{1}{3} \pm \dfrac{\sqrt{11}}{3}i$

12. $y = 2x - 1$　**13.** $2 - 6i$　**14.** $\dfrac{8 - 5\sqrt{2}}{4}$　**15.** $-\dfrac{1}{6} \pm \dfrac{\sqrt{71}}{6}i$　**16.** $1 \pm \dfrac{3\sqrt{2}}{2}$

17. $x = 9$; $y = 4$; $z = 2$　**18.** 4　**19.** $-24 - 22i$　**20.** $-\dfrac{1}{2} - 2i$　**21.** $\dfrac{xy^4 + x^4}{y^{10}}$

22. (a) *SAS* congruency postulate　(b) *HL* congruency postulate
(c) *SSS* congruency postulate　(d) *AAAS* congruency postulate

23. $\Delta AYX \cong \Delta CZX$ by *AAAS* congruency postulate

24. $\Delta ABE \cong \Delta CBD$ by *SAS* congruency postulate　**25.** $x = 2\sqrt{14}$; $y = 2\sqrt{10}$; $z = 2\sqrt{35}$

26. $\dfrac{20}{3}$　**27.** Refer to Lesson 4.　**28.** $\dfrac{215\pi}{6}$ cm^3　**29.** C　**30.** D

problem set 13

1. 96　**2.** 2394　**3.** 0, 2, 4　**4.** 50　**5.** 15　**6.** $\dfrac{27}{5}$　**7.** 4

8. 35　**9.** Interior: 1440°; Exterior: 360°　**10.** Valid.　**11.** $x = 60$; $y = 30$

12. $x = 95$; $y = 120$; $z = 115$　**13.** 1　**14.** $\dfrac{1}{5} \pm \dfrac{2}{5}i$　**15.** $\dfrac{3}{4} \pm \dfrac{\sqrt{41}}{4}$

16. $\dfrac{3}{2} \pm \dfrac{\sqrt{17}}{2}$　**17.** $y = 3x - 3$　**18.** $x = 5$; $y = 2$; $z = -1$　**19.** $\dfrac{10}{3}$　**20.** 1

21. 3　**22.** $-9 + 4\sqrt{5}$　**23.** $-\dfrac{1}{2}i$　**24.** $\Delta ABD \cong \Delta CBD$ by *SAS* congruency postulate

25. $\Delta PQR \cong \Delta RSP$ by *SAS* congruency postulate　**26.** $\dfrac{9}{2}$　**27.** Refer to Lesson 4.

28. $(144 + 129\pi)$ m^3 = 549.27 m^3　**29.** C　**30.** A

problem set 14

1. $N_U = 70$; $N_D = 50$　**2.** $-11, -9, -7$　**3.** Interior: 2700°; Exterior: 360°

4. 10,650.27 ft　**5.** $4.11\underline{/318.05°}$; $4.11\underline{/-41.95°}$; $-4.11\underline{/138.05°}$; $-4.11\underline{/-221.95°}$

6. $7.69\underline{/108.27°}$; $7.69\underline{/-251.73°}$; $-7.69\underline{/288.27°}$; $-7.69\underline{/-71.73°}$ **7.** $0.75\hat{i} + 8.57\hat{j}$

8. $-5.93\hat{i} - 4.47\hat{j}$ **9.** $x = 28$; $y = 20$ **10.** $x = 140$; $y = 80$; $z = 140$

11. $x = 50$; $y = 130$ **12.** $\dfrac{59}{5}$ **13.** $-\dfrac{1}{4} \pm \dfrac{\sqrt{19}}{4}i$ **14.** $\dfrac{7}{4}, -1$ **15.** $\dfrac{1}{3} \pm \dfrac{\sqrt{11}}{3}i$

16. $-\dfrac{1}{5} \pm \dfrac{\sqrt{31}}{5}$ **17.** $y = -\dfrac{3}{2}x - \dfrac{7}{2}$ **18.** $(3\sqrt{3} + 2\sqrt{2} - 12)i$ **19.** $a^{\frac{7x-2}{2}} b^{2x+y}$

20. $\dfrac{1}{10} - \dfrac{7}{10}i$ **21.** $\dfrac{b^7 + a^8 b^5}{a^9}$ **22.** $\triangle ABC \cong \triangle CDE$ by *AAAS* congruency postulate

23. $\dfrac{7 + 3\sqrt{3}}{2}$ **24.** $4x^{\frac{2}{3}} - 16y^{-\frac{2}{5}}$ **25.** $x = 3$; $y = 4$; $z = 4$ **26.** $\dfrac{9}{4}$

27. $a = 2\sqrt{13}$; $b = 3\sqrt{13}$; $h = 6$ **28.** $10\sqrt{3}$ cm   **29.** A   **30.** B

problem set 15

1. $-11, -9, -7, -5$ **2.** 1080   **3.** $y = x + 9$ **4.** 5847.61 ft

5.

STATEMENTS	REASONS
1. $\overline{AC} \cong \overline{BC}$	1. Given
2. $\angle ACD \cong \angle BCD$	2. Given
3. $\overline{CD} \cong \overline{CD}$	3 Reflexive axiom
4. $\triangle ACD \cong \triangle BCD$	4. *SAS* congruency postulate

6.

STATEMENTS	REASONS
1. $\overline{AB} \cong \overline{AD}$	1. Given
2. $\overline{BC} \cong \overline{DC}$	2. Given
3. $\overline{AC} \cong \overline{AC}$	3 Reflexive axiom
4. $\triangle ABC \cong \triangle ADC$	4. *SSS* congruency postulate

7. $8.23\underline{/149.32°}$; $8.23\underline{/-210.68°}$; $-8.23\underline{/329.32°}$; $-8.23\underline{/-30.68°}$

8. $5.16\underline{/324.46°}$; $5.16\underline{/-35.54°}$; $-5.16\underline{/144.46°}$; $-5.16\underline{/-215.54°}$

9. $-13.59\hat{i} - 6.34\hat{j}$ **10.** $31.21\hat{i} - 28.10\hat{j}$ **11.** $\dfrac{20}{7}$ **12.** 21   **13.** $\dfrac{1}{2} \pm \dfrac{\sqrt{39}}{6}i$

14. $-\dfrac{3}{2} \pm \dfrac{3}{2}i$ **15.** $-\dfrac{5}{6} \pm \dfrac{\sqrt{71}}{6}i$ **16.** Line *A*: $y = 3$; Line *B*: $y = \dfrac{3}{2}x - 9$

17. $x = 4$; $y = 6$; $z = 1$ **18.** $-6i$ **19.** $2 + \sqrt{2}$ **20.** $\dfrac{1}{xy(3x - 2y)}$ **21.** $-6 - 25i$

22. $a^{-2z-5} b^{2z+11}$ **23.** $9x - 4z^{\frac{1}{2}}$ **24.** $x = 2$; $y = 4$; $z = 6$

25. $m\angle A = 84°$; $m\angle C = 96°$ **26.** $\dfrac{21}{2}$ **27.** $\sqrt{58 + x^2}$ **28.** $l = 5$ m; $h = 3$ m

29. A   **30.** D

problem set 16

1. $N_C = 5$; $N_R = 8$ **2.** $-14, -12, -10$ **3.** $y = -\dfrac{3}{2}x - 4$ **4.** 114.49 mi

5. $\dfrac{cx + cab}{c - ka}$ **6.** $\dfrac{pc + pb}{2mc + mb}$ **7.** $\dfrac{apc + am}{xpc + xm + cy}$ **8.** $d = \dfrac{pmay}{xyb - pmb}$

9. $c = \dfrac{bx}{xy - ma}$ **10.** $x^2 + 2x + 4 + \dfrac{7}{x - 2}$

11.

STATEMENTS	REASONS
1. $\angle A \cong \angle B$	1. Given
2. $\angle ACD \cong \angle BCE$	2. Vertical angles are congruent.
3. $\angle D \cong \angle E$	3. If two angles in one triangle are congruent to two angles in a second triangle, then the third angles are congruent.
4. $\overline{CD} \cong \overline{CE}$	4. Given
5. $\triangle ACD \cong \triangle BCE$	5. *AAAS* congruency postulate

12.

STATEMENTS	REASONS
1. $\angle Q$ and $\angle S$ are right angles.	1. Given
2. $\triangle PQR$ and $\triangle PSR$ are right triangles.	2. A triangle which contains a right angle is a right triangle.
3. $\overline{PR} \cong \overline{PR}$	3. Reflexive axiom
4. $\overline{PQ} \cong \overline{PS}$	4. Given
5. $\triangle PQR \cong \triangle PSR$	5. *HL* congruency postulate

13. $7.21\underline{/303.69°}$; $7.21\underline{/-56.31°}$; $-7.21\underline{/123.69°}$; $-7.21\underline{/-236.31°}$

14. $10\underline{/233.13°}$; $10\underline{/-126.87°}$; $-10\underline{/53.13°}$; $-10\underline{/-306.87°}$

15. $1.09\hat{i} - 4.06\hat{j}$ **16.** $-10.87\hat{i} + 40.57\hat{j}$ **17.** $\frac{1}{3} \pm \frac{\sqrt{14}}{3}i$ **18.** $-\frac{1}{10} \pm \frac{\sqrt{139}}{10}i$

19. Line A: $x = -4$; Line B: $y = -4x + 10$ **20.** $x = 3$; $y = 2$; $z = 1$ **21.** 9

22. $\frac{3}{5} - \frac{16}{5}i$ **23.** $\frac{-21 - 11\sqrt{3}}{104}$ **24.** $(1 - \sqrt{2})i$ **25.** $\frac{a^6 + a^8 b^6}{b^5}$

26. $x = 10$; $y = \frac{45}{8}$; $z = 110$ **27.** $a = 4\sqrt{2}$; $b = 4\sqrt{14}$; $h = 2\sqrt{7}$

28. $V = 48\pi \text{ cm}^3 = 150.80 \text{ cm}^3$; $A_{\text{surface}} = (36\pi + 12\sqrt{13\pi}) \text{ cm}^2 = 249.02 \text{ cm}^2$

29. B   **30.** C

problem set 17

1. $-8, -6, -4$ and $4, 6, 8$ **2.** $N_O = 8$; $N_S = 30$ **3.** $y = 4x - 5$

4. $\triangle ABC \sim \triangle XYZ$ by *SAS* similarity postulate   **5.** $\triangle GHI \sim \triangle JKL$ by *SSS* similarity postulate

6. $\triangle PQR \sim \triangle STU$ by *AAA*   **7.** $\triangle ABC \sim \triangle DEF$ by *AAA*

8.

STATEMENTS	REASONS
1. $\overline{BC} \parallel \overline{AE}$	1. Given
2. $\angle ADE \cong \angle CDB$	2. Vertical angles are congruent.
3. $\angle A \cong \angle C$	3. If two parallel lines are cut by a transversal, then each pair of alternate interior angles is congruent.
4. $\angle E \cong \angle B$	4. AA $\rightarrow$ AAA
5. $\triangle ADE \sim \triangle CDB$	5. AAA

9. $\frac{a^2 cx - abx^2}{bxc^3 + b^2 c^2}$

10. $\frac{x^2 + x}{x^2 + 4x + 4}$ **11.** $k = \frac{b}{2a - b}$ **12.** $r = \frac{-2ax^2}{bxt - ab^2}$

13. $x^2 - 3x + 11 - \frac{34}{x + 3}$

14.

STATEMENTS	REASONS
1. $\overline{AD} \cong \overline{BD}$	1. Given
2. $\angle ADE \cong \angle BDC$	2. Vertical angles are congruent.
3. $\overline{ED} \cong \overline{CD}$	3. Given
4. $\triangle ADE \cong \triangle BDC$	4. *SAS* congruency postulate

15. $8.60\underline{/54.46°}$; $8.60\underline{/-305.54°}$; $-8.60\underline{/234.46°}$; $-8.60\underline{/-125.54°}$

16. $12.17\underline{/170.54°}$; $12.17\underline{/-189.46°}$; $-12.17\underline{/350.54°}$; $-12.17\underline{/-9.46°}$ **17.** $-3.47\hat{i} - 19.70\hat{j}$

18. $1, -\frac{3}{4}$ **19.** Line A: $y = -3x + 3$; Line B: $x = -3$ **20.** $x = 1$; $y = 1$; $z = -3$

21. $\frac{1}{4}$ **22.** $\frac{7}{2} + \frac{1}{2}i$ **23.** $\frac{-7 + \sqrt{5}}{4}$ **24.** $3x - 5x^{\frac{1}{2}}y^{\frac{3}{2}} - 2y^3$ **25.** $x^{-a+3}b^{\frac{4y-9a}{6}}$

26. 2   **27.** $AD = 5$; $DC = 7$ **28.** $l = 10 \text{ cm}$; $h = 8 \text{ cm}$ **29.** D   **30.** B

problem set 18

1. $N_B = 2$; $N_W = 3$; $N_G = 6$ **2.** $N_N = 8$; $N_D = 9$; $N_Q = 3$ **3.** 10

4. $y = -\frac{2}{5}x + \frac{11}{5}$ **5.** 49   **6.** 106.8 oz   **7.** 891.43 grams

8. $\triangle PQR \sim \triangle STU$ by *SSS* similarity postulate   **9.** $\frac{m^2 x + 7a^2 y}{ap^2 - 3x}$ **10.** $\frac{md + mc}{ad + ac + bd}$

11. $c = \dfrac{kbx}{x^2 + kba}$ **12.** $k = \dfrac{2pm}{m^2c^2 - pa}$ **13.** $x^2 + 1 - \dfrac{1}{x^2 - 1}$

14.

STATEMENTS	REASONS
1. $\angle Q \cong \angle S$	1. Given
2. $\overline{PQ} \parallel \overline{SR}$	2. Given
3. $\angle QPR \cong \angle SRP$	3. If two parallel lines are cut by a transversal, then each pair of alternate interior angles is congruent.
4. $\angle QRP \cong \angle SPR$	4. If two angles in one triangle are congruent to two angles in a second triangle, then the third angles are congruent.
5. $\overline{PR} \cong \overline{PR}$	5. Reflexive axiom
6. $\triangle PQR \cong \triangle RSP$	6. *AAAS* congruency postulate

15. $15.30\underline{/168.69°}$; $15.30\underline{/-191.31°}$; $-15.30\underline{/348.69°}$; $-15.30\underline{/-11.31°}$

16. $14.32\underline{/347.91°}$; $14.32\underline{/-12.09°}$; $-14.32\underline{/167.91°}$; $-14.32\underline{/-192.09°}$ **17.** $-20.57\hat{i} + 24.51\hat{j}$

18. $-37.68\hat{i} - 26.38\hat{j}$ **19.** $\dfrac{5}{6} \pm \dfrac{\sqrt{23}}{6}i$ **20.** $\dfrac{3}{2}, -1$ **21.** $x = 2;\ y = -2;\ z = 3$

22. $-3 + 6i$ **23.** $\dfrac{-18 - 10\sqrt{3}}{3}$ **24.** $a^{\frac{8}{15}}b^{\frac{59}{15}}$ **25.** $\dfrac{7}{4}$ **26.** 13

27. $(50\pi - 100)\,\text{cm}^2 = 57.08\,\text{cm}^2$ **28.** 24 cm   **29.** B   **30.** B

problem set 19

1. $\dfrac{16}{1}$ **2.** $N_R = 5;\ N_B = 5;\ N_G = 10$ **3.** $N_N = 8;\ N_D = 30;\ N_Q = 12$

4. $y = \dfrac{2}{5}x - 5$ **5.** 108   **6.** 56   **7.** 40 ml of 10%, 10 ml of 40%

8. $\left(-\dfrac{1}{2} + \dfrac{\sqrt{17}}{2}, \dfrac{1}{2} + \dfrac{\sqrt{17}}{2}\right), \left(-\dfrac{1}{2} - \dfrac{\sqrt{17}}{2}, \dfrac{1}{2} - \dfrac{\sqrt{17}}{2}\right)$

9. $(1, 2\sqrt{2}), (1, -2\sqrt{2}), (-1, 2\sqrt{2}), (-1, -2\sqrt{2})$

10. $(-1 + \sqrt{5}, -1 - \sqrt{5}), (-1 - \sqrt{5}, -1 + \sqrt{5})$ **11.** $2x^{3n+1}(2x - 3x^n)$

12. $(x^a + y^b)(x^a - y^b)$ **13.** $(3x^4y^2 - z^3)(9x^8y^4 + 3x^4y^2z^3 + z^6)$

14. $(2x^2y + p)(4x^4y^2 - 2x^2yp + p^2)$ **15.** $\triangle UVW \sim \triangle XYZ$ by *SAS* similarity postulate

16. $\dfrac{3a^2cd + 2bc^2d}{a^2b^2d - ab^3c}$ **17.** $\dfrac{17}{25} - \dfrac{19}{25}i$ **18.** $\dfrac{-159 + 56\sqrt{3}}{407}$ **19.** $-\dfrac{11}{41} - \dfrac{17}{41}i$

20. $9a^{\frac{2x}{3}} - b^y$ **21.** $x^{2c-1-d}y^{2-3d-c}$ **22.** $x^3 + 2x^2 + 4x + 6 + \dfrac{13}{x - 2}$

23. $z = \dfrac{36s^2nt + 24m}{5n}$

24.

STATEMENTS	REASONS
1. $\overline{VX} \perp \overline{UW}$	1. Given
2. $\angle UXV$ and $\angle WXV$ are right angles.	2. Perpendicular lines intersect to form right angles.
3. $\triangle UVX$ and $\triangle WVX$ are right triangles.	3. A triangle which contains a right angle is a right triangle.
4. $\overline{UV} \cong \overline{WV}$	4. Given
5. $\overline{VX} \cong \overline{VX}$	5. Reflexive axiom
6. $\triangle UVX \cong \triangle WVX$	6. *HL* congruency postulate

25.

STATEMENTS	REASONS
1. $\overline{HK} \cong \overline{IJ}$	1. Given
2. $\overline{HI} \cong \overline{KJ}$	2. Given
3. $\overline{IK} \cong \overline{IK}$	3. Reflexive axiom
4. $\triangle HIK \cong \triangle JKI$	4. *SSS* congruency postulate

26. 40   **27.** 60

28. (a) $26{,}244\pi\,\text{m}^3$ (b) 3 cm   **29.** C   **30.** C

problem set 20

1. 226.58 m   2. $y = \dfrac{3}{5}x + \dfrac{6}{5}$ 3. $N_R = 20$; $N_G = 80$ 4. $N_R = 10$; $N_B = 4$

5. $N_N = 5$; $N_D = 3$; $N_Q = 4$ 6. 84   7. 12 lb   8. 133.33 oz   9. $3\sqrt{6}$

10. $3\sqrt{6}$ 11. $4\sqrt{3}$ 12. $\triangle VWZ \sim \triangle YXZ$ by *SSS* similarity postulate

13.

STATEMENTS	REASONS
1. $\overline{AB} \parallel \overline{DE}$	1. Given
2. $\angle BAC \cong \angle EDF$	2. If two parallel lines are cut by a transversal, then each pair of corresponding angles is congruent.
3. $\overline{BC} \parallel \overline{EF}$	3. Given
4. $\angle BCA \cong \angle EFD$	4. If two parallel lines are cut by a transversal, then each pair of corresponding angles is congruent.
5. $\angle B \cong \angle E$	5. $AA \rightarrow AAA$
6. $\triangle ABC \sim \triangle DEF$	6. AAA

14. $x = 4$; $y = 3$; $z = 2$ 15. $\left(-\dfrac{2}{5} + \dfrac{2\sqrt{11}}{5}, \dfrac{1}{5} + \dfrac{4\sqrt{11}}{5}\right), \left(-\dfrac{2}{5} - \dfrac{2\sqrt{11}}{5}, \dfrac{1}{5} - \dfrac{4\sqrt{11}}{5}\right)$

16. No solution; $x \neq 3, -1$ 17. $(3xy^2 + 2p)(9x^2y^4 - 6xy^2p + 4p^2)$

18. $(2xy^4 - 3z^3)(4x^2y^8 + 6xy^4z^3 + 9z^6)$ 19. $\dfrac{3tx + xs}{6yt + 2ys - 6zt}$ 20. $\dfrac{1}{8x^{12}y^5}$

21. $(7\sqrt{7} - 5\sqrt{5} - 4)i$ 22. $y = \dfrac{3dfgs^2 + 21x^3}{4g}$ 23. $x^2 + 1 - \dfrac{5}{x^2 - 1}$

24. $14.76\underline{/298.30°}$; $14.76\underline{/-61.70°}$; $-14.76\underline{/118.30°}$; $-14.76\underline{/-241.70°}$ 25. $-\dfrac{5}{6} \pm \dfrac{\sqrt{71}}{6}i$

26.

STATEMENTS	REASONS
1. $\overline{PQ} \parallel \overline{ST}$	1. Given
2. $\angle P \cong \angle T$ and $\angle Q \cong \angle S$	2. If two parallel lines are cut by a transversal, then each pair of alternate interior angles is congruent.
3. $\angle PRQ \cong \angle TRS$	3. Vertical angles are congruent.
4. $\overline{PQ} \cong \overline{ST}$	4. Given
5. $\triangle PRQ \cong \triangle TRS$	5. $AAAS$ congruency postulate

27. 12 m

28. $l = 10$ cm; $h = 8$ cm   29. A   30. A

problem set 21

1. $\dfrac{399}{16}$ 2. $y = -x + 3$ 3. $N_R = 4$; $N_B = 2$; $N_G = 15$

4. $N_N = 5$; $N_D = 20$; $N_S = 10$ 5. 54, 45   6. 224.71 liters   7. (a), (d)

8. (a) Not a function   (b) Function

9. (a) $\{x \in \mathbb{R}\}$ (b) $\{x \in \mathbb{R} \mid x \geq -5\}$ (c) $\{x \in \mathbb{R} \mid x \leq 6\}$ 10. 15   11. $2\sqrt{3}$

12. 8   13. $\triangle PQT \sim \triangle SRT$ by *SAS* similarity postulate

14.

STATEMENTS	REASONS
1. $\overline{ED} \parallel \overline{BC}$	1. Given
2. $\angle ADE \cong \angle ACB$ $\angle AED \cong \angle ABC$	2. If two parallel lines are cut by a transversal, then each pair of corresponding angles is congruent.
3. $\angle A \cong \angle A$	3. Reflexive axiom
4. $\triangle AED \sim \triangle ABC$	4. AAA

15. $\left(\dfrac{3 + \sqrt{33}}{2}, \dfrac{-3 + \sqrt{33}}{2}\right), \left(\dfrac{3 - \sqrt{33}}{2}, \dfrac{-3 - \sqrt{33}}{2}\right)$

16. $8(2ab^3 - p)(4a^2b^6 + 2ab^3p + p^2)$

17. $(3b^3a^2 - 4c)(9b^6a^4 + 12b^3a^2c + 16c^2)$ 18. $\dfrac{a^3y - 6xm^2}{x^2l^2 - 6ty^2}$

19. $4 - 5x^{a-b}y^{a-b} + x^{b-a}y^{b-a}$ **20.** $-6 + (3\sqrt{3} + 17)i$ **21.** $\dfrac{33 - 5\sqrt{3}}{26}$

22. $1 + 2i$ **23.** $d = \dfrac{wr + 1}{2r - 1}$ **24.** $x^2 - 1 - \dfrac{x - 3}{x^2 + 2}$ **25.** $-16.07\hat{i} + 19.15\hat{j}$

26.

STATEMENTS	REASONS
1. $\overline{AB} \cong \overline{DC}$	1. Given
2. $\overline{AD} \cong \overline{BC}$	2. Given
3. $\overline{BD} \cong \overline{BD}$	3. Reflexive axiom
4. $\triangle ABD \cong \triangle CDB$	4. *SSS* congruency postulate

27. 59   **28.** 207π m^3

29. A   **30.** B

problem set 22

1. $y = -\dfrac{1}{3}x - \dfrac{1}{3}$ **2.** 2, 4, 6   **3.** 91.15 m   **4.** $N_P = 10;\ N_N = 10;\ N_Q = 4$

5. 62, 26   **6.** (a)    (b)

7.   **8.**

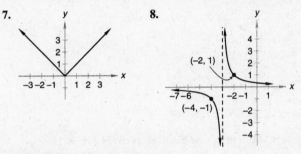

9. (a) Function   (b) Not a function

10. (a) Function, 1 to 1   (b) Function, not 1 to 1   (c) Not a function   (d) Function, 1 to 1

11. (a) $\{x \in \mathbb{R} \mid x \geq 8\}$ (b) $\{x \in \mathbb{R}\}$ (c) $\{x \in \mathbb{R} \mid x \neq -3\}$ **12.** 32   **13.** $\sqrt{6}$

14. $\dfrac{9}{2}$ **15.**

STATEMENTS	REASONS
1. $\dfrac{AC}{BC} = \dfrac{BC}{DC}$	1. Given
2. $\angle C \cong \angle C$	2. Reflexive axiom
3. $\triangle ABC \sim \triangle BDC$	3. *SAS* similarity postulate

16. $(3, 3), (3, -3), (-3, 3), (-3, -3)$ **17.** $(x^2 + y^2)(x + y)$

18. $(2xb^2 - 3p)(4x^2b^4 + 6xb^2p + 9p^2)$ **19.** $\dfrac{3sl + 3sk}{2ml + 2mk - zl}$ **20.** $\dfrac{4}{3} + 4i$

21. $x^{2a+\frac{3}{2}}y^{a+4}$ **22.** $\dfrac{a^3 + b}{b}$

23. $13.45\underline{/228.01°};\ 13.45\underline{/-131.99°};\ -13.45\underline{/48.01°};\ -13.45\underline{/-311.99°}$ **24.** $\dfrac{3}{4} \pm \dfrac{\sqrt{11}\,i}{4}$

25.

STATEMENTS	REASONS
1. $\overline{BC} \cong \overline{EF}$	1. Given
2. $\overline{BC} \parallel \overline{EF}$	2. Given
3. $\angle ACB \cong \angle DFE$	3. If two parallel lines are cut by a transversal, then each pair of corresponding angles is congruent.
4. $\overline{AC} \cong \overline{DF}$	4. Given
5. $\triangle ABC \cong \triangle DEF$	5. *SAS* congruency postulate

26.

STATEMENTS	REASONS
1. $\overline{RP} \perp \overline{PS}, \overline{RP} \perp \overline{QR}$	1. Given
2. $\angle PRQ$ and $\angle RPS$ are right angles.	2. Perpendicular lines intersect to form right angles.
3. $\triangle PRQ$ and $\triangle RPS$ are right triangles.	3. A triangle which contains a right angle is a right triangle.
4. $\overline{PQ} \cong \overline{SR}$	4. Given
5. $\overline{RP} \cong \overline{RP}$	5. Reflexive axiom
6. $\triangle PRQ \cong \triangle RPS$	6. *HL* congruency postulate

27. 38   **28.** 300π cm^3

29. A   **30.** C

problem set 23

1. $y = -\frac{3}{2}x + \frac{5}{2}$ **2.** 15   **3.** $N_N = 9$; $N_D = 4$; $N_Q = 8$

4. $N_G = 5$; $N_R = 10$; $N_B = 2$ **5.** 42, 24   **6.** 9 gallons   **7.**

8.

9. (a)

(b)

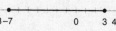

10.

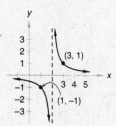

11. (b), (d)

12. (a) $\{x \in \mathbb{R}\}$ (b) $\{x \in \mathbb{R}\}$ (c) $\{x \in \mathbb{R} \mid x \neq 2\}$

13. 2   **14.** $8\sqrt{3}$ **15.** 33   **16.**

STATEMENTS	REASONS
1. $\overline{RQ} \perp \overline{QP}, \overline{RS} \perp \overline{ST}$	1. Given
2. $\angle PQR$ and $\angle TSR$ are right angles.	2. Perpendicular lines intersect to form right angles.
3. $\angle PQR \cong \angle TSR$	3. All right angles are congruent.
4. $\angle PRQ \cong \angle TRS$	4. Vertical angles are congruent.
5. $\angle P \cong \angle T$	5. $AA \rightarrow AAA$
6. $\triangle PQR \sim \triangle TSR$	6. AAA

17. $x = -2$; $y = 3$; $z = 3$ **18.** (3, 3)   **19.** $-2 \pm 2\sqrt{3}$

20. $a^3 b^3 \left(2b + 3a^2\right)\left(4b^2 - 6ba^2 + 9a^4\right)$ **21.** $\frac{2(yk - z)}{yk - z + 3xk}$

22. $\sqrt{10} + \sqrt{5} - 10 - 3\sqrt{2}i$ **23.** $\frac{38 + 23\sqrt{3}}{13}$ **24.** mn **25.** $x^2 - x + 4 - \frac{12}{x + 3}$

26.

STATEMENTS	REASONS
1. $\angle I \cong \angle L$	1. Given
2. J is the midpoint of $\overline{IL}$	2. Given
3. $\overline{IJ} \cong \overline{LJ}$	3. A midpoint divides a segment into two congruent segments.
4. $\angle IJH \cong \angle LJK$	4. Vertical angles are congruent.
5. $\angle H \cong \angle K$	5. If two angles in one triangle are congruent to two angles in a second triangle, then the third angles are congruent.
6. $\triangle HIJ \cong \triangle KLJ$	6. $AAAS$ congruency postulate

27. $AB = 9$; $CD = 11$

28. $900\pi \ \text{m}^2$ **29.** B   **30.** B

problem set 24

1. $y = \frac{3}{5}x - \frac{9}{5}$ **2.** 4, 6, 8, 10 and $-12, -10, -8, -6$ **3.** $N_D = 10$; $N_Q = 2$; $N_H = 2$

4. $N_R = 3$; $N_G = 4$; $N_B = 2$ **5.** 73, 37   **6.** 264 ml   **7.**

8.   **9.**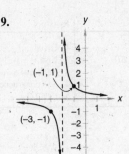

10. (a) Not a function   (b) Not a function

11. (a) Not a function   (b) Function, not 1 to 1   (c) Not a function   (d) Function, not 1 to 1

12. (a) $\{x \in \mathbb{R} \mid x \geq -6\}$ (b) $\{x \in \mathbb{R}\}$ (c) $\{x \in \mathbb{R} \mid x \neq 0\}$ **13.** $\dfrac{1 + \sqrt{2}}{2}$

14. (a) 16   (b) -4 (c) 13   **15.** $1 + \dfrac{2\sqrt{3}}{3}$ **16.** 33

17. $\left(\dfrac{2 + \sqrt{19}}{5}, \dfrac{1 - 2\sqrt{19}}{5}\right), \left(\dfrac{2 - \sqrt{19}}{5}, \dfrac{1 + 2\sqrt{19}}{5}\right)$ **18.** $x^{5N+2}\left(4 + 3x^{3N+1}\right)$

19. $\dfrac{ac^3 - 6m^3xy}{xy^2d^2 - gx^3y}$ **20.** $-\dfrac{31}{15} - \dfrac{8}{15}i$ **21.** $a^{\frac{19}{12}}b^{\frac{1}{4}}$ **22.** xy

23. $9.43\underline{/302.01°}$; $9.43\underline{/-57.99°}$; $-9.43\underline{/122.01°}$; $-9.43\underline{/-237.99°}$ **24.** $-\dfrac{1}{6} \pm \dfrac{\sqrt{33}}{6}$

25. $2x + 2$ **26.**

STATEMENTS	REASONS
1. $\overline{BE} \cong \overline{CE}$	1. Given
2. $\overline{AE} \cong \overline{DE}$	2. Given
3. $\angle BEA \cong \angle CED$	3. Vertical angles are congruent.
4. $\triangle ABE \cong \triangle DCE$	4. *SAS* congruency postulate

27. $120°$

28. $150\pi \text{ cm}^2$ **29.** B   **30.** A

problem set 25

1. Orville = 25 yr; Wilbur = 15 yr   **2.** $\dfrac{32}{13}$ hr   **3.** $\dfrac{2}{5}\dfrac{\text{sandcastles}}{\text{hr}}$ **4.** 162 men

5. 68   **6.** $y = \dfrac{1}{2}x - \dfrac{1}{2}$ **7.** [graph with points (1, 4), (0, 1)]   **8.** [graph with points (−1, 4), (0, 1)]

9. (a) [number line: open circle at −9, open circle at 3]   (b) [number line: closed at −4/−3, closed at 7/8]

10. (a) Function, not 1 to 1   (b) Not a function   (c) Function, 1 to 1   (d) Function, 1 to 1

11. (a) $\left\{x \in \mathbb{R} \mid x \geq \dfrac{1}{2}\right\}$ (b) $\{x \in \mathbb{R} \mid x > 3\}$ (c) $\{x \in \mathbb{R} \mid x \neq 1, -6\}$

12. (a) 0   (b) $\dfrac{1}{2} - \sqrt{3}$ **13.** (a) -12 (b) $-\dfrac{4}{3}$ (c) -15 **14.** $\dfrac{1}{2}$ **15.** $\dfrac{\sqrt{2}}{2} - \dfrac{2\sqrt{3}}{3}$

16. 32   **17.** $(\sqrt{5}, 2), (\sqrt{5}, -2), (-\sqrt{5}, 2), (-\sqrt{5}, -2)$ **18.** $\left(x^{2a} + y^{2a}\right)\left(x^a - y^a\right)$

19. $\left(2xy^2 - 3a^2b^3\right)\left(4x^2y^4 + 6xy^2a^2b^3 + 9a^4b^6\right)$ **20.** $\dfrac{3smr - 3sq}{2mr - 2q - 6rl}$

21. $\dfrac{-48 + 25\sqrt{3}}{11}$ **22.** $9x - 4z^{\frac{1}{2}}$ **23.** $x^3 - 4x^2 - x - 2 - \dfrac{9}{x - 2}$

24. $z = \dfrac{18ktm}{5sm^2 + 12k^2}$ **25.** $x^2 + 6x + 8$

26.

STATEMENTS	REASONS
1. $\overline{AB} \cong \overline{CB}$	1. Given
2. $\angle ABD \cong \angle CBD$	2. Given
3. $\overline{BD} \cong \overline{BD}$	3. Reflexive axiom
4. $\triangle ABD \cong \triangle CBD$	4. *SAS* congruency postulate
5. $\overline{AD} \cong \overline{CD}$	5. *CPCTC*

27. 35   **28.** $12\sqrt{3}$ m

29. A   **30.** C

problem set 26

1. Charlotte = 30 yr; Emily = 10 yr   **2.** $\frac{80}{7}$ min   **3.** 8 days

4. Donnie = 65 mph; time = 5 hr; Sarah = 45 mph; time = 10 hr   **5.** 800 liters

6. (a) $\log_k 7 = p$ (b) $k^p = 7$ **7.** (a) $b^a = 12$ (b) $\log_b 12 = a$ **8.** 3   **9.** −3

10. 16   **11.** (a) (b)   **12.**

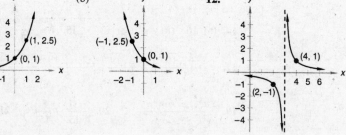

13. (a) Not a function (b) Function, 1 to 1 (c) Function, not 1 to 1 (d) Function, not 1 to 1

14. (a) $\left\{ x \in \mathbb{R} \mid x \geq -\frac{1}{2} \right\}$ (b) $\{x \in \mathbb{R} \mid x \geq 0\}$ (c) $\left\{ x \in \mathbb{R} \mid x \neq -\frac{1}{2}, 3 \right\}$

15. 0   **16.** 0   **17.** 0   **18.** $\frac{\sqrt{2}}{2} - 1$ **19.** (a) −2 (b) 0 (c) 0

20.

STATEMENTS	REASONS
1. $AC \cdot DC = BC \cdot BC$	1. Given
2. $\frac{AC}{BC} = \frac{BC}{DC}$	2. Division
3. $\angle C \cong \angle C$	3. Reflexive axiom
4. $\triangle ABC \sim \triangle BDC$	4. *SAS* similarity postulate

21. $x = 1$; $y = -1$ **22.** −2

23. $x^2 + xy + y^2$ **24.** $\left(4x^4y^2 - 3a^2b^3\right)\left(16x^8y^4 + 12x^4y^2a^2b^3 + 9a^4b^6\right)$

25. 8.06$\underline{/119.74°}$; 8.06$\underline{/-240.26°}$; −8.06$\underline{/299.74°}$; −8.06$\underline{/-60.26°}$ **26.** $\frac{x-4}{x-7}$ **27.** 65

28. 10 m   **29.** B   **30.** A

problem set 27

1. Marshall = 6 yr; George = 13 yr   **2.** $\frac{40}{3}$ min   **3.** 1 day

4. $N_B = 7$; $N_R = 4$; $N_W = 8$ **5.** 36 acorns   **6.** $y = \frac{2}{3}x - \frac{7}{3}$ **7.** $\log_3 7 = k$

8. $m^n = 8$ **9.** 4   **10.** −3   **11.** 4

12. (a) (b)   **13.**

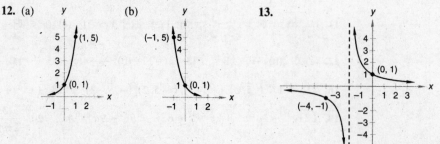

14. (a) Not a function (b) Not a function (c) Function, 1 to 1 (d) Function, not 1 to 1

15. (a) $\left\{ x \in \mathbb{R} \mid x \leq \frac{1}{3} \right\}$ (b) $\{x \in \mathbb{R} \mid x \geq -10, x \neq 2\}$ (c) $\{x \in \mathbb{R} \mid x \neq -3, 1\}$

16. $\dfrac{3}{2}$ **17.** $\dfrac{3\sqrt{3}}{4}$ **18.** -1 **19.** (a) -100 (b) $\dfrac{1}{51}$ (c) 6 **20.** $(0, 4), \left(-\dfrac{12}{5}, -\dfrac{16}{5}\right)$

21. $3y^{2n+1}\left(1 + 4y^{n+1}\right)$ **22.** $\dfrac{8}{5} + \dfrac{16}{5}i$ **23.** $a = \dfrac{3zp}{50pr + k}$ **24.** $\dfrac{1}{4} \pm \dfrac{\sqrt{7}}{4}i$

25. $\dfrac{2}{x + h}$ **26.**

STATEMENTS	REASONS
1. C is the midpoint of $\overline{BE}$	1. Given
2. $\overline{BC} \cong \overline{EC}$	2. A midpoint divides a segment into two congruent segments.
3. $\angle B \cong \angle E$	3. Given
4. $\angle BCA \cong \angle ECD$	4. Vertical angles are congruent.
5. $\angle A \cong \angle D$	5. If two angles in one triangle are congruent to two angles in a second triangle, then the third angles are congruent.
6. $\triangle ABC \cong \triangle DEC$	6. AAAS congruency postulate
7. $\overline{AC} \cong \overline{DC}$	7. CPCTC

27. 66 **28.** 6 cm

29. A   **30.** A

problem set 28

1. $\dfrac{xp}{x - 2p}\dfrac{\text{mi}}{\text{hr}}$ **2.** $\dfrac{RT + 20}{R + 5}$ hr   **3.** Thomas = 7 yr; Dylan = 14 yr   **4.** $\dfrac{80}{13}$ hr

5. $\dfrac{14}{3}$ days   **6.** 840   **7.** 10,080   **8.** $\log_2 9 = k$ **9.** $m^n = 6$

10. 3   **11.** -4 **12.** 16

13. (a)   (b)   **14.**

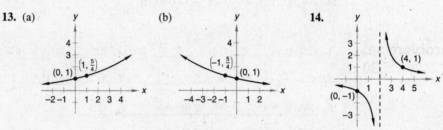

15. (a) $\{x \in \mathbb{R} \mid x \geq -4\}$ (b) $\{x \in \mathbb{R} \mid x \neq 0, 1\}$ (c) $\{x \in \mathbb{R} \mid x \geq 4\}$

16. $\sqrt{3}$ **17.** $\dfrac{3}{2}$ **18.** (a) -6 (b) -3 (c) -3 **19.** $(2, 0), (-2, 0)$

20. $\dfrac{x^2 y - y^3 zca}{s^2 tca - r^2 z}$ **21.** $6 + 3i$ **22.** $\dfrac{2 - \sqrt{2}}{2}$ **23.** $x^{a+2}y^{a-4}$

24. $x^3 - 2x^2 - 2x - \dfrac{6}{x - 1}$ **25.** $1 - x^2$

26.

STATEMENTS	REASONS
1. $\angle 1 \cong \angle 4$	1. Given
2. $\angle 2 \cong \angle 3$	2. Given
3. $\overline{PR} \cong \overline{PR}$	3. Reflexive axiom
4. $\angle Q \cong \angle S$	4. If two angles in one triangle are congruent to two angles in a second triangle, then the third angles are congruent.
5. $\triangle PQR \cong \triangle RSP$	5. AAAS congruency postulate
6. $\overline{QR} \cong \overline{SP}$	6. CPCTC

27. $x = 60$; $y = 65$; $z = 85$

28. $l = 20$ m; $h = 12$ m

29. D   **30.** B

problem set 29

1. $(ag + pax)$ mi   **2.** $\dfrac{1}{2}\dfrac{\text{henway}}{\text{day}}$ **3.** 8 days   **4.** Nat = 65 yr; Odessa = 75 yr

5. $N_P = 10$; $N_N = 15$; $N_D = 5$ **6.** 10,080   **7.** 270,270   **8.** $\log_3 12 = k$ **9.** $b^3 = 5$

10. 7   **11.** -3 **12.** 64   **13.**   **14.**

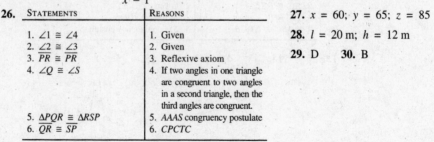

15. (a) Function, not 1 to 1   (b) Not a function   (c) Function, 1 to 1   (d) Not a function

16. (a) $\left\{ x \in \mathbb{R} \mid x \geq \dfrac{5}{4} \right\}$ (b) $\{ x \in \mathbb{R} \mid x > -3 \}$ (c) $\left\{ x \in \mathbb{R} \mid x \geq -2, x \neq -\dfrac{1}{2}, 1 \right\}$

17. 0   **18.** 0   **19.** $\dfrac{3}{2}$ **20.** $\dfrac{\sqrt{3}}{2} + 1$ **21.** (a) $-15\dfrac{1}{2}$ (b) 8   (c) 2

22. (a) $4a^{3m}(a+2)(a-2)$ (b) $\left(2ab - 3c^2 d^2\right)\left(4a^2 b^2 + 6abc^2 d^2 + 9c^4 d^4\right)$

23. $\dfrac{3z + 12}{2cz + 8c + tz}$ **24.** $-5 + \dfrac{1}{6}i$

25. $5.83\underline{/329.04°}$; $5.83\underline{/-30.96°}$; $-5.83\underline{/149.04°}$; $-5.83\underline{/-210.96°}$

26. $\sqrt{x+h} + x^2 + 2xh + h^2$ **27.**

Statements	Reasons
1. $\overline{AC}$ bisects $\angle BAD$	1. Given
2. $\angle BAC \cong \angle DAC$	2. A bisector divides an angle into two congruent angles.
3. $\angle ABC \cong \angle ADC$	3. Given
4. $\angle ACB \cong \angle ACD$	4. If two angles in one triangle are congruent to two angles in a second triangle, then the third angles are congruent.
5. $\overline{AC} \cong \overline{AC}$	5. Reflexive axiom
6. $\triangle ABC \cong \triangle ADC$	6. AAAS congruency postulate
7. $\overline{BC} \cong \overline{DC}$	7. CPCTC

28. $x = 60$; $y = 80$ **29.** A   **30.** B

problem set 30

1. 1280 boys   **2.** 14, 41   **3.** 12.5 liters of 90%, 7.5 liters of 58%   **4.** 422.86 ml

5. $y = -\dfrac{3}{2}x + 1$ **6.** $6.58\underline{/203.07°}$ **7.** $20.72\underline{/136.64°}$

8.

Statements	Reasons
1. $\overline{PQ} \cong \overline{SR}$	1. Given
2. $\angle PQR$ and $\angle SRQ$ are right angles.	2. Given
3. $\angle PQR \cong \angle SRQ$	3. All right angles are congruent.
4. $\overline{QR} \cong \overline{QR}$	4. Reflexive axiom
5. $\triangle PQR \cong \triangle SRQ$	5. SAS congruency postulate

9.

Statements	Reasons
1. $\overline{AB} \cong \overline{DC}$	1. Given
2. $\overline{AC} \cong \overline{DB}$	2. Given
3. $\overline{BC} \cong \overline{BC}$	3. Reflexive axiom
4. $\triangle ABC \cong \triangle DCB$	4. SSS congruency postulate

10. 21   **11.** $\dfrac{1}{3}$ **12.** 3

13. 25   **14.**   **15.**

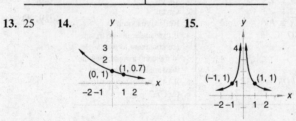

16. (a) $\{ x \in \mathbb{R} \mid x \neq 0 \}$ (b) $\left\{ x \in \mathbb{R} \mid x > -\dfrac{7}{2} \right\}$ (c) $\{ x \in \mathbb{R} \mid x \geq 3 \}$

17. (a) $-\dfrac{3}{2}$ (b) $\sqrt{3} + 1 + \sqrt{2}$ **18.** $-\dfrac{3}{2}$ **19.** $5\sqrt{3} - \dfrac{11}{2}$ **20.** (a) x (b) x

21. $(3, 1), (3, -1), (-3, 1), (-3, -1)$ **22.** $x^a + y^b$ **23.** $2x^{3N+1}\left(1 + 3x^{2N+1}\right)$

24. $\dfrac{kxd + kc}{axd + ac + bd}$ **25.** $\dfrac{2}{3}i$ **26.** $x^2 + 2xh + h^2 - x - h$ **27.** $x = 70$; $y = 75$

28. 2304 cm^2 **29.** A   **30.** C

problem set 31

1. $\dfrac{pm + 5p}{m + p} \dfrac{\text{mi}}{\text{hr}}$ 2. Lannes = 20 yr; Davout = 40 yr   3. $-14, -13, -12, -11$

4. $N_B = 12$; $N_G = 6$; $N_R = 4$ 5. $y = -x + 9$

6. (a) x axis, no; y axis, yes; origin, no   (b) x axis, yes; y axis, yes; origin, yes

7. $y = (x - 2)^2$ 8.   9. $3.25\underline{/5.56°}$

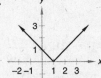

10.

STATEMENTS	REASONS
1. $\angle ZXV \cong \angle ZYU$	1. Given
2. $\overline{XV} \cong \overline{YU}$	2. Given
3. $\angle Z \cong \angle Z$	3. Reflexive axiom
4. $\angle ZVX \cong \angle ZUY$	4. If two angles in one triangle are congruent to two angles in a second triangle, then the third angles are congruent.
5. $\triangle XZV \cong \triangle YZU$	5. *AAAS* congruency postulate

11. 35 12. 2 13. -2 14. $\dfrac{1}{27}$ 15.

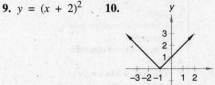

16. (a) Function, not 1 to 1   (b) Function, not 1 to 1   (c) Not a function   (d) Function, 1 to 1

17. $\left\{ x \in \mathbb{R} \mid x \geq -3, x \neq -\dfrac{1}{2}, \dfrac{3}{2} \right\}$ 18. 0 19. $\sqrt{3}$ 20. (a) -1 (b) -1 (c) 0

21. $x = 5$; $y = 4$ 22. $7a^{5n+2}\left(7 - a^{n+1}\right)$ 23. $\dfrac{3a^2 c - 2b^2 c}{a^2 b^2 + bc^2}$ 24. $\dfrac{y^3 + x^3}{xy^3}$

25. $2x^2 - 2x + 3 - \dfrac{4}{x + 1}$ 26. $\dfrac{6 - yr}{5y - 3p}$ 27. $-\dfrac{3}{8} \pm \dfrac{\sqrt{41}}{8}$ 28. $2xh + h^2$

29. B   30. B

problem set 32

1. $\dfrac{xp + 10p}{x - 2p} \dfrac{\text{mi}}{\text{hr}}$ 2. 84 min   3. 4 days   4. 22 ft

5. Laertes = 40 yr; Ophelia = 36 yr   6. $y = \dfrac{1}{3}x - \dfrac{4}{3}$ 7. (a) $60°$ (b) $\dfrac{\sqrt{3}}{2}$ (c) $\dfrac{5\sqrt{41}}{41}$

8. (a) x axis, yes; y axis, no; origin, no   (b) x axis, no; y axis, yes; origin, no

9. $y = (x + 2)^2$ 10.   11. $6.94\underline{/65.70°}$

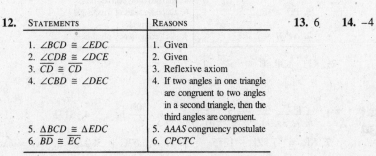

12.

STATEMENTS	REASONS
1. $\angle BCD \cong \angle EDC$	1. Given
2. $\angle CDB \cong \angle DCE$	2. Given
3. $\overline{CD} \cong \overline{CD}$	3. Reflexive axiom
4. $\angle CBD \cong \angle DEC$	4. If two angles in one triangle are congruent to two angles in a second triangle, then the third angles are congruent.
5. $\triangle BCD \cong \triangle EDC$	5. *AAAS* congruency postulate
6. $\overline{BD} \cong \overline{EC}$	6. *CPCTC*

13. 6 14. -4 15. 81

16.   **17.** 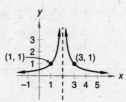   **18.** $\{x \in \mathbb{R} \mid x \geq 0, x \neq 1\}$

19. $-2\sqrt{2} - \dfrac{1}{2}$ **20.** -1 **21.** (a) $-\dfrac{31}{16}$ (b) -32 (c) 4 **22.** $(0, 2), \left(\dfrac{3}{2}, -\dfrac{5}{2}\right)$

23. $\dfrac{2x + 6}{6bx + 18b + 3tx}$ **24.** $\dfrac{-2}{17} + \dfrac{25}{17}i$ **25.** $z^{\frac{3}{2}b + \frac{9}{2}}$ **26.** $\dfrac{1}{6} \pm \dfrac{\sqrt{5}i}{6}$

27. $h^2 + 2xh + 3h$ **28.** $600\pi\,\text{m}^2$ **29.** D   **30.** A

problem set 33

1. $N_N = 3; N_D = 4; N_Q = 4$ **2.** 375 lb   **3.** $y = -\dfrac{1}{2}x + 3$ **4.** C   **5.** 48 m²

6. $y = -\dfrac{1}{4}x + \dfrac{7}{4}$ **7.** (a) 60°   (b) $\dfrac{\sqrt{3}}{2}$ (c) $-\dfrac{3}{4}$

8. (a) x axis, no; y axis, no; origin, yes   (b) x axis, yes; y axis, yes; origin, yes

9. $y = |x| + 3$ **10.** 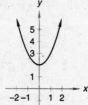   **11.** $3.88\underline{/270.47°}$ **12.** 495

13. 6   **14.** −6   **15.** 8   **16.** 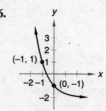   **17.**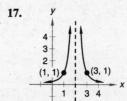

18. $\{x \in \mathbb{R} \mid x \geq 2, x \leq -2, x \neq 3\}$ **19.** $\sqrt{6} - 1$ **20.** (a) 80   (b) 9   (c) 4

21. $x = 2; y = 0$ **22.** $4a^{x+2}(1 - 3a)$ **23.** $\dfrac{a^2b - fg^2c}{x^2yd^2 + cz^3}$ **24.** $-\dfrac{5}{4} + \dfrac{1}{4}i$

25. $g = \dfrac{8dsr}{hfr - 4ds}$ **26.** $h^2 + 2h + 2xh$

27.

STATEMENTS	REASONS
1. PQRS is a rectangle.	1. Given
2. ∠PQT and ∠SRT are right angles.	2. A rectangle contains four right angles.
3. ∠PQT ≅ ∠SRT	3. All right angles are congruent.
4. T is the midpoint of $\overline{QR}$.	4. Given
5. $\overline{QT} ≅ \overline{RT}$	5. A midpoint divides a segment into two congruent segments.
6. $\overline{PQ} ≅ \overline{SR}$	6. Opposite sides of a rectangle are congruent.
7. △PQT ≅ △SRT	7. SAS congruency postulate

28. $x = 115; y = 41; z = 89$

29. C   **30.** B

problem set 34

1. $\dfrac{mz}{m - 3z} \dfrac{\text{mi}}{\text{hr}}$ **2.** $\dfrac{21}{10}$ hr   **3.** $\dfrac{300}{17}$ hr   **4.** \$135   **5.** 21   **6.** −5

7. Mo $= -7.5Zr + 1375$ **8.** H $= 6.67C - 580$ **9.** $f(x) = \sqrt{x}; g(x) = x + 1$

10. A   **11.** 10   **12.** $y = 3x + \dfrac{5}{2}$ **13.** (a) 45° (b) $\dfrac{3}{4}$ (c) $\dfrac{\sqrt{10}}{10}$

14. (a) x axis, yes; y axis, yes; origin, yes   (b) x axis, no; y axis, no; origin, yes

15. $y = |x| - 3$ **16.**   **17.** $5\underline{/223°}$ **18.** 5   **19.** −5   **20.** 25

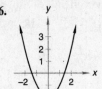

21. (a) Not a function   (b) Not a function   (c) Function, 1 to 1   (d) Function, not 1 to 1

22. $\{x \in \mathbb{R} \mid x \geq -11, x \neq 4, -3\}$ **23.** $\dfrac{3}{4}$ **24.** (a) 8 (b) 8 (c) 19

25. (3, 1), (3, −1), (−3, 1), (−3, −1)   **26.** $\dfrac{-h}{x^2 + hx}$

27.

STATEMENTS	REASONS
1. $\overline{BD}$ bisects $\overline{AC}$	1. Given
2. $\overline{AD} \cong \overline{CD}$	2. A bisector divides a segment into two congruent segments.
3. $\overline{AB} \cong \overline{CB}$	3. Given
4. $\overline{BD} \cong \overline{BD}$	4. Reflexive axiom
5. $\triangle ABD \cong \triangle CBD$	5. SSS congruency postulate
6. $\angle A \cong \angle C$	6. CPCTC

28. $144\sqrt{3}$ cm^2

29. C   **30.** C

problem set 35

1. $N_W = 25$; $N_R = 10$; $N_B = 30$ **2.** 500 lb   **3.** $\dfrac{9}{8} \dfrac{\text{jobs}}{\text{hr}}$ **4.** Multiply by 9

5. $\dfrac{21}{5}$ **6.** $\dfrac{17}{12}$ **7.** $\sqrt{(x - 3)^2 + (y + 2)^2}$ **8.** $\dfrac{11}{15}$ **9.** $\dfrac{49}{4}$

10. $Y = -45B + 4550$ **11.** $f(x) = x^2$ **12.** C   **13.** 6   **14.** $y = \dfrac{6}{5}x - \dfrac{8}{5}$

15. 30°   **16.** $-\dfrac{4}{5}$ **17.** $\dfrac{2\sqrt{5}}{5}$

18. (a) x axis, no; y axis, yes; origin, no   (b) x axis, yes; y axis, no; origin, no

19. $y = -\sqrt{x}$ **20.** $y = (x - 3)^3$ **21.** $4.96\underline{/309.01°}$ **22.** (a) $\dfrac{4}{3}$ (b) $-\dfrac{3}{2}$ (c) 27

23. (a) Domain = $\{x \in \mathbb{R} \mid -4 \leq x \leq 6\}$; Range = $\{y \in \mathbb{R} \mid -2 \leq y \leq 3\}$

(b) Domain = $\{x \in \mathbb{R} \mid -4 \leq x \leq 4\}$; Range = $\{y \in \mathbb{R} \mid -2 \leq y \leq 2\}$

24. $-\dfrac{\sqrt{3}}{3}$ **25.** (a) x (b) x **26.** $\dfrac{-h}{x(x + h)}$ **27.** 69

28.

STATEMENTS	REASONS
1. $\overline{AC} \cong \overline{EC}$	1. Given
2. $\overline{BC} \cong \overline{DC}$	2. Given
3. $\angle BCA \cong \angle DCE$	3. Vertical angles are congruent.
4. $\triangle ABC \cong \triangle EDC$	4. SAS congruency postulate
5. $\overline{AB} \cong \overline{ED}$	5. CPCTC

29. A   **30.** A

problem set 36

1. Plane = 240 mph; wind = 60 mph   **2.** $N_R = 10$; $N_W = 100$; $N_B = 50$ **3.** $3\sqrt{3}$

4. $\dfrac{mp}{m + 2p} \dfrac{\text{mi}}{\text{hr}}$ **5.** Decreased by 4%   **6.** $-\dfrac{12}{7}$ **7.** $\sqrt{(x + 2)^2 + (y - 5)^2}$

8. $\dfrac{37}{20}$ **9.** $R = -10W + 620$ **10.** $f(x) = \sqrt{x}$; $g(x) = x - 1$ **11.** 7

12. $y = 3x + 7$ **13.** $-30°$ **14.** $\dfrac{2\sqrt{10}}{7}$

15. (a) x axis, no; y axis, no; origin, yes   (b) x axis, no; y axis, yes; origin, no

16. $y = \sqrt{-x}$ **17.** $y = (x + 3)^3$ **18.** $4.79\underline{/281.36°}$ **19.** 360

20. (a) $3\sqrt{3}$ (b) $-\dfrac{11}{2}$ (c) $\dfrac{1}{9}$ **21.**

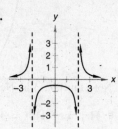

22. (a) Function, not 1 to 1   (b) Function, not 1 to 1   (c) Not a function   (d) Function, not 1 to 1

23. $\left\{ x \in \mathbb{R} \mid x \leq 3,\ x \neq -\dfrac{5}{2}, -2 \right\}$ **24.** (a) $1 - \dfrac{\sqrt{2}}{2}$ (b) $\dfrac{-1 + \sqrt{2}}{2}$ **25.** $-\sqrt{3}$

26. (a) $\dfrac{1}{18}$ (b) $\dfrac{1}{9}$ (c) $\dfrac{9}{8}$ **27.** $h^2 + 2xh - 2h$

28.

STATEMENTS	REASONS
1. $\overline{AB} \perp \overline{BC}$, $\overline{CD} \perp \overline{DA}$	1. Given
2. $\angle ABC$ and $\angle CDA$ are right angles.	2. Perpendicular lines intersect to form right angles.
3. $\triangle ABC$ and $\triangle CDA$ are right triangles.	3. A triangle which contains a right angle is a right triangle.
4. $\overline{AC} \cong \overline{AC}$	4. Reflexive axiom
5. $\overline{AB} \cong \overline{CD}$	5. Given
6. $\triangle ABC \cong \triangle CDA$	6. HL congruency postulate
7. $\overline{BC} \cong \overline{DA}$	7. CPCTC

29. C   **30.** C

problem set 37

1. Plane = 120 mph; wind = 20 mph   **2.** $384   **3.** $\dfrac{3}{8}$ **4.** $4000

5. $\dfrac{mk + 10m}{k - 2m} \dfrac{\text{mi}}{\text{hr}}$ **6.** $y = -\dfrac{7}{5}x - \dfrac{6}{5}$ **7.** $\left(-\dfrac{1}{2}, \dfrac{9}{2} \right)$ **8.** $-\dfrac{96}{35}$ **9.** 46

10. $O = 6.67I - 106.7$ **11.** $f(x) = \sqrt{x}$ **12.** A   **13.** 6   **14.** $y = \dfrac{1}{4}x - \dfrac{1}{6}$

15. (a) $0°$ (b) $\dfrac{\sqrt{5}}{5}$

16. (a) x axis, no; y axis, no; origin, yes   (b) x axis, yes; y axis, no; origin, no

17. $y = -(3^x)$ **18.** $y = 4^x + 3$ **19.** (a) 2   (b) $-\dfrac{7}{2}$ (c) $2\sqrt{2}$

20. (a) Domain = $\{x \in \mathbb{R} \mid -3 \leq x \leq 5\}$; Range = $\{y \in \mathbb{R} \mid 1 \leq y \leq 7\}$

(b) Domain = $\{x \in \mathbb{R} \mid -2 \leq x \leq 2\}$; Range = $\{y \in \mathbb{R} \mid -8 \leq y \leq 8\}$

21. (a) $\dfrac{-1 - \sqrt{2}}{2}$ (b) $\dfrac{2 + \sqrt{2}}{2}$ **22.** (a) 2   (b) 3   (c) 4   **23.** $(0, 2), \left(\dfrac{8}{5}, -\dfrac{6}{5} \right)$

24. 2   **25.** $x^3 + x + 1$ **26.** $2x + h$

27.

STATEMENTS	REASONS
1. $\overline{PQ} \cong \overline{SR}$	1. Given
2. $\overline{QS} \cong \overline{RP}$	2. Given
3. $\overline{PS} \cong \overline{PS}$	3. Reflexive axiom
4. $\triangle PQS \cong \triangle SRP$	4. SSS congruency postulate
5. $\angle PQS \cong \angle SRP$	5. CPCTC

28. 4572π cm^3 **29.** B   **30.** A

problem set 38

1. Boat = 12 mph; current = 3 mph   **2.** $\dfrac{RT + 100}{T + P} \dfrac{\text{mi}}{\text{hr}}$ **3.** 50 mph

4. 4 liters of 90%, 16 liters of 75%   **5.** 5 hr   **6.** 120   **7.** 3125   **8.** 243

9. $x^2 - \dfrac{14}{15}x - \dfrac{8}{15} = 0$ **10.** $y = 8x + \dfrac{5}{2}$ **11.** $\left(\dfrac{7}{2}, 4\right)$ **12.** $-\dfrac{5}{4}$

13. $V = -1.54K + 173.7$ **14.** $f(x) = x^3$; $g(x) = 2x + 3$ **15.** C   **16.** $32\ \text{cm}^2$

17. (a) $-45°$ (b) $\dfrac{2\sqrt{29}}{29}$ **18.** $y = 3^{-x}$ **19.** $y = 4^x - 3$ **20.** $19.89\underline{/327.02°}$

21. (a) 2   (b) $-\dfrac{11}{3}$ (c) 9   **22.** $\{x \in \mathbb{R} \mid x \geq -100, x \neq -5, -2\}$

23. (a) $\dfrac{1}{2}$ (b) $-\dfrac{\sqrt{2}}{2} - \dfrac{\sqrt{3}}{3}$ **24.** (a) x (b) x

25. $(\sqrt{3}, 2), (\sqrt{3}, -2), (-\sqrt{3}, 2), (-\sqrt{3}, -2)$ **26.** $g = \dfrac{2(x - x_0 - v_0 t)}{t^2}$

27. $h + 2x - 2$ **28.**   **29.** B   **30.** A

STATEMENTS	REASONS
1. *ABCD* is a square.	1. Given
2. $\angle BAD$ and $\angle CDA$ are right angles.	2. A square contains four right angles.
3. $\angle BAD \cong \angle CDA$	3. All right angles are congruent.
4. $\overline{AB} \cong \overline{DC}$	4. All sides of a square are congruent.
5. $\overline{AD} \cong \overline{AD}$	5. Reflexive axiom
6. $\triangle BAD \cong \triangle CDA$	6. *SAS* congruency postulate
7. $\overline{BD} \cong \overline{CA}$	7. *CPCTC*

problem set 39

1. 2453.58 mi   **2.** 31.42 ft   **3.** 24   **4.** 210   **5.** 20 mph   **6.** $\dfrac{2y}{s + 10}\ \dfrac{\text{yd}}{\text{s}}$

7. 25 days   **8.** $x - 2y + 8 = 0$ **9.** $\dfrac{x}{-2} + \dfrac{y}{3} = 1$ **10.** $\dfrac{\sqrt{3} + 1}{2}$ **11.** $-\dfrac{\sqrt{3}}{4}$

12. $\dfrac{1}{2}$ **13.** $x^2 - 3 = 0$ **14.** $y = -\dfrac{9}{4}x + \dfrac{1}{8}$ **15.** $\left(2, \dfrac{9}{2}\right)$ **16.** $\dfrac{14}{3}$ **17.** $\dfrac{5}{4}$

18. $S = -5.71P + 334.2$ **19.** $f(x) = \sqrt{x}$ **20.** No. Isosceles trapezoid.   **21.** $\dfrac{1}{2}$

22. (a) $-45°$ (b) $\dfrac{2\sqrt{6}}{5}$

23. (a) x axis, yes; y axis, yes; origin, yes   (b) x axis, no; y axis, yes; origin, no

24. (a) 3   (b) -3 (c) $\sqrt[3]{9}$

25. (a) Domain $= \{x \in \mathbb{R} \mid -4 \leq x \leq 4\}$; Range $= \{y \in \mathbb{R} \mid 0 \leq y \leq 3\}$

     (b) Domain $= \{x \in \mathbb{R} \mid -5 \leq x \leq 2\}$; Range $= \{y \in \mathbb{R} \mid -4 \leq y \leq 5\}$

26. (a) x (b) x **27.**   **28.** $2052\pi\ \text{m}^2$

STATEMENTS	REASONS
1. *ABCD* is a rectangle.	1. Given
2. $\angle B$ and $\angle C$ are right angles.	2. A rectangle contains four right angles.
3. $\angle B \cong \angle C$	3. All right angles are congruent.
4. $\overline{AB} \cong \overline{CD}$	4. Opposite sides of a rectangle are congruent.
5. *E* is the midpoint of $\overline{BC}$.	5. Given
6. $\overline{BE} \cong \overline{CE}$	6. A midpoint divides a segment into two congruent segments.
7. $\triangle ABE \cong \triangle DCE$	7. *SAS* congruency postulate
8. $\overline{AE} \cong \overline{DE}$	8. *CPCTC*

29. B   **30.** B

problem set 40

1. 18.33 ft   **2.** 17 mph   **3.** Plane $= 120$ mph; wind $= 20$ mph   **4.** 10 lb   **5.** 625

6. 1,860,480   **7.** 14   **8.** 2   **9.** 3   **10.** 9   **11.** Yes   **12.** $x + 3y - 9 = 0$

13. $\dfrac{x}{-\frac{5}{2}} + \dfrac{y}{\frac{5}{4}} = 1$ **14.** $\dfrac{\sqrt{3}}{4}$ **15.** -1 **16.** 1   **17.** $x^2 + \dfrac{19}{15}x - \dfrac{2}{3} = 0$

18. $9x + y - 7 = 0$ **19.** $N = -\dfrac{9}{8}R + 202.5$ **20.** $f(x) = x + 1$; $g(x) = x^2$

21. (a) $-60°$ (b) $\dfrac{3\sqrt{13}}{13}$ **22.** $y = -x^2$ **23.** $y = \dfrac{1}{x - 3}$ **24.** $\{x \in \mathbb{R} \mid x > 0, x \neq 1\}$

25. $y^6(5x - 6ay)(25x^2 + 30xay + 36a^2y^2)$ **26.** $6x + 3h - 4$

27.

STATEMENTS	REASONS
1. $\overline{PR}$ bisects $\angle QPS$	1. Given
2. $\overline{PR}$ bisects $\angle QRS$	2. Given
3. $\angle QPR \cong \angle SPR$	3. A bisector divides an angle
$\angle QRP \cong \angle SRP$	into two congruent angles.
4. $\overline{PR} \cong \overline{PR}$	4. Reflexive axiom
5. $\angle Q \cong \angle S$	5. If two angles in one triangle
	are congruent to two angles
	in a second triangle, then the
	third angles are congruent.
6. $\triangle PQR \cong \triangle PSR$	6. AAAS congruency postulate

28. $\dfrac{2}{3}$ **29.** C   **30.** B

problem set 41

1. 30.54 ft   **2.** 18 mph   **3.** 200 men   **4.** 9:00 p.m.   **5.** $\dfrac{m}{h - 3} \dfrac{\text{mi}}{\text{hr}}$

6. $\dfrac{6 - 2\sqrt{3}}{3}$ **7.** $2 - \sqrt{3}$ **8.** (a) 5040   (b) 154,440   **9.** 13

10. No solution   **11.** 3   **12.** 8   **13.** No   **14.** $x + 3y - 7 = 0$

15. $\dfrac{x}{-\frac{6}{5}} + \dfrac{y}{2} = 1$ **16.** $x^2 - \dfrac{1}{6}x - \dfrac{1}{3} = 0$ **17.** $\dfrac{x}{-\frac{8}{3}} + \dfrac{y}{8} = 1$ **18.** $-\dfrac{3}{4}$ **19.** -4

20. $H = S$ **21.** C   **22.** 6 cm   **23.** (a) $150°$ (b) $\dfrac{\sqrt{5}}{3}$ **24.** $y = \dfrac{1}{x + 3}$

25. $y = |x - 3| + 2$ **26.** $6.04\underline{/153.30°}$

27. (a) Domain $= \{x \in \mathbb{R} \mid -6 \leq x \leq 5\}$; Range $= \{y \in \mathbb{R} \mid -3 \leq y \leq 4\}$

     (b) Domain $= \{x \in \mathbb{R} \mid -4 \leq x \leq 4\}$; Range $= \{y \in \mathbb{R} \mid -2 \leq y \leq 6\}$

28. $\dfrac{-1}{x(x + h)}$ **29.** C   **30.** A

problem set 42

1. 1047.20 ft   **2.** $B = 20$ mph; $C = 5$ mph   **3.** 0.88   **4.** 16 hr   **5.** 3 days

6. \$300   **7.** $(x - 3)^2 + (y - 4)^2 = 3^2$ **8.**

9.

10. $\sqrt{2}$ **11.** $-2 + \sqrt{3}$ **12.** 151,200   **13.** 6

14. 49   **15.** 4   **16.** No   **17.** $2x + 5y - 13 = 0$ **18.** $\dfrac{x}{\frac{1}{2}} + \dfrac{y}{-\frac{3}{5}} = 1$

19. $x^2 - \dfrac{3}{10}x - \dfrac{2}{5} = 0$ **20.** $2x + y - 1 = 0$ **21.** $I = 1.22A - 7.1$ **22.** A

23. 9 cm   **24.** (a) $-60°$ (b) $\dfrac{\sqrt{7}}{4}$ **25.** $y = |x + 3| + 2$

26. $g(x) = |x - 2| + 3$

27. $\left\{ x \in \mathbb{R} \mid x \geq 0, x \neq \dfrac{1}{2} \right\}$

28.

STATEMENTS	REASONS
1. $\overline{AD} \cong \overline{BD}$	1. Given
2. $\overline{ED} \cong \overline{CD}$	2. Given
3. $\angle BDC \cong \angle ADE$	3. Vertical angles are congruent.
4. $\triangle BDC \cong \triangle ADE$	4. *SAS* congruency postulate
5. $\angle A \cong \angle B$	5. *CPCTC*

29. C   **30.** D

problem set 43

1. 43.63 ft   **2.** 523.60 ft   **3.** 20 days   **4.** 50 hr   **5.** $\dfrac{2000}{130 + f + s}$ gal

6. $S = 31$ yr; $J = 33$ yr   **7.** $y = -4 \cos \theta$ **8.** $y = 5 \sin x$

9. $(x + 2)^2 + (y - 3)^2 = 4^2$ **10.**   **11.** $-\sqrt{3}$ **12.** $-\sqrt{2} - 1$

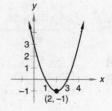

13. 13,440   **14.** 1   **15.** 4   **16.** 10   **17.** 4   **18.** Yes   **19.** $x^2 - 2x - 2 = 0$

20. $y = -\dfrac{3}{2}x + \dfrac{3}{2}$ **21.** $\left(\dfrac{1}{2}, 3 \right)$ **22.** $\dfrac{35}{9}$ **23.** 0   **24.** H = -8C + 922

25. (a) $-30°$ (b) $-\dfrac{3}{5}$

26. (a) Domain = $\{x \in \mathbb{R} \mid -6 \leq x \leq 2\}$; Range = $\{y \in \mathbb{R} \mid -2 \leq y \leq 6\}$

   (b) Domain = $\{x \in \mathbb{R} \mid -5 \leq x \leq 5\}$; Range = $\{y \in \mathbb{R} \mid -4 \leq y \leq 4\}$

27. $y = (x - 1)^2 - 1$ **28.** $g(x) = (x - 2)^2 - 1$ **29.** D   **30.** A

problem set 44

1. $\dfrac{100d}{x - 5d}$ drums   **2.** $\dfrac{hw}{w + m}$ hr   **3.** $\dfrac{mc}{c + n}$ min   **4.** 100 mi   **5.** 120

6. 314.16 yd   **7.** $y = -10 \cos x$ **8.** $y = 11 \sin x$ **9.** $(x - h)^2 + (y - k)^2 = 5^2$

10.   **11.** $-\sqrt{2} + \dfrac{1}{2}$ **12.** $\dfrac{-4\sqrt{3}}{3}$ **13.** 7   **14.** $\dfrac{46}{3}$ **15.** $\dfrac{27}{11}$

16. 2   **17.** 4   **18.** Yes   **19.** $x^2 - \dfrac{11}{4}x - \dfrac{3}{4} = 0$

20. $x + 4y - 10 = 0$ **21.** $x + y = 0$ **22.** $\left(\dfrac{5}{2}, \dfrac{1}{2} \right)$ **23.** $\dfrac{-61}{12}$

24. F = 55.56D $-$ 1555.68   **25.** $f(x) = \log_3 x$; $g(x) = x + 2$ **26.** (a) $45°$ (b) $\dfrac{3}{5}$

27. $y = (x + 3)^2 - 1$ **28.** 2   **29.** B   **30.** B

**problem set
45**

1. 25   **2.** 8640   **3.** $\dfrac{fk(c + 10)}{c(k - x)}$ hr   **4.** 2799.16 mi

5. $R_O = 4$ mph; $T_O = 6$ hr; $R_B = 8$ mph; $T_B = 3$ hr   **6.** 2400 liters

7. $N_G = 20$; $N_B = 10$; $N_W = 5$

8. Cu $= -0.2317$Pb $+ 55.2056$; $r = -0.8109$; not a good correlation

9. Rh $= 0.7686$Dy $- 2.2571$; $r = 0.9944$; good correlation   **10.** $y = -10 \sin \theta$

11. $y = 8 \cos x$ **12.** $(x + 2)^2 + (y - 5)^2 = 6^2$ **13.**

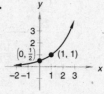

14. $\dfrac{9\sqrt{2} + 4\sqrt{3}}{6}$ **15.** $-\dfrac{\sqrt{3}}{6}$ **16.** 90   **17.** 1   **18.** 30   **19.** $\dfrac{1}{14}$ **20.** 3

21. Yes   **22.** $x^2 - 4x - 1 = 0$ **23.** $y = -\dfrac{8}{9}x + \dfrac{3}{2}$ **24.** $f(x) = 2x + 3$

25. $\left\{ x \in \mathbb{R} \mid x \geq 0, x \neq \dfrac{1}{4} \right\}$ **26.** $y = \sqrt{x - 2} + 3$

27. $g(x) = \sqrt{x - 3} + 2$

```
        y
        3
        2
        1    (3, 2)
   -1  1 2 3 4 5 6    x
```

28.

Statements	Reasons	
1. $\overline{PQ} \parallel \overline{ST}$	1. Given	**29.** B **30.** A
2. $\angle Q \cong \angle S$ $\angle P \cong \angle T$	2. If parallel lines are intersected by a transversal, then each pair of alternate interior angles is congruent.	
3. R is the midpoint of $\overline{QS}$.	3. Given	
4. $\overline{QR} \cong \overline{RS}$	4. A midpoint divides a segment into two congruent segments.	
5. $\angle QRP \cong \angle SRT$	5. Vertical angles are congruent.	
6. $\triangle QRP \cong \triangle SRT$	6. AAAS congruency postulate	
7. $\overline{PR} \cong \overline{TR}$	7. CPCTC	

**problem set
46**

1. 25   **2.** 34,560   **3.** $\dfrac{dy}{y + 50}$ days   **4.** $\dfrac{200b}{d + 2b}$ balls   **5.** 628.32 m

6. $R_O = 9$ mph; $R_B = 18$ mph   **7.** 500 liters   **8.** $N_R = 12$; $N_E = 4$; $N_D = 2$

9. $x^2 - 4x + 13 = 0$ **10.** $\left(x + \dfrac{3}{2} - \dfrac{\sqrt{15}}{2}i \right)\left(x + \dfrac{3}{2} + \dfrac{\sqrt{15}}{2}i \right)$

11. C $= -0.1138$H $+ 50.1680$; $r = -0.9439$; good correlation

12. $y = -12 \cos x$ **13.** $y = -9 \sin \theta$ **14.** $(x - h)^2 + (y - k)^2 = 6^2$

15.

```
        y
        3
        2    (1, 1/3)
   (0, 1/9)
             x
        1 2 3
```

16. (a) $\dfrac{\sqrt{3} - \sqrt{2}}{2}$ (b) $-2\sqrt{2}$ **17.** 1624

18. 0   **19.** $\dfrac{35}{2}$ **20.** $\dfrac{2}{9}$ **21.** 27   **22.** Yes   **23.** $\dfrac{1}{3}$

24. (a) $\dfrac{-5\sqrt{194}}{194}$ (b) $\dfrac{\sqrt{7}}{4}$ **25.** $y = \sqrt{x - 1} - 4$

26. $g(x) = \sqrt{x - 4} - 5$

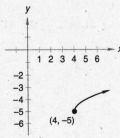

(4, –5)

27. (a) Domain = $\{x \in \mathbb{R} \mid -4 \le x \le 6\}$; Range = $\{y \in \mathbb{R} \mid -2 \le y \le 3\}$

(b) Domain = $\{x \in \mathbb{R} \mid -3 \le x \le 2\}$; Range = $\{y \in \mathbb{R} \mid -4 \le y \le 4\}$

28. $1 - 2x - h$ **29.** B   **30.** C

problem set 47

1. 12   **2.** $\dfrac{dm}{40}$ days   **3.** $\dfrac{dk}{k - y}$ hr   **4.** $\dfrac{dm}{12}$ dollars   **5.** 13.96 ft

6. $B = 40$ mph; $W = 10$ mph   **7.** $y = -5 - 25 \sin \theta$ **8.** $y = -3 + 7 \cos x$

9. (a) $-45°$ (b) $-30°$ **10.** $x^2 - 6x + 13 = 0$ **11.** $2(x + 1 - i)(x + 1 + i)$

12. $O = 0.2434N - 1.1762$; $r = 0.9596$; good correlation   **13.** $(x - 2)^2 + (y - 1)^2 = 3^2$

14.

(0, 8)

(–1, 4)

15. (a) $\dfrac{-3 - \sqrt{2}}{2}$ (b) 1   **16.** 5   **17.** $\dfrac{15}{4}$ **18.** 3

19. 8   **20.** $\dfrac{x}{\frac{3}{2}} + \dfrac{y}{-\frac{1}{2}} = 1$ **21.** (1, 1)   **22.** $\dfrac{8}{3}$ **23.** 5   **24.** (a) $150°$ (b) $-\dfrac{3\sqrt{7}}{7}$

25. (a) x axis, yes; y axis, no; origin, no   (b) x axis, no; y axis, yes; origin, no

26. $y = \sqrt{x + 4} + 2$ **27.** $g(x) = \sqrt{x + 4} + 1$

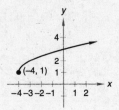

(–4, 1)

28. (a) $\dfrac{74}{3}$ (b) $\dfrac{81}{7}$ (c) $\dfrac{727}{27}$ **29.** C   **30.** B

problem set 48

1. 80   **2.** 324   **3.** 2930.48 mi   **4.** 1920 cal   **5.** $m = \dfrac{W_1 W_2}{W_1 + W_2}$

6. 450 ml of 40%, 150 ml of 80%   **7.** $N_R = 4$; $N_B = 2$; $N_W = 6$ **8.** $5000   **9.** 1

10. $\dfrac{7}{3}$ **11.** $\dfrac{x}{\frac{7}{2}} + \dfrac{y}{-\frac{7}{4}} = 1$ **12.** $y = \dfrac{3}{4}x + \dfrac{5}{4}$ **13.** $y = -5 - 20 \cos x$

14. $y = 6 - 14 \sin \theta$ **15.** (a) $60°$ (b) $-30°$ **16.** $x^2 - 2x + 10 = 0$

17. $(x - 1 - \sqrt{2}i)(x - 1 + \sqrt{2}i)$

18. $I = 4.2727E - 19.4935$; $r = 0.8253$; good correlation   **19.** $(x - 3)^2 + (y - 2)^2 = 4^2$

20.

21. 432   **22.** 11   **23.** 0   **24.** 50   **25.** (a) −90° (b) $\dfrac{\sqrt{5}}{3}$

26. $y = \sqrt{x + 1} - 3$ **27.** $g(x) = \sqrt{x + 9} - 2$

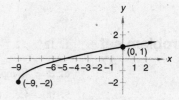

28.

STATEMENTS	REASONS
1. $\overline{BD}$ is perpendicular bisector of $\overline{AC}$	1. Given
2. $\overline{AD} \cong \overline{DC}$ $\angle ADB \cong \angle CDB$	2. Perpendicular bisector bisects segment into two congruent segments and forms congruent right angles.
3. $\overline{DB} \cong \overline{DB}$	3. Reflexive axiom
4. $\triangle ADB \cong \triangle CDB$	4. *SAS* congruency postulate
5. $\overline{AB} \cong \overline{CB}$	5. *CPCTC*

29. C   **30.** D

problem set 49

1. 288   **2.** 480   **3.** 3013.42 mi   **4.** 51 days   **5.** $432   **6.** $\dfrac{7dp}{4c}$ dollars

7. $\dfrac{11KS}{G(S + 14)}$ days   **8.** Refer to Lesson 49.   **9.** $\dfrac{1}{3}$ **10.** 5   **11.** $x + y - 2 = 0$

12. $\dfrac{x}{-\frac{2}{5}} + \dfrac{y}{-\frac{2}{9}} = 1$ **13.** $x - 5y - 19 = 0$ **14.** $y = 1 + 5\sin x$ **15.** $y = 5 - 15\cos\theta$

16. (a) −45° (b) −60°   **17.** $x^2 - 4x + 5 = 0$ **18.** $3(x - 2 - 2i)(x - 2 + 2i)$

19. Ca $= 0.5176$K $+ 6.6444$; $r = 0.9352$; good correlation   **20.** $(x + 2)^2 + (y + 3)^2 = 3^2$

21.

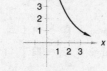

22. 0   **23.** (a) 38 (b) 3   **24.** 10 ft   **25.** $y = |x - 1| - 4$

26. $g(x) = |x - 4| - 3$

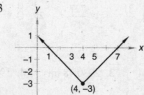

27. (a) Domain $= \{x \in \mathbb{R} \mid -2 < x \le 4\}$; Range $= \{y \in \mathbb{R} \mid -3 < y \le 3\}$

(b) Domain $= \{x \in \mathbb{R} \mid -3 \le x < 6\}$; Range $= \{y \in \mathbb{R} \mid -4 \le y \le 5\}$

28. $2x$ **29.** A   **30.** C

problem set 50

1. 40   **2.** 40   **3.** 2695.49 mi   **4.** $J = 30$ yr; $S = 45$ yr   **5.** $\dfrac{177}{2}$ hr   **6.** 2 qt

7. $\dfrac{d}{h - 4}\dfrac{\text{mi}}{\text{hr}}$ **8.** 45°, 315°   **9.** 30°, 330°   **10.** Refer to Lesson 49.

11. (a) -1 (b) $3 + 3\sqrt{3}$ **12.** -2 **13.** $5x + y - 7 = 0$

14. $y = -3x + 16$ **15.** $y = 5 + 25 \cos x$ **16.** $y = 15 - 25 \cos \theta$

17. $x^2 - 2x + 4 = 0$ **18.** $(x - 1 - \sqrt{3}i)(x - 1 + \sqrt{3}i)$

19. $C = 0.1178H - 4.1948$; $r = 0.9112$; good correlation   **20.** $(x + 2)^2 + (y - 4)^2 = 4^2$

21.   **22.** (a) $\dfrac{26}{5}$ (b) 81 **23.** $\dfrac{31}{4}$ **24.** (a) $150°$ (b) $\dfrac{\sqrt{33}}{7}$

25. $y = |x + 3| - 3$ **26.** $g(x) = |x + 4| - 5$;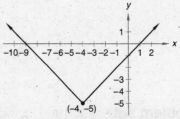

27. (a) Domain $= \{x \in \mathbb{R} \mid -5 \le x < 4\}$; Range $= \{y \in \mathbb{R} \mid -2 \le y \le 7\}$

  (b) Domain $= \{x \in \mathbb{R} \mid -4 < x < 3\}$; Range $= \{y \in \mathbb{R} \mid -4 < y \le 4\}$

28.

STATEMENTS	REASONS
1. $\overline{AB} \parallel \overline{DC}$	1. Given
2. $\overline{AD} \parallel \overline{BC}$	2. Given
3. $\angle DBC \cong \angle BDA$ $\angle ABD \cong \angle CDB$	3. If two parallel lines are intersected by a transversal, then each pair of alternate interior angles is congruent.
4. $\overline{BD} \cong \overline{BD}$	4. Reflexive axiom
5. $\angle BAD \cong \angle BCD$	5. If two angles in one triangle are congruent to two angles in a second triangle, then the third angles are congruent.
6. $\triangle ABD \cong \triangle CDB$	6. *AAAS* congruency postulate
7. $\overline{AB} \cong \overline{DC}$	7. *CPCTC*

29. D   **30.** B

problem set 51

1. 18 **2.** 130 **3.** 314.16 m   **4.** 15 hr   **5.** $\dfrac{100d}{3}$ stamps   **6.** 8 packages

7. $\dfrac{60d}{m - 60}$ mph   **8.** (a) 0.5441 (b) 1.2528 **9.** $e^{8.1887}$ **10.** $240°, 300°$

11. $240°, 300°$ **12.** Refer to Lesson 49.   **13.** -2 **14.** $\left(\dfrac{3}{2}, 3\right)$ **15.** $6x - 4y - 5 = 0$

16. $5x + y - 4 = 0$ **17.** $y = 5 + 25 \sin x$ **18.** $y = 10 - 20 \cos \theta$

19. $x^2 - 6x + 10 = 0$ **20.** $4(x + 1 - \sqrt{6}i)(x + 1 + \sqrt{6}i)$

21. $H = 0.8072P + 55.9193$; $r = 0.9111$; good correlation

22. $(x + 3)^2 + (y - 2)^2 = 5^2$ **23.**   **24.** 6384 **25.** (a) 34 (b) $\dfrac{8}{9}$

26. Yes   **27.** (a) $\dfrac{\sqrt{7}}{4}$ (b) $-\dfrac{5\sqrt{6}}{12}$ (c) $30°$ **28.** $y = -\sqrt{x - 2}$ **29.** B   **30.** $2x + 1$

problem set 52

1. 1080 **2.** 80 **3.** 2681.66 mi **4.** $\frac{56}{13}$ hr **5.** \$210 **6.** \$56

7. $\frac{D}{S - 120}$ $\frac{\text{ft}}{\text{s}}$ **8.** $W = 5 \frac{\text{mi}}{\text{hr}}$; $B = 10 \frac{\text{mi}}{\text{hr}}$ **9.** 60°, 120°, 240°, 300°

10. 15°, 75°, 135°, 195°, 255°, 315° **11.** 120°, 240° **12.** (a) 1.2122 (b) 2.7912

13. $e^{8.2428}$ **14.** $\frac{11}{6}$ **15.** $\frac{5}{3}$ **16.** $\frac{x}{10} + \frac{y}{2} = 1$ **17.** $y = 4 - 7 \sin x$

18. $y = 2 - 8 \cos \theta$ **19.** $x^2 + 4x + 5 = 0$ **20.** $(x + 2 - i)(x + 2 + i)$

21. $W = 13.4787H - 761.8723$; $r = 0.7815$; not a good correlation

22. $(x - h)^2 + (y - k)^2 = r^2$ **23.** **24.** $\frac{20}{9}$

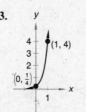

25. $\frac{21}{2}$ **26.** 25 **27.** No **28.** 5 **29.** $y = -\sqrt{x + 4}$ **30.** A

problem set 53

1. 180 **2.** 9424.78 m **3.** 6 days **4.** $\frac{hm}{m + p}$ hr **5.** $\frac{3Y}{S + 20}$ $\frac{\text{yd}}{\text{s}}$ **6.** 400 francs

7. $\frac{(50)(5280)(12)(2.54)}{60}$ $\frac{\text{cm}}{\text{min}}$ **8.** $\frac{30(10)^3}{(2.54)^3}$ in.^{3} **9.** $\frac{(50)(5280)(12)}{(15)(60)(60)(2\pi)}$ $\frac{\text{rev}}{\text{s}}$

10. 60°, 120° **11.** 0°, 120°, 240° **12.** 180° **13.** $10^{3.7924}$ **14.** $e^{8.5942}$

15. $-\frac{2}{3}$ **16.** $\frac{11}{4}$ **17.** $2x - 5 = 0$ **18.** $y = 1 + 5 \cos x$ **19.** $y = -1 - 7 \cos \theta$

20. $x^2 + 2x + 9 = 0$ **21.** $V = 59.88W + 323.76$; $r = 0.9815$; good correlation

22. $\left(x - \sqrt{3}\right)^2 + (y + 2)^2 = 5^2$ **23.**

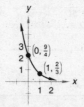

24. $\frac{225}{2}$ **25.** 4 **26.** Yes **27.** 2 **28.** $y = -x^2 + 4$ **29.** D **30.** $2x - 1$

problem set 54

1. $\frac{(1.5)(30)(60)(2\pi)}{5280}$ $\frac{\text{mi}}{\text{hr}}$ **2.** $\frac{(30)(1000)(100)}{(60)(70)}$ $\frac{\text{rad}}{\text{min}}$ **3.** 36 **4.** 418.88 m

5. $\frac{R}{m - 2}$ $\frac{\text{mi}}{\text{hr}}$ **6.** 16 hr **7.** 20 liters

8. $y = (x - 3)^2 - 5$

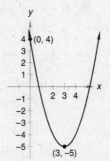

9. $y = -(x + 2)^2 + 10$

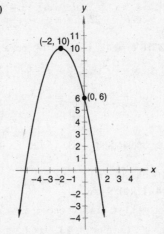

10. $\dfrac{(40)(5280)(12)(2.54)}{(60)(60)} \dfrac{cm}{s}$ **11.** $(12)(10)^3(60)(60) \dfrac{cm^3}{hr}$ **12.** $135°, 225°$

13. $10°, 50°, 130°, 170°, 250°, 290°$ **14.** $0°, 180°$ **15.** $10^{3.4914}$ **16.** $e^{8.0392}$

17. $\dfrac{1}{3}$ **18.** -1 **19.** $(2, 6)$ **20.** $\dfrac{x}{-\frac{7}{4}} + \dfrac{y}{7} = 1$ **21.** $y = 9 - \sin x$

22. $y = 6 + 6 \cos \theta$ **23.** $5\left(x + \dfrac{3}{2} - \dfrac{3\sqrt{3}}{2}i\right)\left(x + \dfrac{3}{2} + \dfrac{3\sqrt{3}}{2}i\right)$

24. $S = -0.089T + 14.47$; $r = -0.9047$; good correlation   **25.** $(x - 3)^2 + (y - 2)^2 = 6^2$

26.   **27.** (a) $\dfrac{1}{6}$ (b) $\dfrac{25}{8}$ **28.** $-\dfrac{25}{6}$ **29.** $y = -|x| - 2$ **30.** C

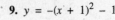

problem set 55   **1.** 2   **2.** 6   **3.** 10,080   **4.** $\dfrac{(10)(1000)}{(60)(60)(3)} \dfrac{rad}{s}$

5. $\dfrac{(0.5)(40)(60)}{36} \dfrac{yd}{min}$ **6.** 100 mph   **7.** $N_R = 6$; $N_W = 4$; $N_G = 5$

8. $y = (x - 4)^2 - 4$ **9.** $y = -(x + 1)^2 - 1$

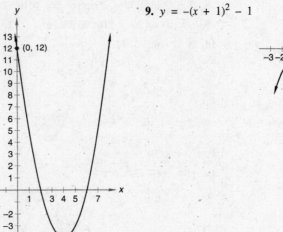

10. $\dfrac{(20)(100)(60)(60)}{(2.54)(12)(5280)} \dfrac{mi}{hr}$ **11.** $\dfrac{(12)(10)^3}{(2.54)^3(60)} \dfrac{in.^3}{min}$ **12.** $30°, 210°$

13. $10°, 70°, 130°, 190°, 250°, 310°$ **14.** $45°, 225°$ **15.** $10^{3.7634}$ **16.** $e^{8.6656}$

17. $-\dfrac{1}{3}$ **18.** $\dfrac{2}{3}$ **19.** $x + y - 1 = 0$ **20.** $y = 7 + 3 \sin \theta$

21. $y = 8 - 9\cos\theta$ **22.** $\left(x - \dfrac{5}{2} - \dfrac{\sqrt{7}}{2}i\right)\left(x - \dfrac{5}{2} + \dfrac{\sqrt{7}}{2}i\right)$

23. $P = 1.057H + 60.43$; $r = 0.1018$; not a good correlation

24. $(x - 2)^2 + (y - 5)^2 = 7^2$ **25.** 630 **26.** (a) 6 (b) 31 **27.** Yes

28. (a) $-\dfrac{3}{4}$ (b) $\dfrac{\sqrt{7}}{4}$ **29.** $y = \sqrt{-x} + 3$ **30.** B

problem set 56

1. 125 **2.** 39,916,800 **3.** 15,120 **4.** $\dfrac{(40)(2\pi)(10)(2.54)}{60}\ \dfrac{\text{cm}}{\text{s}}$

5. $\dfrac{(260)(1000)(100)}{(60)(2.54)(12)(2\pi)}\ \dfrac{\text{rev}}{\text{min}}$ **6.** \$594 **7.** 74

8. Youngster = 13 yr; Ancient one = 53 yr **9.** $14.74\ \text{m}^2$ **10.** $18.43\ \text{cm}^2$

11. $234.73\ \text{m}^2$ **12.** $5\ \text{m}^2$ **13.** $9.06\ \text{ft}^2$ **14.** B

15. $y = (x - 2)^2 + 2$ **16.** $y = -(x + 3)^2 + 3$

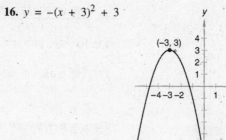

17. $135°, 315°$ **18.** $80°, 100°, 200°, 220°, 320°, 340°$ **19.** $135°, 315°$ **20.** $10^{4.8129}$

21. $e^{11.0821}$ **22.** 3 **23.** $x + 4y + 3 = 0$ **24.** $(8, 2)$ **25.** $y = 3 - 9\cos x$

26. $3(x + 3 - i)(x + 3 + i)$ **27.** $P = 0.0996I + 47.9949$; $r = 0.1503$; not a good correlation

28. $(x - 4)^2 + (y - 5)^2 = 5^2$ **29.** (a) 7 (b) $\dfrac{4}{3}$ **30.** $2x - 2$

problem set 57

1. 13,860 **2.** 83,160 **3.** $\dfrac{(4)(400)(60)}{(2.54)(12)(5280)}\ \dfrac{\text{mi}}{\text{hr}}$ **4.** $\dfrac{(40)(1000)(100)}{(5)(60)(60)}\ \dfrac{\text{rad}}{\text{s}}$

5. $B = 6\ \text{mph}$; $W = 2\ \text{mph}$ **6.** $4010.77\ \text{km}$ **7.** 2000 boys **8.** $y = 6\sin(\theta - 90°)$

9. $y = 10\sin 2\theta$ **10.** $43.26\ \text{cm}^2$ **11.** $25.80\ \text{cm}^2$ **12.** $217.51\ \text{ft}^2$ **13.** $4.80\ \text{m}^2$

14. $20.57\ \text{cm}^2$ **15.**

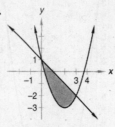

16. $y = -(x + 2)^2 + 8$ **17.** $60°, 300°$

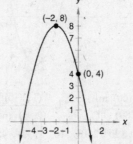

18. $20°, 100°, 140°, 220°, 260°, 340°$ **19.** $30°, 90°, 150°, 210°, 270°, 330°$ **20.** 10^4

21. $e^{9.2103}$ **22.** $\dfrac{x}{\frac{7}{4}} + \dfrac{y}{1} = 1$ **23.** $\dfrac{\pi}{6}$ **24.** 4   **25.** $\left(x - \dfrac{3}{2} - \dfrac{\sqrt{7}}{2}i\right)\left(x - \dfrac{3}{2} + \dfrac{\sqrt{7}}{2}i\right)$

26. (a) 33   (b) $\dfrac{13}{3}$ **27.** Yes   **28.** 5   **29.** $y = \sqrt{-(x-4)}$ **30.** D

problem set 58

1. 126   **2.** 30   **3.** 24   **4.** $\dfrac{(10)(525)(2.54)(60)(60)}{(100)(1000)} \ \dfrac{\text{km}}{\text{hr}}$ **5.** $\dfrac{(100)(5280)(12)(2.54)}{(60)(60)(40)} \ \dfrac{\text{rad}}{\text{s}}$

6. 3640   **7.** 11   **8.** 3.57 atm   **9.** $\dfrac{12\sqrt{5}}{5}$ **10.** $y = -2(x+2)^2 + 4$

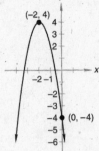

11. $y = -3 + 5\cos(\theta - 135°)$ **12.** $y = 2 + 6\cos 2\theta$ **13.** 34.47 m^2 **14.** 344,720 cm^2

15. 4.05 ft^2 **16.** 0.12 m^2 **17.** C **18.** $\dfrac{(250)(1000)(100)(60)(60)}{(2.54)(12)(5280)} \ \dfrac{\text{mi}}{\text{hr}}$ **19.** 30°, 330°

20. 6°, 66°, 78°, 138°, 150°, 210°, 222°, 282°, 294°, 354°   **21.** 45°, 105°, 165°, 225°, 285°, 345°

22. $3x + y - 7 = 0$ **23.** $\dfrac{\sqrt{15}}{4}$ **24.** 1   **25.** 5   **26.** (a) 1   (b) 2   **27.** No

28. (a) Domain = $\{x \in \mathbb{R} \mid -5 < x < 2\}$; Range = $\{y \in \mathbb{R} \mid -3 \le y < 6\}$

(b) Domain = $\{x \in \mathbb{R} \mid -5 \le x < 5\}$; Range = $\{y \in \mathbb{R} \mid -4 \le y \le 4\}$

29. $y = \sqrt{-x} - 2$ **30.** B

problem set 59

1. 2,494,800   **2.** 720   **3.** 648   **4.** $\dfrac{(400)(60)(60)}{5280} \ \dfrac{\text{mi}}{\text{hr}}$ **5.** $\dfrac{(40)(1000)(100)}{(2.54)(60)(8)(2\pi)} \ \dfrac{\text{rev}}{\text{min}}$

6. $\dfrac{20(x+1)}{y}$ pencils   **7.** $\dfrac{66}{13}$ days   **8.** 30 gal of 80%, 20 gal of 20%   **9.** 3   **10.** 2

11. $\dfrac{4}{7}$ **12.** 6   **13.** 30   **14.** $\dfrac{2\sqrt{5}}{5}$ **15.** $y = 3(x-1)^2 + 2$

16. $y = 3 + 8\sin(\theta - 45°)$ **17.** $y = 4 + 7\sin 2\theta$ **18.** 285,316.95 cm^2

19. 5,496,510.22 cm^2 **20.** 0.61 m^2 **21.**

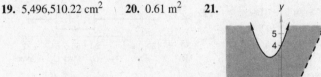

22. $\dfrac{(30)(60)(60)}{(100)(1000)} \dfrac{\text{km}}{\text{hr}}$ **23.** 30°, 210° **24.** 10°, 70°, 130°, 190°, 250°, 310° **25.** $10^{4.3010}$

26. $e^{9.9035}$ **27.** (a) $\dfrac{3}{4}$ (b) $-\dfrac{\pi}{6}$ (c) $1 - \sqrt{3}$ **28.** $(x - 3)^2 + (y - 2)^2 = 10^2$

29. $y = \sqrt{-(x + 3)}$ **30.** A

problem set 60

1. 12 **2.** 6,652,800 **3.** $\dfrac{(16)(367)(60)}{(12)(5280)} \dfrac{\text{mi}}{\text{hr}}$ **4.** $\dfrac{(5)(1000)(100)}{(60)(5)} \dfrac{\text{rad}}{\text{min}}$

5. $J = 400$ mph; $W = 50$ mph **6.** $N_R = 4$; $N_W = 8$; $N_G = 10$ **7.** 0°, 90°, 270°

8. 90°, 270° **9.** 2 **10.** 5 **11.** 1 **12.** 7 **13.** 3 **14.** $4\sqrt{2}$

15. $y = 3(x + 1)^2 - 3$ **16.** $y = -5 + 15 \cos (\theta - 45°)$

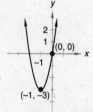

17. $y = -10 + 20 \cos 2x$ **18.** 190.53 m^2 **19.** 77.41 cm^2 **20.** 279.25 cm^2

21. 0.60 ft^2 **22.** A **23.** 30°, 150°, 270° **24.** 1 **25.** (a) $\dfrac{\pi}{4}$ (b) $\dfrac{15}{16}$ (c) 0

26. $\dfrac{x}{\frac{5}{4}} + \dfrac{y}{-5} = 1$ **27.** $x^2 + 2x + 4 = 0$ **28.** Yes

29. $g(x) = |x|$ **30.** $2x + 3$

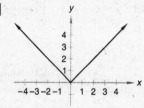

problem set 61

1. 1320 **2.** 12 **3.** $\dfrac{(40)(1000)(100)}{(2.54)(60)(60)(14)} \dfrac{\text{rad}}{\text{s}}$ **4.** $\dfrac{(16)(40)(2\pi)(60)(60)}{(2.54)(12)(5280)} \dfrac{\text{mi}}{\text{hr}}$

5. $\dfrac{2ud}{u + d}$ knots **6.** $247 **7.** $E = 35$ yr; $L = 31$ yr **8.** 483

9. Range = 5; mean = 5.83; median = 6; mode = 8; variance = 3.81; standard deviation = 1.95

10. 68% of the data lie between 62 and 68; 95% of the data lie between 59 and 71; 99% of the data lie between 56 and 74.

11.

STEM	LEAF
3	1, 0
4	0, 4, 2, 7
5	5, 7, 3, 2
6	2, 9

12.

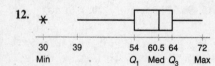

13. 45°, 75°, 165°, 195°, 285°, 315° **14.** 30°, 150°, 210°, 330° **15.** 60°, 90°, 270°, 300°

16. 2 **17.** 10 **18.** 23 **19.** $\dfrac{3\sqrt{2}}{2}$

20. $y = 2(x - 1)^2 - 9$

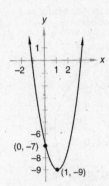

(0, -7)

(1, -9)

21. $y = -2 + 6 \sin\left(x - \dfrac{\pi}{4}\right)$

22. $y = 2 + 5 \sin 4\theta$ **23.** 541.27 cm^2 **24.** 8000 cm^2 **25.** 105.90 cm^2

26.

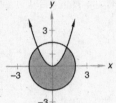

27. 0   **28.** 0   **29.** $-\dfrac{5}{13}$ **30.** $y = -4x + 3$

problem set 62

1. $C = 10N + 50$ **2.** 30,240   **3.** 6930   **4.** 24   **5.** $\dfrac{(20)(723)}{(2.54)(12)(60)} \dfrac{\text{ft}}{\text{s}}$

6. $W = 2 \text{ mph}; D = 4 \text{ mph}$ **7.** 40 atm   **8.** 1920   **9.** $y = \dfrac{mf - cd}{me - nd}$

10. Range = 6; mean = 4; median = 3.5; mode = 7; variance = 5.33; standard deviation = 2.31

11. (a) 78 to 90   (b) 72 to 96

12. Mean = 557.11; standard deviation = 74.38

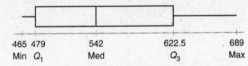

465 479   542   622.5   689
Min Q_1 Med Q_3 Max

13. $0°, 90°, 180°, 270°$ **14.** $45°, 135°, 225°, 315°$ **15.** 2   **16.** $\dfrac{3}{2}$ **17.** 9

18. $\sqrt{2}$ **19.** $y = -1 + 4 \cos(\theta - 135°)$ **20.** $y = -3 + 5 \cos \dfrac{1}{3}x$

21. 626.72 cm^2 **22.** 89.88 cm^2 **23.** 57.43 cm^2 **24.**

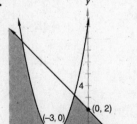

(-3, 0)   (0, 2)

25. 0   **26.** $\dfrac{4}{3}$ **27.** $-\dfrac{5}{12}$ **28.** $5x + 3y - 2 = 0$ **29.** D   **30.** Yes

problem set 63

1. $N_R = 27$ **2.** 35   **3.** 48   **4.** 12   **5.** $\dfrac{(60)(100)(1000)}{(2.54)(12)(60)(60)} \dfrac{\text{rad}}{\text{s}}$

6. $\dfrac{ma - mb}{ab} \text{ hr}$ **7.** $\dfrac{1000b}{a + bc} \text{ hr}$ **8.** Onlookers = 850; bystanders = 200

9. $(x + 4)^2 + (y - 3)^2 = 6^2$; center = $(-4, 3)$; radius = 6

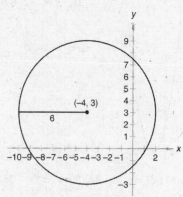

10. $(x - 4)^2 + (y + 1)^2 = 2^2$; center = $(4, -1)$; radius = 2

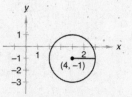

11. $x = \dfrac{cn - bf}{an - mb}$ **12.** Point = 14; range = 14; median = 18; standard deviation = 5.22

13. 68% of the data lie between 72 and 80; 95% of the data lie between 68 and 84; 99% of the data lie between 64 and 88.

14.

Stem	Leaf
5	6
6	2, 7, 3, 5, 4
7	6, 0, 8, 2, 4
8	9, 3, 0, 1

15. 60°, 120°, 240°, 300°   **16.** 0°, 180°   **17.** $2\sqrt{3}$ **18.** 7

19. $6\sqrt{2}$ **20.** $y = 2(x - 3)^2 - 9$ **21.** $y = 4 + 8 \sin\left(x - \dfrac{\pi}{4}\right)$

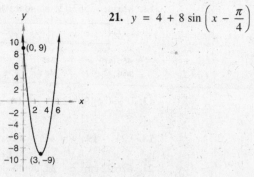

22. $y = -3 + 5 \sin \dfrac{1}{2}x$ **23.** 1542.69 cm²   **24.** 1920 cm²   **25.** 122.53 cm²

26.   **27.** 1   **28.** 0   **29.** $\dfrac{\sqrt{11}}{6}$ **30.** 26

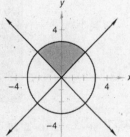

**problem set
64**

1. $25,000   **2.** 50   **3.** 35   **4.** $\dfrac{(10)(75)(2.54)(60)}{(100)(1000)} \dfrac{\text{km}}{\text{hr}}$ **5.** $\dfrac{150(x + y)}{m + k}$ hr

6. $\dfrac{mr - mb}{br}$ hr   **7.** $\dfrac{100k^2t}{d}$ pencils   **8.** (a) 6.32 cis 18.43°   (b) $\dfrac{5\sqrt{3}}{2} + \dfrac{5}{2}i$

9. $6\sqrt{3} - 6i$ **10.** -6

11. $(x - 2)^2 + y^2 = 2^2$; center $= (2, 0)$; radius $= 2$

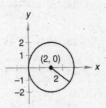

12. $(x + 3)^2 + (y - 2)^2 = 2^2$; center $= (-3, 2)$; radius $= 2$

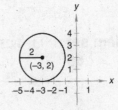

13. $y = \dfrac{cf - dp}{cq - bp}$ **14.** 7 to 27

15. Mean $= 28.93$; standard deviation $= 9.67$;

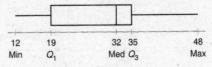

16. $270°$ **17.** $60°, 120°, 240°, 300°$ **18.** $0°, 45°, 180°, 225°$ **19.** 1   **20.** 3

21. 163   **22.** $7\sqrt{2}$ **23.** $y = -1 + 5\cos(x - 135°)$ **24.** $y = 6 - 4\cos\dfrac{2}{3}x$

25. $138.56\,\text{cm}^2$ **26.** $676.30\,\text{cm}^2$ **27.**

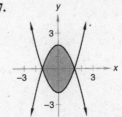

28. 1   **29.** 1

30. $\dfrac{x}{\frac{12}{5}} + \dfrac{y}{12} = 1$

problem set 65

1. \$1000   **2.** 26   **3.** 34,650   **4.** $\dfrac{(45)(1000)(100)}{(30)(60)}\dfrac{\text{rad}}{\text{min}}$ **5.** 2944.30 miles

6. $\dfrac{50(2h + 4)}{m + x}$ hr   **7.** $\dfrac{Rx - px}{Rp}$ hr   **8.** $\dfrac{500(k^2x + m)}{d}$ pencils   **9.** $45°, 315°$

10. $\dfrac{\pi}{3}, \dfrac{2\pi}{3}, \dfrac{7\pi}{6}, \dfrac{11\pi}{6}$ **11.**

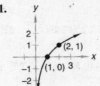

12. (a) $5.83 \text{ cis } 59.04°$ (b) $3 + 3\sqrt{3}i$

13. $30i$ **14.** $9 + 9\sqrt{3}i$

15. $(x + 5)^2 + y^2 = 10^2$; center $= (-5, 0)$; radius $= 10$

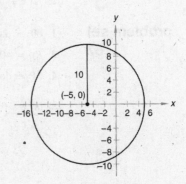

16. $x = \dfrac{gf - hd}{af - cd}$ **17.** Range = 8; mean = 5.67; median = 6; mode = 9; variance = 8.89; standard deviation = 2.98

18. 68%   **19.** 50°, 70°, 170°, 190°, 290°, 310°   **20.** 2   **21.** 4   **22.** 9

23. $y = 1 + 5 \sin\left(x - \dfrac{3\pi}{4}\right)$ **24.** $y = 6 + 10 \sin \dfrac{2}{7}\theta$ **25.** 0.0046 m^2 **26.** $\dfrac{7\sqrt{85}}{85}$

27. $\dfrac{5}{4}$ **28.** $\dfrac{(600)(1000)(100)}{(2.54)(12)(5280)} \dfrac{\text{mi}}{\text{hr}}$ **29.** $\left(x + \dfrac{3}{2} - \dfrac{\sqrt{19}}{2}i\right)\left(x + \dfrac{3}{2} + \dfrac{\sqrt{19}}{2}i\right)$ **30.** D

problem set 66

1. \$925   **2.** 84   **3.** 120   **4.** $\dfrac{(12)(5280)(12)}{(60)(13)} \dfrac{\text{rad}}{\text{min}}$ **5.** $\dfrac{740(2p + 6)}{k + z}$ hr

6. $\dfrac{mz - ma}{az}$ hr   **7.** $\dfrac{10{,}000\,p^2 k}{m}$ cars   **8.** $y = -1 - 8 \cos 2x$

9. $y = 3 + 5 \sin\left(x - \dfrac{3\pi}{4}\right)$ **10.** 30°, 210°   **11.** $\dfrac{\pi}{3}, \dfrac{7\pi}{6}, \dfrac{5\pi}{3}, \dfrac{11\pi}{6}$

12.

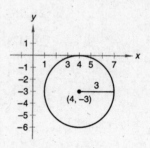

13. (a) 5 cis 36.87°   (b) $-\dfrac{5}{2}\sqrt{3} + \dfrac{5}{2}i$ **14.** 6 cis (350°)

15. $8\sqrt{3} - 8i$

16. $(x - 4)^2 + (y + 3)^2 = 3^2$; center = (4, –3); radius = 3

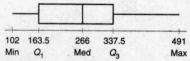

17. $x = \dfrac{cf - bg}{af - bd}$ **18.** 3

19. Range = 7; mean = 3; median = 2; mode = 2; variance = 6.67; standard deviation = 2.58

20. Mean = 264.13; standard deviation = 110.25

102	163.5	266	337.5	491
Min	Q_1	Med	Q_3	Max

21. 10°, 50°, 130°, 170°, 250°, 290°   **22.** $x = 2, 4$ **23.** $x = 4$ **24.** $\dfrac{145}{8}$

25. 8.86 m^2 **26.** 1440.54 cm^2 **27.** –8   **28.** $\dfrac{3}{2}$ **29.** $x^2 - 4x + 9 = 0$

30. $\dfrac{-1}{2(x + h)(x - h)}$

problem set 67

1. 60   **2.** $B = 20$ mph; $W = 4$ mph

3. $R_H = 400$ mph; $T_H = 3$ hr; $R_F = 200$ mph; $T_F = 9$ hr

4. \$1 per doz eggs; 50¢ per lb of flour   **5.** 98   **6.** 25   **7.** (a) 39.67   (b) 204,173.79

8. (a) 9   (b) $\dfrac{1}{9}$ **9.**   **10.** $y = 4 + 6 \sin \dfrac{2}{3}\theta$

11. $y = 3 + 5 \cos \frac{1}{2}(x - 270°)$ **12.** (a) 13 cis 292.62° (b) $-\frac{7\sqrt{3}}{2} - \frac{7}{2}i$

13. $4 + 4\sqrt{3}i$ **14.** $-3\sqrt{3} - 3i$

15. $(x - 2)^2 + (y + 3)^2 = 4^2$; center = $(2, -3)$; radius = 4

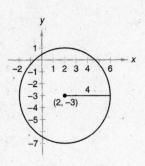

16. $y = \dfrac{bc - ad}{cg - df}$ **17.** $-\dfrac{1}{13}$ **18.** 47.5%

19.

STEM	LEAF
1	7
2	
3	
4	6
5	6, 8
6	4, 6, 8
7	3, 5, 0, 1
8	3, 7, 5, 2
9	2

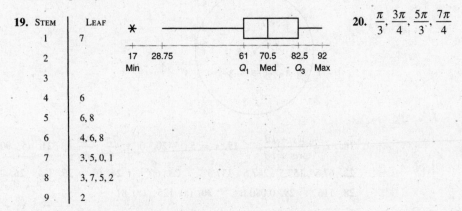

20. $\dfrac{\pi}{3}, \dfrac{3\pi}{4}, \dfrac{5\pi}{3}, \dfrac{7\pi}{4}$

21. 30°, 150°   **22.** 40°, 80°, 160°, 200°, 280°, 320°   **23.** $-\dfrac{1}{2}$ **24.** 1, 3   **25.** 3

26. 3   **27.**

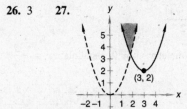

28. 395.98 cm^2 **29.** $(x - 2 - \sqrt{2}i)(x - 2 + \sqrt{2}i)$

30. $\dfrac{(80)(1000)(100)}{(2.54)(5280)(12)} \dfrac{\text{mi}}{\text{hr}}$

problem set 68

1. \$475   **2.** 126   **3.** 60   **4.** $\dfrac{(15)(5280)(12)}{(60)(400)}$ in.   **5.** $\dfrac{100(2u + 2)}{m + s}$ hr

6. $\dfrac{750w^3a^2}{g}$ stereos   **7.** 0, 1, 2, 3   **8.** Vertex = $(0, 0)$; parabola: $y = \dfrac{1}{12}x^2$

9. Directrix: $y = -1$; axis of symmetry: $x = 0$; parabola: $y = \dfrac{1}{8}x^2 + 1$

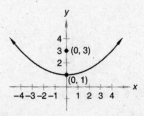

10. 25 ft   **11.** (a) 68% (b) 34%

12.

STEM	LEAF
2	53, 94, 11, 75, 92, 52
3	78, 12, 87, 10, 66, 96, 51
4	22, 08, 00

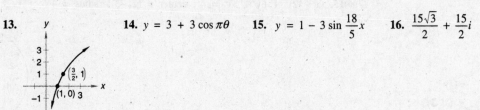

211   283.5   331.5   391.5 422
Min Q_1 Med Q_3 Max

13.

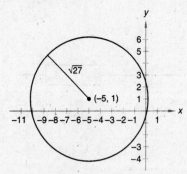

14. $y = 3 + 3 \cos \pi\theta$ **15.** $y = 1 - 3 \sin \dfrac{18}{5}x$ **16.** $\dfrac{15\sqrt{3}}{2} + \dfrac{15}{2}i$

17. $(x + 5)^2 + (y - 1)^2 = \left(\sqrt{27}\right)^2$; center = $(-5, 1)$; radius = $\sqrt{27}$

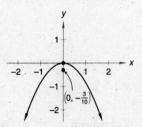

18. $x = \dfrac{ws + kd}{wa + bd}$ **19.** $x = 5$ **20.** $0, \pi, \dfrac{7\pi}{6}, \dfrac{11\pi}{6}$ **21.** $45°, 90°, 225°, 270°$

22. $67.5°, 157.5°, 247.5°, 337.5°$ **23.** $60°$ **24.** 0 **25.** 1 **26.** $2, 3$ **27.** $5\sqrt{5}$

28. 116 **29.** 0.080 ft^2 **30.** (a) 125 (b) 81

problem set 69

1. $R_G = 40$ mph; $R_B = 80$ mph   **2.** p is multiplied by 32.   **3.** $20°$ **4.** $\dfrac{x}{k - 20} \dfrac{\text{mi}}{\text{min}}$

5. $\$8000$ **6.** -38 **7.** $\dfrac{1 \pm \sqrt{41}}{2}$

8. Directrix: $y = \dfrac{3}{10}$; axis of symmetry: $x = 0$; parabola: $y = -\dfrac{5}{6}x^2$

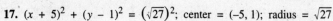

9. Parabola: $y = -\dfrac{1}{12}(x + 3)^2 + 2$; directrix: $y = 5$; axis of symmetry: $x = -3$

10. Mean = 0.17; median = -0.5; variance = 9.14; mode does not exist; standard deviation = 3.02

11. 81.5% **12.**

13. $y = 5 + 4 \cos 2\left(x + \dfrac{3\pi}{8}\right)$

14. $y = -3 + 10 \sin 3(\theta - 20°)$ **15.** $6 + 6\sqrt{3}i$

16. (a) $6.32 \text{ cis } 341.57°$ (b) $-\dfrac{5\sqrt{2}}{2} + \dfrac{5\sqrt{2}}{2}i$ **17.** $y = \dfrac{ad - pc}{aq - pb}$

18.

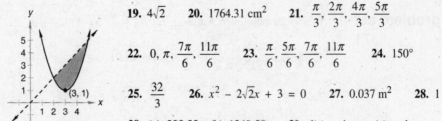

19. $4\sqrt{2}$ **20.** 1764.31 cm^2 **21.** $\dfrac{\pi}{3}, \dfrac{2\pi}{3}, \dfrac{4\pi}{3}, \dfrac{5\pi}{3}$

22. $0, \pi, \dfrac{7\pi}{6}, \dfrac{11\pi}{6}$ **23.** $\dfrac{\pi}{6}, \dfrac{5\pi}{6}, \dfrac{7\pi}{6}, \dfrac{11\pi}{6}$ **24.** 150°

25. $\dfrac{32}{3}$ **26.** $x^2 - 2\sqrt{2}x + 3 = 0$ **27.** 0.037 m^2 **28.** 1

29. (a) 223.55   (b) 1249.58   **30.** $f(x) = \ln x$; $g(x) = \log x$

problem set 70

1. 45 squirrels   **2.** 4 hr   **3.** $B = 20$ mph; $W = 2$ mph   **4.** J is doubled

5. 1,108,800   **6.** 81.85%   **7.** 93.32%   **8.** 3   **9.** 3, –2

10. Parabola: $y = \dfrac{1}{20}(x - 2)^2 - 1$;

directrix: $y = -6$; axis of symmetry: $x = 2$

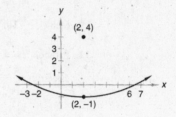

11.

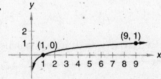

12. $(x - 2)^2 + (y + 3)^2 = \left(\sqrt{21}\right)^2$; center = $(2, -3)$; radius = $\sqrt{21}$

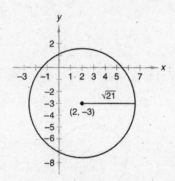

13. $y = -9 + 31\sin\dfrac{3}{2}(x + 10°)$ **14.** $y = 12 + 2\cos\dfrac{2}{3}\left(x - \dfrac{\pi}{2}\right)$

15. $x = \dfrac{js + aw}{jd + kw}$ **16.** $\dfrac{15}{2} - \dfrac{15\sqrt{3}}{2}i$ **17.** $6 - 6\sqrt{3}i$ **18.** $\dfrac{\pi}{6}, \dfrac{\pi}{4}, \dfrac{3\pi}{4}, \dfrac{11\pi}{6}$

19. $\dfrac{\pi}{3}, \pi, \dfrac{5\pi}{3}$ **20.** –30°   **21.** $\dfrac{3}{2}$

22. Mean = 4; median = 3.5; mode = 1; variance = 7.33; standard deviation = 2.71

23.

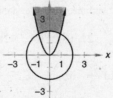

24. 0.040 ft^2 **25.** $x^2 - 4\sqrt{3}x + 16 = 0$

26. 1   **27.** 14.10 in.^{2} **28.** $\dfrac{7\sqrt{5}}{25}$ **29.** $\dfrac{8}{7}$ **30.** D

problem set 71

1. $B = 20$ mph; $W = 4$ mph   2. $N_B = 2$; $N_R = 4$; $N_W = 7$ 3. 72   4. $\dfrac{20}{9}$ hr

5. x is multiplied by $\dfrac{9}{4}$ 6. Length $= 100$ cm; width $= 17$ cm; height $= 33$ cm

7.

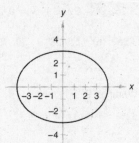

8. $\dfrac{x^2}{4} + \dfrac{y^2}{9} = 1$

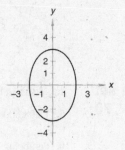

9. 6.68%   10. ±2

11. Parabola: $y = -\dfrac{1}{8}x^2$;

    directrix: $y = 2$; axis of symmetry: $x = 0$

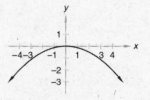

12. Parabola: $y = \dfrac{1}{8}(x - 1)^2 + 2$; directrix: $y = 0$; axis of symmetry: $x = 1$

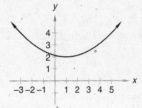

13.

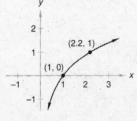

14. $(x + 4)^2 + (y - 6)^2 = 3^2$; center $= (-4, 6)$; radius $= 3$

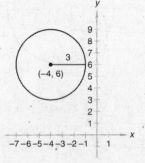

15. $y = -3 + 8 \cos \dfrac{1}{4}(x - 180°)$ 16. $y = 1 + 2 \cos \dfrac{1}{2}\left(x + \dfrac{\pi}{2}\right)$

17. (a) 10.63 cis 228.81° (b) $0 - 7i$ 18. $3\sqrt{3} - 3i$ 19. 120°, 225°, 240°, 315°

20. 30°, 150°, 210°, 330°   21. 90°, 135°, 270°, 315°   22. −1   23. 1

24. Mean $= 3.83$; median $= 4$; mode $= 5$; variance $= 4.14$; standard deviation $= 2.03$

25.

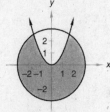

26. $\dfrac{14\sqrt{29}}{29}$ 27. 0.024 ft^2 28. 1

29. (a) 0 (b) $\dfrac{7}{2}$ (c) 11

30. $\left(x + \dfrac{7}{2} - \dfrac{\sqrt{11}}{2}i\right)\left(x + \dfrac{7}{2} + \dfrac{\sqrt{11}}{2}i\right)$

problem set 72

1. 90,720 **2.** $\dfrac{y}{m-2}\dfrac{\text{yd}}{\text{min}}$ **3.** $\dfrac{1000\,wm}{z}$ men **4.** 2380 beauties **5.** 143 **6.** 6°

7. $A = 110°$; $a = 15.04$; $m = 10.28$ **8.** $B = 28°$; $c = 5.87$; $b = 7.35$

9.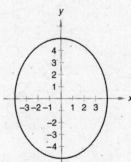

10. $\dfrac{x^2}{16} + \dfrac{y^2}{4} = 1$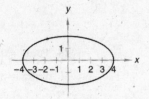

11. 73.33% **12.** $-2, 3$

13. Focus $= (0, -2)$; vertex $= (0, 0)$; directrix: $y = 2$

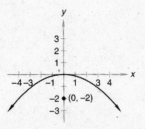

14. 12.5 ft **15.** 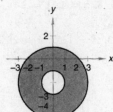 **16.** $y = -3 + 5\sin\dfrac{1}{2}\left(x - \dfrac{\pi}{2}\right)$

17. $y = -10 + 20\sin 2x$ **18.** (a) 10 cis 143.13° (b) $\dfrac{3}{2} - \dfrac{3\sqrt{3}}{2}i$ **19.** $-18 + 0i$

20. $\dfrac{\pi}{2}, \dfrac{3\pi}{2}$ **21.** $\dfrac{\pi}{6}, \dfrac{5\pi}{6}, \dfrac{3\pi}{2}$ **22.** $\dfrac{\pi}{6}, \dfrac{2\pi}{3}, \dfrac{7\pi}{6}, \dfrac{5\pi}{3}$ **23.** 1 **24.** 2

25. Mean $= 5.5$; median $= 6.5$; mode $= 7$; variance $= 4.92$; standard deviation $= 2.22$

26. 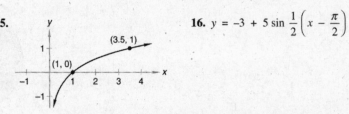 **27.** 1 **28.** 1 **29.** $\left(x + \dfrac{3}{2} - \dfrac{\sqrt{31}}{2}i\right)\left(x + \dfrac{3}{2} + \dfrac{\sqrt{31}}{2}i\right)$

30. Yes

problem set 73

1. 210 **2.** $\dfrac{5000}{M(M-5)}$ dollars **3.** $\dfrac{h-w}{h}$ **4.** 6 times **5.** 28, 42 **6.** $\dfrac{x+2}{x+1}$

7. 93.53 in.^{2} **8.** 482.84 cm^2 **9.** $\dfrac{1}{81}$ **10.** $A = 20°$; $a = 6.70$; $b = 9.79$

11. $\dfrac{x^2}{9} + \dfrac{y^2}{4} = 1$ 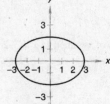 **12.** 64.49% **13.** $-2, 0$

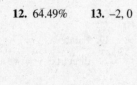

14. Parabola: $y = \dfrac{1}{28}(x - 3)^2 - 2$;

directrix: $y = -9$; axis of symmetry: $x = 3$

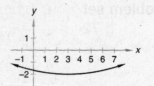

15. Focus $= \left(0, \dfrac{9}{4}\right)$; directrix: $y = -\dfrac{9}{4}$;

vertex $= (0, 0)$; axis of symmetry: $x = 0$

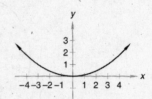

16.

17. $y = -3 + 2\cos \dfrac{5}{3}(x - 81°)$

18. $y = -2 + 6\sin\left(x - \dfrac{\pi}{4}\right)$ **19.** $6\sqrt{3} + 6i$

20. $y = \dfrac{ag - cd}{af - bd}$ **21.** $y = -\dfrac{1}{7}$

22. $0°, 30°, 150°, 180°$ **23.** $60°, 120°, 240°, 300°$

24. $120°, 240°$ **25.** -4 **26.** $\dfrac{3}{4}$ **27.**

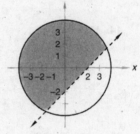

28. $\dfrac{2}{3}$

29. 4 **30.** $y = -2x + \dfrac{9}{2}$

problem set 74

1. 495 **2.** $\dfrac{1}{13}$ **3.** $(36y - 12f - n)$ in.   **4.** \$6.44 per hour   **5.** $\dfrac{E - P}{E}$

6. $\dfrac{D - P}{N}$ $\dfrac{\text{dollars}}{\text{item}}$ **7.** $\dfrac{2pk}{k + p}$ mph   **8.** $x = 1; y = 2$ **9.** $x = -1; y = 1$

10. 300 cm^2 **11.** 4 cm   **12.** $\dfrac{9}{4}$ **13.** $A = 135°; a = 28.28; b = 10.35$

14. $\dfrac{x^2}{16} + \dfrac{y^2}{25} = 1$ **15.** 0.62% **16.** $-4, 5$

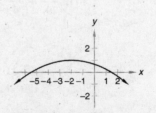

17. Parabola: $y = -\dfrac{1}{12}(x + 2)^2 + 1$;

directrix: $y = 4$; axis of symmetry: $x = -2$

18.

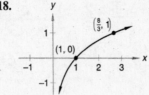

19. $(x + 5)^2 + (y - 2)^2 = 3^2$; center $= (-5, 2)$; radius $= 3$

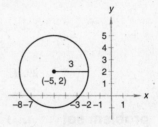

20. $y = 3 + 11 \sin \dfrac{3}{2}(x - 40°)$ **21.** $y = -1 + 14 \sin (x + 45°)$ **22.** $-24 + 0i$

23. (a) $3.61 \text{ cis } 303.69°$ (b) $-\dfrac{13\sqrt{3}}{2} + \dfrac{13}{2}i$ **24.** $\dfrac{\pi}{6}, \dfrac{5\pi}{6}, \dfrac{7\pi}{6}, \dfrac{11\pi}{6}$

25. $\dfrac{\pi}{3}, \dfrac{2\pi}{3}, \dfrac{4\pi}{3}, \dfrac{5\pi}{3}$ **26.** 0 **27.** 2 **28.** $\dfrac{3}{2}$ **29.** (a) 36 (b) -2 (c) 5

30. $(x - 2\sqrt{5}\,i)(x + 2\sqrt{5}\,i)$

**problem set
75**

1. $\$1.10 + \$1.10m$ **2.** $\dfrac{20D}{p^2 - 20p} \dfrac{\text{dollars}}{\text{student}}$ **3.** p is multiplied by $\dfrac{16}{3}$ **4.** 14 miles

5. 56 triangles   **6.** 70 **7.** $x = -\dfrac{25}{17}$; $y = -\dfrac{6}{17}$ **8.** 293.89 cm^2

9. Area $= 77.25 \text{ cm}^2$; radius $= 4.83 \text{ cm}$ **10.** $\dfrac{25}{4}$ **11.** $A = 50°$; $a = 7.08$; $b = 8.68$

12. $\dfrac{x^2}{8} + \dfrac{y^2}{5} = 1$ **13.** 1

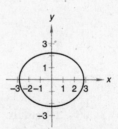

14. Focus $= (0, -4)$; vertex $= (0, 0)$; directrix: $y = 4$

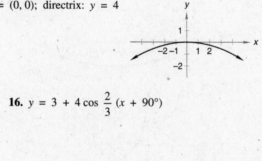

15.

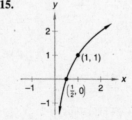

16. $y = 3 + 4 \cos \dfrac{2}{3}(x + 90°)$

17. $y = 10 + 6 \sin \dfrac{1}{2}\left(x - \dfrac{\pi}{2}\right)$ **18.** $-10 + 0i$ **19.** (a) $7.81 \text{ cis } 50.19°$ (b) $\dfrac{7\sqrt{2}}{2} - \dfrac{7\sqrt{2}}{2}i$

20. $60°, 120°, 240°, 300°$ **21.** $90°$ **22.** $90°$ **23.** 0

24. Mean $= 2.67$; median $= 1.5$; mode $= 0$; variance $= 14.56$; standard deviation $= 3.82$

25.

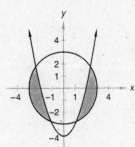

26. $\dfrac{2\sqrt{10}}{5}$ **27.** $\dfrac{1}{2}$ **28.** (a) $\dfrac{2}{3}$ (b) 14   (c) 0

29. (a) $\dfrac{1}{36}$ (b) $\dfrac{1}{64}$ **30.** $2\left(x - \dfrac{5}{4} - \dfrac{\sqrt{23}}{4}i\right)\left(x - \dfrac{5}{4} + \dfrac{\sqrt{23}}{4}i\right)$

**problem set
76**

1. 45 committees   **2.** 210 groups   **3.** $460; $34,960   **4.** $M = 29$ yr; $R = 28$ yr

5. $\dfrac{y}{m - 15}\dfrac{\text{yards}}{\text{minutes}}$ **6.** $\cos x \tan x = \cos x \dfrac{\sin x}{\cos x} = \sin x = \dfrac{1}{\dfrac{1}{\sin x}} = \dfrac{1}{\csc x}$

7. $\dfrac{\cot x}{\csc x} = \dfrac{\dfrac{\cos x}{\sin x}}{\dfrac{1}{\sin x}} = \dfrac{\cos x}{\sin x} \cdot \dfrac{\sin x}{1} = \cos x$

8. $-\sin(-\theta)\cos(90° - \theta) = -(-\sin\theta)\sin\theta = \sin^2\theta$ **9.** $x = \dfrac{17}{12}$; $y = \dfrac{7}{8}$

10. Area $= 342.38$ in.^{2}; radius $= 9.71$ in.   **11.** 6.53 in.

12. $B = 30°$; $a = 11.70$ ft; $b = 6.22$ ft   **13.** $\dfrac{x^2}{6} + \dfrac{y^2}{12} = 1$

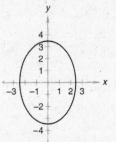

14. 30.5%   **15.** $-1, 4$

16. Parabola: $y = \dfrac{1}{28}(x + 3)^2 - 2$; directrix: $y = -9$; axis of symmetry: $x = -3$

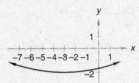

17.

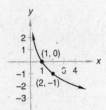

18. $(x - 1)^2 + (y + 1)^2 = 2^2$; center $= (1, -1)$; radius $= 2$

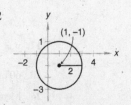

19. $y = 3 + 6 \cos \frac{2}{3}(\theta - 135°)$ **20.** $y = -3 + \frac{3}{2} \sin 4(x + 30°)$ **21.** $-9\sqrt{2} + 9\sqrt{2}i$

22. $\frac{\pi}{2}, \frac{3\pi}{2}$ **23.** $\frac{\pi}{6}, \frac{\pi}{3}, \frac{2\pi}{3}, \frac{5\pi}{6}, \frac{7\pi}{6}, \frac{4\pi}{3}, \frac{5\pi}{3}, \frac{11\pi}{6}$ **24.** π **25.** 0

26. $\frac{2\sqrt{13}}{13}$ **27.** 3   **28.** 4   **29.** (a) 12   (b) 0   **30.** (a) 205.70   (b) 38.80

problem set 77

1. 126 teams   **2.** 42.86 mph   **3.** \$656   **4.** \$1024   **5.** 4, 5, 6   **6.** $\frac{x + 2}{x + 1}$

7. $x^4 + 4x^3y + 6x^2y^2 + 4xy^3 + y^4$ **8.** $21x^5y^2$

9. $\sin x \sec x = \sin x \frac{1}{\cos x} = \frac{\sin x}{\cos x} = \tan x$

10. $\sec x \cot x = \frac{1}{\cos x} \cdot \frac{\cos x}{\sin x} = \frac{1}{\sin x} = \csc x$

11. $\sin(-\theta) \tan(90° - \theta) = (-\sin \theta) \cot \theta = (-\sin \theta)\left(\frac{\cos \theta}{\sin \theta}\right) = -\cos \theta$

12. $x = 4; y = 5$

13. Radius of circumscribed circle = 6 cm; radius of inscribed circle = 5.20 cm

14. $A = 30°$; $a = 10$ cm   **15.** $\frac{x^2}{2} + \frac{y^2}{8} = 1$

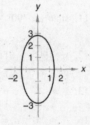

16. 8.08%   **17.** $\frac{-3 \pm \sqrt{17}}{4}$

18. Parabola: $y = -\frac{1}{12}(x - 4)^2 + 3$; directrix: $y = 6$; axis of symmetry: $x = 4$

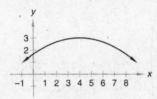

19. $y = 11 + \cos \frac{3}{4}\left(x + \frac{\pi}{3}\right)$ **20.** $y = -3 + 7 \sin \frac{2}{3}(x - 60°)$ **21.** $4 + 4\sqrt{3}i$

22. 60°, 120°, 240°, 300°   **23.** 7.5°, 52.5°, 97.5°, 142.5°, 187.5°, 232.5°, 277.5°, 322.5°

24. 1   **25.** $\frac{7\sqrt{2}}{2}$ **26.**   **27.** $\frac{5}{2}$ **28.** $\frac{17}{8}$

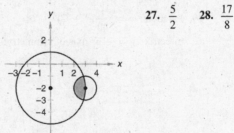

29. (a) 6   (b) 4   (c) $\frac{1}{2}$ **30.** $4x - 3 + 2h$

problem set 78

1. 126 committees   **2.** 62   **3.** 98°   **4.** $(25Q - Ka)$ cents   **5.** 2 hr
6. A: \$1000; B: \$2000

7. Vertices = $(4, 0)$; $(-4, 0)$; asymptotes: $y = \frac{1}{2}x$; $y = -\frac{1}{2}x$

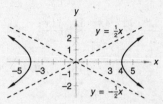

8. $\frac{y^2}{9} - \frac{x^2}{4} = 1$; vertices = $(0, 3)$; $(0, -3)$; asymptotes: $y = \frac{3}{2}x$; $y = -\frac{3}{2}x$

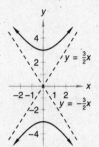

9. $a^5 + 5a^4b + 10a^3b^2 + 10a^2b^3 + 5ab^4 + b^5$ **10.** $15a^2b^4$

11. $\sin\theta \csc(90° - \theta) = \sin\theta \sec\theta = \sin\theta \dfrac{1}{\cos\theta} = \tan\theta$

12. $\sec(90° - \theta)\tan\theta = \csc\theta \tan\theta = \dfrac{1}{\sin\theta} \cdot \dfrac{\sin\theta}{\cos\theta} = \dfrac{1}{\cos\theta} = \sec\theta$

13. $x = \dfrac{29}{10}$; $y = \dfrac{11}{5}$ **14.** Side = 5 cm; radius = 8.09 cm   **15.** $\dfrac{9}{25}$

16. $A = 30°$; $a = 8.77$ m; $b = 13.44$ m

17. $\dfrac{x^2}{4} + \dfrac{y^2}{49} = 1$ **18.** $0, \dfrac{17}{2}$

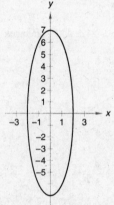

19. Parabola: $y = \dfrac{1}{40}(x + 2)^2 - 6$;

directrix: $y = -16$; axis of symmetry: $x = -2$

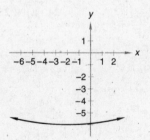

20.

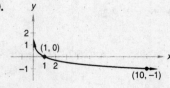

21. $(x + 1)^2 + (y + 1)^2 = (\sqrt{13})^2$; center $= (-1, -1)$; radius $= \sqrt{13}$

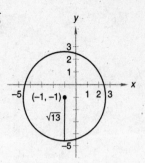

22. $y = 5 + 4 \sin \dfrac{2}{3}\left(x - \dfrac{3\pi}{2}\right)$ **23.** $3 - 3\sqrt{3}i$ **24.** $\dfrac{\pi}{3}, \pi, \dfrac{5\pi}{3}$

25. $\dfrac{\pi}{4}, \dfrac{\pi}{2}, \dfrac{3\pi}{4}, \dfrac{5\pi}{4}, \dfrac{7\pi}{4}$ **26.** (a) $120°$ (b) $-\dfrac{\pi}{3}$

27. Mean $= 3.83$; median $= 4$; mode $= 5$; variance $= 4.14$; standard deviation $= 2.03$

28. $\dfrac{13\sqrt{17}}{17}$ **29.** $2 \pm \sqrt{3}$ **30.** $\dfrac{3\sqrt{5}}{5}$

problem set 79

1. 220 committees   **2.** 20,160   **3.** \$1100   **4.** $B = 18$ mph; $W = 6$ mph   **5.** 6 days

6. $27 \operatorname{cis} 105°$ **7.** $16 + 16\sqrt{3}i$ **8.** $2 \operatorname{cis} 30°$; $2 \operatorname{cis} 150°$; $2 \operatorname{cis} 270°$ **9.** $i; -i$

10. Vertices $= (4, 0)$; $(-4, 0)$; asymptotes: $y = \dfrac{3}{4}x$; $y = -\dfrac{3}{4}x$

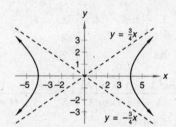

11. $\dfrac{x^2}{4} - \dfrac{y^2}{9} = 1$; vertices $= (2, 0)$; $(-2, 0)$; asymptotes: $y = \dfrac{3}{2}x$; $y = -\dfrac{3}{2}x$

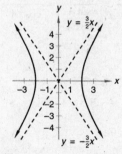

12. $x^6 + 6x^5y + 15x^4y^2 + 20x^3y^3 + 15x^2y^4 + 6xy^5 + y^6$ **13.** $126a^4b^5$

14. $\dfrac{\tan \theta}{\sec \theta} = \dfrac{\dfrac{\sin \theta}{\cos \theta}}{\dfrac{1}{\cos \theta}} = \dfrac{\sin \theta}{\cos \theta} \cdot \dfrac{\cos \theta}{1} = \sin \theta$

15. $\sin(90° - \theta)\sec(90° - \theta) = \cos \theta \csc \theta = \cos \theta \cdot \dfrac{1}{\sin \theta} = \dfrac{\cos \theta}{\sin \theta} = \cot \theta$

16. $x = \dfrac{31}{22}$; $y = -\dfrac{7}{22}$ **17.** 8.07 ft   **18.** Side $= 8$ ft; area $= 716.55$ ft^2

19. $B = 40°$; $a = 12.66$ cm; $b = 9.40$ cm

20. $\dfrac{x^2}{4} + \dfrac{y^2}{16} = 1$

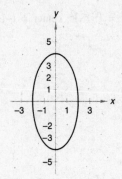

21. 30.85%   **22.** $-1, 2$

23. Parabola: $y = \dfrac{1}{16}(x + 4)^2 + 2$; directrix: $y = -2$; axis of symmetry: $x = -4$

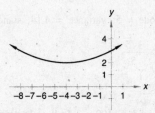

24. $y = -1 + 5\cos 3(x - 50°)$ **25.** $8i$ **26.** $45°, 135°$

27. $30°, 60°, 120°, 150°, 210°, 240°, 300°, 330°$ **28.** $\dfrac{3\sqrt{10}}{10}$ **29.** $\dfrac{7}{4}$ **30.** $y = \dfrac{5}{3}x - \dfrac{10}{3}$

problem set 80

1. 24   **2.** $(300 - hm)\,\text{mi}$ **3.** $\dfrac{1}{3}$ cup   **4.** $\dfrac{3}{2}$ hr   **5.** $\dfrac{M}{25}$ days   **6.** 728

7. $\dfrac{\sec^2 x - \tan^2 x}{1 + \cot^2 x} = \dfrac{1}{\csc^2 x} = \sin^2 x$

8. $\dfrac{\cos A}{1 + \sin A} + \dfrac{1 + \sin A}{\cos A} = \dfrac{\cos^2 A + (1 + \sin A)^2}{(1 + \sin A)\cos A} = \dfrac{\cos^2 A + 1 + 2\sin A + \sin^2 A}{(1 + \sin A)\cos A}$

$= \dfrac{2 + 2\sin A}{(1 + \sin A)\cos A} = \dfrac{2(1 + \sin A)}{(1 + \sin A)\cos A} = \dfrac{2}{\cos A} = 2\sec A$

9. $\dfrac{1}{\tan A} + \tan A = \dfrac{1 + \tan^2 A}{\tan A} = \dfrac{\sec^2 A}{\tan A} = \dfrac{\dfrac{1}{\cos^2 A}}{\dfrac{\sin A}{\cos A}} = \dfrac{1}{\cos^2 A} \cdot \dfrac{\cos A}{\sin A}$

$= \dfrac{1}{\cos A} \cdot \dfrac{1}{\sin A} = \sec A \csc A$

10. $64 \operatorname{cis} 0°$ **11.** $3 \operatorname{cis} 12°$; $3 \operatorname{cis} 132°$; $3 \operatorname{cis} 252°$

12. $\sqrt{2} + \sqrt{2}i$; $\sqrt{2} - \sqrt{2}i$; $-\sqrt{2} + \sqrt{2}i$; $-\sqrt{2} - \sqrt{2}i$

13. $\dfrac{x^2}{25} - \dfrac{y^2}{16} = 1$; vertices $= (5, 0)$; $(-5, 0)$;

asymptotes: $y = \dfrac{4}{5}x$; $y = -\dfrac{4}{5}x$

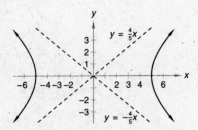

14. $a^3 + 3a^2 b + 3ab^2 + b^3$ **15.** $15x^4 y^2$

16. $x = \dfrac{23}{11}$; $y = \dfrac{15}{22}$

17. Side $= 3$ in.; area $= 118.67$ in.^{2}; radius $= 6.27$ in.

18. $C = 15°$; $b = 20.12$ in.; $c = 9.08$ in.

19. $\dfrac{x^2}{25} + \dfrac{y^2}{9} = 1$

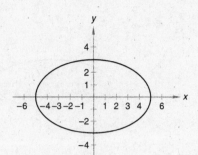

20. $\dfrac{7}{6} \pm \dfrac{\sqrt{73}}{6}$

21. Parabola: $y = \dfrac{5}{28}x^2$; directrix: $y = -\dfrac{7}{5}$; axis of symmetry: $x = 0$

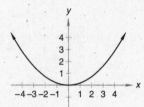

22.

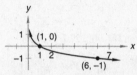

23. $(x + 1)^2 + (y - 2)^2 = \left(\dfrac{7}{3}\right)^2$; center $= (-1, 2)$; radius $= \dfrac{7}{3}$

24. $y = -4 + 6 \cos \dfrac{3}{2}(x + 110°)$ **25.** $-12i$ **26.** $\dfrac{\pi}{4}, \dfrac{7\pi}{4}$ **27.** $\dfrac{2\pi}{3}$ **28.** $-\dfrac{4}{3}$

29. $\dfrac{14}{13}$ **30.** 5

problem set 81

1. 210 teams **2.** 20 **3.** 81 and 69 **4.** 45°; 55°; 80° **5.** 6 workers

6. $B = 91.43°$; $C = 48.57°$; $a = 5.14$ in. **7.** $A = 40.54°$; $B = 111.80°$; $C = 27.66°$

8. 69 ft **9.** $\dfrac{1 - \cos^2 x}{\sec^2 x - 1} = \dfrac{\sin^2 x}{\tan^2 x} = \dfrac{\sin^2 x}{\dfrac{\sin^2 x}{\cos^2 x}} = \dfrac{\sin^2 x}{1} \cdot \dfrac{\cos^2 x}{\sin^2 x} = \cos^2 x$

10. $\dfrac{1}{1 + \sin A} + \dfrac{1}{1 - \sin A} = \dfrac{1 - \sin A + 1 + \sin A}{(1 + \sin A)(1 - \sin A)} = \dfrac{2}{1 - \sin^2 A} = \dfrac{2}{\cos^2 A} = 2 \sec^2 A$

11. $-8i$ **12.** 2 cis 15°; 2 cis 135°; 2 cis 255°

13. $\dfrac{3\sqrt{2}}{2} + \dfrac{3\sqrt{2}}{2}i$; $-\dfrac{3\sqrt{2}}{2} + \dfrac{3\sqrt{2}}{2}i$; $-\dfrac{3\sqrt{2}}{2} - \dfrac{3\sqrt{2}}{2}i$; $\dfrac{3\sqrt{2}}{2} - \dfrac{3\sqrt{2}}{2}i$

14. $\dfrac{x^2}{25} - \dfrac{y^2}{4} = 1$; vertices $= (5, 0)$; $(-5, 0)$;

asymptotes: $y = \dfrac{2}{5}x$; $y = -\dfrac{2}{5}x$

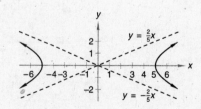

15. $m^4 + 4m^3 n + 6m^2 n^2 + 4mn^3 + n^4$ **16.** $35x^4 y^3$

17. Area $= 100.77$ in.^{2}; radius $= 5.80$ in.

18. $\dfrac{x^2}{25} + \dfrac{y^2}{4} = 1$

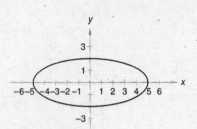

19. 44.35%

20. Parabola: $y = -\dfrac{1}{16}(x - 4)^2 + 2$;

directrix: $y = 6$; axis of symmetry: $x = 4$

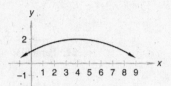

21.

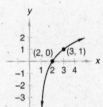

22. $y = 10 + 2 \sin \dfrac{9}{8}(\theta - 90°)$ **23.** $4 - 4\sqrt{3}i$

24. 50°, 110°, 170°, 230°, 290°, 350°   **25.** 90°, 270°   **26.** $\dfrac{3}{5}$

27.

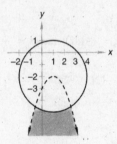

28. $\dfrac{10}{11}$ **29.** $\dfrac{11}{10}$ **30.** $\dfrac{1}{4}$

**problem set
82**

1. 38,798,760 patterns   **2.** 22, 33, 44   **3.** Height = 8 ft; length = 6 ft; width = 4 ft

4. $(t - rh)$ miles   **5.** 35 days   **6.** $\dfrac{39b}{ab + 9}$ days   **7.** −1.91   **8.** −0.75

9. $B = 74.74°$; $C = 60.26°$; $a = 7.33$ cm   **10.** $A = 51.32°$; $B = 110.49°$; $C = 18.19°$

11. $\dfrac{\sin A}{1 + \cos A} + \dfrac{1 + \cos A}{\sin A} = \dfrac{\sin^2 A + (1 + \cos A)^2}{(1 + \cos A)\sin A} = \dfrac{\sin^2 A + 1 + 2\cos A + \cos^2 A}{(1 + \cos A)\sin A}$

$= \dfrac{2 + 2\cos A}{(1 + \cos A)\sin A} = \dfrac{2(1 + \cos A)}{(1 + \cos A)\sin A} = \dfrac{2}{\sin A} = 2\csc A$

12. $\dfrac{\csc^2 \theta - \cot^2 \theta}{1 + \cot^2 \theta} = \dfrac{1}{\csc^2 \theta} = \sin^2 \theta$

13. $\dfrac{\sin x}{\csc x} + \dfrac{\cos x}{\sec x} = \dfrac{\sin x}{\dfrac{1}{\sin x}} + \dfrac{\cos x}{\dfrac{1}{\cos x}} = \sin^2 x + \cos^2 x = 1$ **14.** $1 \operatorname{cis} 0°$

15. $2 \operatorname{cis} 15°$; $2 \operatorname{cis} 105°$; $2 \operatorname{cis} 195°$; $2 \operatorname{cis} 285°$ **16.** $\dfrac{1}{2} + \dfrac{\sqrt{3}}{2}i$; -1; $\dfrac{1}{2} - \dfrac{\sqrt{3}}{2}i$

17. $\dfrac{x^2}{36} - \dfrac{y^2}{9} = 1$; vertices = $(6, 0)$; $(-6, 0)$; asymptotes: $y = \dfrac{1}{2}x$; $y = -\dfrac{1}{2}x$

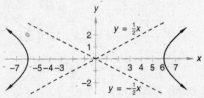

18. $p^5 + 5p^4q + 10p^3q^2 + 10p^2q^3 + 5pq^4 + q^5$ **19.** $252x^5$

20. Radius of circumscribed circle = 6.74; radius of inscribed circle = 6.57

21. $\dfrac{x^2}{36} + \dfrac{y^2}{9} = 1$

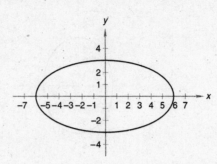

22. Parabola: $y = \dfrac{1}{24}x^2$; directrix: $y = -6$; axis of symmetry: $x = 0$

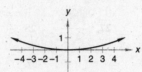

23. $(x + 1)^2 + (y - 3)^2 = \left(\dfrac{\sqrt{38}}{2}\right)^2$; center = $(-1, 3)$; radius = $\dfrac{\sqrt{38}}{2}$

24. $y = 2 + 9 \sin 4\left(x - \dfrac{\pi}{8}\right)$ **25.** $\dfrac{\pi}{6}, \dfrac{5\pi}{6}, \dfrac{7\pi}{6}, \dfrac{11\pi}{6}$ **26.** $\dfrac{\pi}{4}, \dfrac{3\pi}{4}, \dfrac{5\pi}{4}, \dfrac{7\pi}{4}$

27. Mean = $\dfrac{2}{3}$; median = 0; mode = 0; variance = 3.56; standard deviation = 1.89

28. $\dfrac{2\sqrt{5}}{5}$ **29.** $\dfrac{18}{5}$ **30.** 51.38%

**problem set
83**

1. 82.75 ft   **2.** \$130   **3.** $\dfrac{Mk}{J(M - 5)}$ days   **4.** $\dfrac{1}{6}$ **5.** $\dfrac{60}{289}$ **6.** $\dfrac{15}{68}$

7. -11.75 **8.** -1.95 **9.** $B = 79.11°$; $C = 40.89°$; $a = 10.58$ in.

10. $A = 44.41°$; $B = 101.54°$; $C = 34.05°$

11. $\dfrac{\sin A}{1 - \cos A} + \dfrac{1 - \cos A}{\sin A} = \dfrac{\sin^2 A + (1 - \cos A)^2}{(1 - \cos A)\sin A} = \dfrac{\sin^2 A + 1 - 2\cos A + \cos^2 A}{(1 - \cos A)\sin A}$

$= \dfrac{2 - 2\cos A}{(1 - \cos A)\sin A} = \dfrac{2(1 - \cos A)}{(1 - \cos A)\sin A} = \dfrac{2}{\sin A} = 2\csc A$

12. $\dfrac{\sec^2 \theta - \tan^2 \theta}{\tan^2 \theta + 1} = \dfrac{1}{\sec^2 \theta} = \cos^2 \theta$

13. $\dfrac{1}{\tan(-x)} + \tan(-x) = \dfrac{1}{-\tan x} - \tan x = \dfrac{-1 - \tan^2 x}{\tan x} = \dfrac{-(1 + \tan^2 x)}{\tan x} = \dfrac{-\sec^2 x}{\tan x}$

$= \dfrac{-\dfrac{1}{\cos^2 x}}{\dfrac{\sin x}{\cos x}} = -\dfrac{1}{\cos^2 x} \cdot \dfrac{\cos x}{\sin x} = -\dfrac{1}{\cos x} \cdot \dfrac{1}{\sin x} = -\sec x \csc x$

14. $-32i$ **15.** 2 cis 12°; 2 cis 84°; 2 cis 156°; 2 cis 228°; 2 cis 300°   **16.** 1; i; -1; $-i$

17. $\dfrac{y^2}{16} - \dfrac{x^2}{9} = 1$; vertices = $(0, 4)$; $(0, -4)$;

asymptotes: $y = \dfrac{4}{3}x$; $y = -\dfrac{4}{3}x$

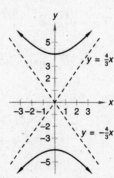

18. $20x^3z^3$ **19.** $x = -2;\ y = 3$ **20.** Area $= 716.55\ \text{cm}^2;$ radius $= 14.93\ \text{cm}$

21. $\dfrac{x^2}{9} + \dfrac{y^2}{16} = 1$ **22.** $y = -8 + 6\cos\dfrac{9}{2}(x - 30°)$

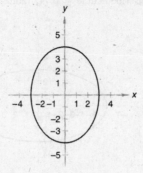

23. $0°, 120°, 240°$ **24.** $15°, 75°, 195°, 255°$ **25.** $-\dfrac{3}{4}$

26.   **27.** $\dfrac{7\sqrt{13}}{13}$ **28.** $\dfrac{2}{3}$

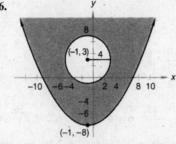

29. 3 **30.** $\left(x - 3\sqrt{3}i\right)\left(x + 3\sqrt{3}i\right)$

problem set 84

1. $\dfrac{1}{8}$ **2.** (a) $\dfrac{16}{49}$ (b) $\dfrac{2}{7}$ **3.** $40°$ **4.** $\dfrac{k}{p + m}\,\dfrac{\text{yd}}{\text{min}}$ **5.** $\dfrac{10k}{3p}$ days **6.** 2 jobs

7.   **8.**

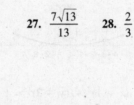

9. $\dfrac{\csc^4 x - \cot^4 x}{\csc^2 x + \cot^2 x} + \cot^2 x = \dfrac{\left(\csc^2 x + \cot^2 x\right)\left(\csc^2 x - \cot^2 x\right)}{\csc^2 x + \cot^2 x} + \cot^2 x$

$= \csc^2 x - \cot^2 x + \cot^2 x = \csc^2 x$

10. $\cos x - \cos x \sin^2 x = \cos x\left(1 - \sin^2 x\right) = \cos x \cos^2 x = \cos^3 x$

11. $\dfrac{\sec^2 \theta - 1}{\cot \theta} = \dfrac{\tan^2 \theta}{\cot \theta} = \dfrac{\tan^2 \theta}{\dfrac{1}{\tan \theta}} = \tan^3 \theta$

12. $\cos(-\theta)\csc(-\theta) = \cos \theta(-\csc \theta) = \cos \theta\left(-\dfrac{1}{\sin \theta}\right) = -\dfrac{\cos \theta}{\sin \theta} = -\cot \theta = \cot(-\theta)$

13. 1.22 **14.** 4.15 **15.** $A = 44.05°;\ B = 83.33°;\ C = 52.62°$ **16.** $q = 16.34\ \text{cm}$

17. $\dfrac{1}{8}\operatorname{cis} 300°$ **18.** $\sqrt{3} + i;\ -1 + \sqrt{3}i;\ 1 - \sqrt{3}i;\ -\sqrt{3} - i$ **19.** $2;\ -1 + \sqrt{3}i;\ -1 - \sqrt{3}i$

20. $\dfrac{x^2}{100} - \dfrac{y^2}{16} = 1;$ vertices $= (10, 0);\ (-10, 0);$ asymptotes: $y = \dfrac{2}{5}x;\ y = -\dfrac{2}{5}x$

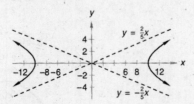

21. $a^7 + 7a^6c + 21a^5c^2 + 35a^4c^3 + 35a^3c^4 + 21a^2c^5 + 7ac^6 + c^7$

22. Radius $= 9.71$ cm; area $= 276.99$ cm^2

23. $\dfrac{x^2}{25} + \dfrac{y^2}{2} = 1$

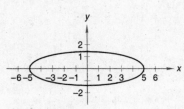

24. $(x + 3)^2 + (y - 2)^2 = \left(\sqrt{28}\right)^2$; center $= (-3, 2)$; radius $= 2\sqrt{7}$

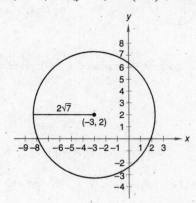

25. 10   **26.** No solution   **27.** $\dfrac{\pi}{6}, \dfrac{5\pi}{6}, \dfrac{7\pi}{6}, \dfrac{11\pi}{6}$ **28.** $\dfrac{\sqrt{10}}{10}$ **29.** $\sqrt{2}$ **30.** 24.20%

**problem set
85**

1. $32\dfrac{8}{11}$ min   **2.** $49\dfrac{1}{11}$ min   **3.** 100 mi   **4.** $\dfrac{4}{7}$ **5.** $\dfrac{7}{18}$

6. 120 seating arrangements   **7.** 167.13 ft   **8.** 4, 6, 8   **9.** 60°, 300°

10. 120°, 180°, 240°   **11.** 0°

12.   **13.**

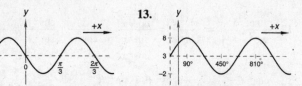

14. $\dfrac{\cos^4 x - \sin^4 x}{\cos^2 x - \sin^2 x} = \dfrac{(\cos^2 x - \sin^2 x)(\cos^2 x + \sin^2 x)}{\cos^2 x - \sin^2 x} = \cos^2 x + \sin^2 x = 1$

15. $\tan x + \cot x = \dfrac{\sin x}{\cos x} + \dfrac{\cos x}{\sin x} = \dfrac{\sin^2 x + \cos^2 x}{\cos x \sin x} = \dfrac{1}{\cos x \sin x} = \sec x \csc x$

16. $\dfrac{1}{1 + \cos x} + \dfrac{1}{1 - \cos x} = \dfrac{1 - \cos x + 1 + \cos x}{1 - \cos^2 x} = \dfrac{2}{\sin^2 x} = 2\csc^2 x$

17. 3.46   **18.** 28.05   **19.** $A = 101.54°$; $B = 44.42°$; $C = 34.04°$

20. $p = 16.93$ cm; area $= 25.71$ cm^2 **21.** $-8 + 8\sqrt{3}i$

22. $1 + \sqrt{3}i$; $-\sqrt{3} + i$; $-1 - \sqrt{3}i$; $\sqrt{3} - i$

23. $\dfrac{y^2}{36} - \dfrac{x^2}{16} = 1$;
vertices $= (0, 6)$; $(0, -6)$;

asymptotes: $y = \dfrac{3}{2}x$; $y = -\dfrac{3}{2}x$

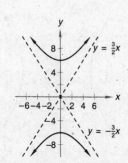

24. $x = \dfrac{16}{7}$; $y = \dfrac{20}{7}$ **25.** Area $= 77.25$ cm^2; radius $= 5.23$ cm

26. $\dfrac{x^2}{8} + \dfrac{y^2}{18} = 1$ **27.** $-18i$

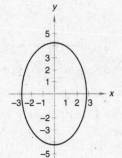

28. Mean $= 0$; median $= 0$; mode $= -2$; variance $= 3.60$; standard deviation $= 1.90$

29. $-\dfrac{6}{11}$ **30.** 5.33 cm^2

problem set 86

1. $16\dfrac{4}{11}$ minutes   **2.** $\dfrac{13}{68}$ **3.** $\dfrac{5}{18}$ **4.** $O = 4I + 5$ **5.** $112\dfrac{16}{17}$ km   **6.** 2, 4, and 6

7. $-10, -4, 2, 8, 14$ **8.** -111 **9.** $-1, -5, -9$ **10.** $-93, -86, -79, -72, -65$

11. $9x + 10y$ **12.** $\dfrac{7\pi}{6}, \dfrac{3\pi}{2}, \dfrac{11\pi}{6}$ **13.** 0 **14.** $\dfrac{5\pi}{3}$

15.   **16.**

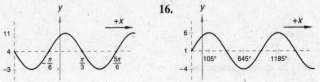

17. $\dfrac{\sec^2 x}{\sec^2 x - 1} = \dfrac{\sec^2 x}{\tan^2 x} = \dfrac{\frac{1}{\cos^2 x}}{\frac{\sin^2 x}{\cos^2 x}} = \dfrac{1}{\cos^2 x} \cdot \dfrac{\cos^2 x}{\sin^2 x} = \dfrac{1}{\sin^2 x} = \csc^2 x$

18. $\dfrac{\cos^2 \theta}{\sin \theta} + \sin \theta = \dfrac{\cos^2 \theta + \sin^2 \theta}{\sin \theta} = \dfrac{1}{\sin \theta} = \csc \theta$

19. $\dfrac{\cos(-x)}{\sin(-x)\cot(-x)} = \dfrac{\cos x}{(-\sin x)(-\cot x)} = \dfrac{\cos x}{\sin x\left(\dfrac{\cos x}{\sin x}\right)} = 1$

20. 1.44 **21.** 1 **22.** 5.39 m

23. $A = 83.33°$; $B = 52.62°$; $C = 44.05°$ **24.** $2i$; $-\sqrt{3} - i$; $\sqrt{3} - i$

25. $\dfrac{x^2}{9} - \dfrac{y^2}{16} = 1$; vertices $= (3, 0)$; $(-3, 0)$; asymptotes: $y = \dfrac{4}{3}x$; $y = -\dfrac{4}{3}x$

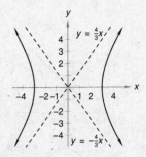

26. $r^3 + 3r^2 s + 3rs^2 + s^3$ **27.** Yes, percentile $= 0.9332$

28.

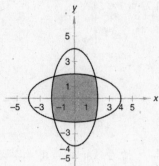

29. $2\sqrt{2}$ **30.** $\dfrac{24}{5}$

problem set 87

1. $27\dfrac{3}{11}$ min   **2.** $\dfrac{13}{36}$ **3.** (a) $\dfrac{2}{27}$ (b) $\dfrac{1}{12}$ **4.** 360 km   **5.** $\dfrac{x}{y-k}\dfrac{\text{yd}}{\text{min}}$

6. 18, 21, 24   **7.** $\dfrac{\sqrt{6}-\sqrt{2}}{4}$ **8.** $\dfrac{\sqrt{2}}{2}(\cos\theta+\sin\theta)$ **9.** Refer to Lesson 87.

10. $2+\sqrt{3}$ **11.** -21 **12.** 26, 46, 66, 86   **13.** 3, 7, 11, 15   **14.** 270°

15. 0°, 60°, 300°   **16.** 60°, 120°, 240°, 300°

17.   **18.**

   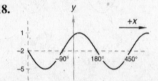

19. $\sec x + \sec x \tan^2 x = \sec x\left(1+\tan^2 x\right) = \sec x \sec^2 x = \sec^3 x$

20. $\dfrac{\sin^2 x}{\cos x} + \cos x = \dfrac{\sin^2 x + \cos^2 x}{\cos x} = \dfrac{1}{\cos x} = \sec x$

21. $\dfrac{\tan(-\theta)\cos(-\theta)}{\sin(-\theta)} = \dfrac{-\tan\theta\cos\theta}{-\sin\theta} = \dfrac{\dfrac{\sin\theta}{\cos\theta}\cdot\cos\theta}{\sin\theta} = \dfrac{\sin\theta}{\sin\theta} = 1$

22. 0.60   **23.** -2.85 **24.** $B = 64.89°$; $C = 95.11°$; $a = 3.78$ cm

25. 2 cis 10°; 2 cis 100°; 2 cis 190°; 2 cis 280°

26. $\dfrac{y^2}{4} - \dfrac{x^2}{25} = 1$; vertices $= (0,2)$; $(0,-2)$; asymptotes: $y = \dfrac{2}{5}x$; $y = -\dfrac{2}{5}x$

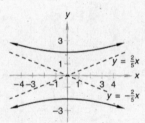

27. $x = -\dfrac{44}{23}$; $y = -\dfrac{49}{23}$ **28.** Area $= 64.95$ in.^{2}; radius $= 4.33$ in.   **29.** 4   **30.** $\dfrac{9}{7}$

problem set 88

1. $A_t = 400e^{0.23t}$; 6320 bacteria

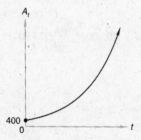

2. $A_t = 40e^{-0.014t}$; 9.86 grams

3. $A_t = 100e^{-0.40t}$; half-life $= 1.73$ yr

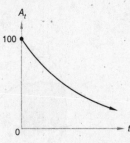

4. 3:16:22   **5.** $\dfrac{25}{102}$ **6.** $\dfrac{1}{36}$ **7.** 2, 3, 4, 5   **8.** $\dfrac{\sqrt{6} - \sqrt{2}}{4}$

9. $\dfrac{\sqrt{3}}{2} \sin \theta - \dfrac{1}{2} \cos \theta$ **10.** Refer to Lesson 87.   **11.** –74   **12.** 6, 4, 2

13. $\dfrac{\pi}{6}, \dfrac{2\pi}{3}, \dfrac{7\pi}{6}, \dfrac{5\pi}{3}$ **14.** $0, \dfrac{\pi}{4}, \pi, \dfrac{5\pi}{4}$ **15.** $0, \dfrac{\pi}{2}, \pi, \dfrac{3\pi}{2}$

16.   **17.**

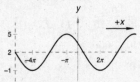

18. $\dfrac{\cos \theta}{1 - \sin \theta} - \dfrac{\cos \theta}{1 + \sin \theta} = \dfrac{\cos \theta(1 + \sin \theta) - \cos \theta(1 - \sin \theta)}{1 - \sin^2\theta}$

$= \dfrac{2 \cos \theta \sin \theta}{\cos^2\theta} = \dfrac{2 \sin \theta}{\cos \theta} = 2 \tan \theta$

19. $(1 - \sin \theta)(1 + \sin \theta) = 1 - \sin^2 \theta = \cos^2 \theta$

20. $\dfrac{\cos^3 x + \sin^3 x}{\cos x + \sin x} = \dfrac{(\cos x + \sin x)(\cos^2 x - \sin x \cos x + \sin^2 x)}{\cos x + \sin x} = 1 - \sin x \cos x$

21. $\dfrac{5}{3}$ **22.** 0.12   **23.** $a = 14.73$ m; area $= 31.18$ m^2

24. 3 cis 10°; 3 cis 130°; 3 cis 250°   **25.** $x = \dfrac{22}{17}$; $y = \dfrac{8}{17}$

26. Area of pentagon $= 61.94$ cm^2; area of circle $= 81.84$ cm^2 **27.** Yes, percentile $= 0.9713$

28. $-\dfrac{14}{27}$ **29.** 2   **30.** 75

**problem set
89**

1. $A_t = 40e^{0.65t}$; 7251 rabbits

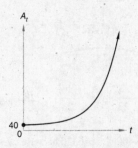

2. $A_t = 40{,}000e^{-0.029t}$; 23.90 hr

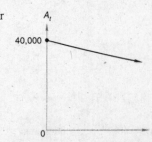

3. $10\dfrac{10}{11}$ min   **4.** $\dfrac{13}{34}$

5. $\dfrac{3}{49}$ **6.** 4, 6, 8   **7.** $\dfrac{x^2}{16} + \dfrac{y^2}{7} = 1$

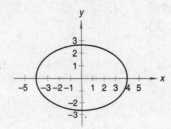

8. $\dfrac{x^2}{24} + \dfrac{y^2}{49} = 1$

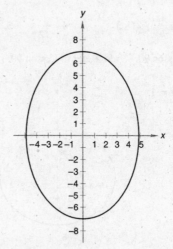

9. $\dfrac{x^2}{4} + \dfrac{y^2}{25} = 1$ **10.** $-\cos x$ **11.** $2 + \sqrt{3}$ **12.** $2 - \sqrt{3}$

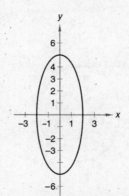

13. -42 **14.** $2, -4, -10, -16$ **15.** $60°, 150°, 240°, 330°$ **16.** $120°, 240°$

17. $52.5°, 82.5°, 142.5°, 172.5°, 232.5°, 262.5°, 322.5°, 352.5°$

18.   **19.**

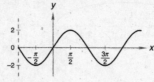   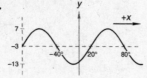

20. $\dfrac{\sin\theta}{1-\cos\theta} - \dfrac{\sin\theta}{1+\cos\theta} = \dfrac{\sin\theta(1+\cos\theta) - \sin\theta(1-\cos\theta)}{1-\cos^2\theta} = \dfrac{2\sin\theta\cos\theta}{\sin^2\theta}$

$= \dfrac{2\cos\theta}{\sin\theta} = 2\cot\theta$

21. $\dfrac{\tan^3 x + 1}{\tan x + 1} = \dfrac{(\tan x + 1)(\tan^2 x - \tan x + 1)}{\tan x + 1} = \sec^2 x - \tan x$

22. $-\dfrac{6}{7}$ **23.** 0 **24.** $9.06°$ **25.** -1 **26.** $-2\sqrt{2} + 2\sqrt{2}i;\ 2\sqrt{2} - 2\sqrt{2}i$

27. Radius of circumscribed circle $= 4.25$ cm; radius of inscribed circle $= 3.44$ cm

28. $\dfrac{1}{2}$ **29.** $\dfrac{101}{100}$ **30.** $4x^4 + 4x^2 + 2$

problem set 90

1. $A_0 = 80$; $k = 0.80$; $A_t = 80e^{0.80t}$; $t = 4.02$ yr

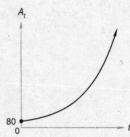

2. $A_t = 2000e^{-0.35t}$ **3.** $\dfrac{1}{16}$ **4.** $\dfrac{1}{72}$ **5.** $\dfrac{1}{2}$ **6.** \$170   **7.** Refer to Lesson 90.

8. Refer to Lesson 90.   **9.** Refer to Lesson 90.

10. $\dfrac{x^2}{25} + \dfrac{y^2}{16} = 1$

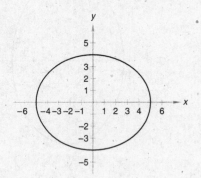

11. $\dfrac{x^2}{48} + \dfrac{y^2}{64} = 1$

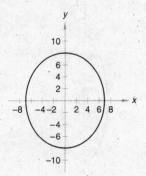

12. $\dfrac{x^2}{36} + \dfrac{y^2}{4} = 1$

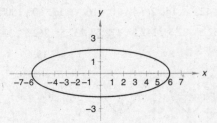

13. $\dfrac{\sqrt{6} + \sqrt{2}}{4}$ **14.** 38   **15.** $-4, -6, -8$ **16.** $\dfrac{\pi}{6}, \dfrac{5\pi}{6}$ **17.** $\dfrac{\pi}{3}, \dfrac{2\pi}{3}, \dfrac{4\pi}{3}, \dfrac{5\pi}{3}$

18.

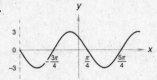

19.

20. $\sec^2 x \sin^2 x + \sin^2 x \csc^2 x = \dfrac{1}{\cos^2 x} \sin^2 x + \sin^2 x \dfrac{1}{\sin^2 x} = \tan^2 x + 1 = \sec^2 x$

21. $\sin^2 \theta + \tan^2 \theta + \cos^2 \theta = 1 + \tan^2 \theta = \sec^2 \theta$ **22.** $82.82°$ **23.** $x = -\dfrac{10}{13}$; $y = -\dfrac{14}{13}$

24.

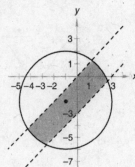

25. 2   **26.** -2.60   **27.** 2   **28.** 7

29. (a) $\frac{1}{4}$ (b) 3   **30.** 2.28%

problem set 91

1. $43\frac{7}{11}$ min   **2.** 16,000 marbles   **3.** $\frac{1}{54}$

4. $A_0 = 30$; $k = 1.13$; $A_t = 30e^{1.13t}$

5. $A_t = 42e^{-0.18t}$; $t = 1.87$ yr   **6.** 12 hr   **7.** 128   **8.** 12, 36

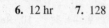

9. 4, 8, 16 or -4, 8, -16   **10.** Refer to Lesson 90.   **11.** $\frac{\sqrt{2-\sqrt{3}}}{2}$ **12.** Refer to Lesson 90.

13. $\frac{\sqrt{2+\sqrt{3}}}{2}$ **14.** $\frac{x^2}{36} + \frac{y^2}{32} = 1$

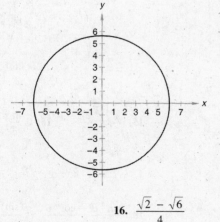

15. $\frac{x^2}{25} + \frac{y^2}{49} = 1$ **16.** $\frac{\sqrt{2}-\sqrt{6}}{4}$

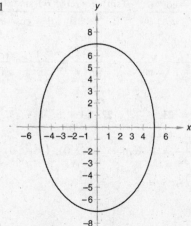

17. 6, 2, -2, -6   **18.** 60°, 300°   **19.** 50°, 70°, 170°, 190°, 290°, 310°

20. 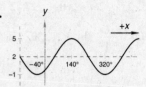   **21.**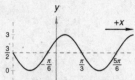

22. $\dfrac{1 - \cos^2 \theta}{1 + \tan^2 \theta} = \dfrac{\sin^2 \theta}{\sec^2 \theta} = \sin^2 \theta \cos^2 \theta$

23. $\csc^2 y \sec^2 y - \sec^2 y = \sec^2 y \left(\csc^2 y - 1\right) = \sec^2 y \cot^2 y$

$= \dfrac{1}{\cos^2 y} \cdot \dfrac{\cos^2 y}{\sin^2 y} = \dfrac{1}{\sin^2 y} = \csc^2 y$

24. $A = 26.27°$; $B = 23.73°$ **25.** Radius $= 8$ in.; area $= 166.28$ in.^{2} **26.** $\dfrac{3\sqrt{10}}{10}$

27. $\dfrac{21}{8}$ **28.** $\dfrac{3}{25}$ **29.** $\dfrac{1}{2}$ **30.** 0

problem set 92

1. $16\dfrac{4}{11}$ min   **2.** $A_t = 10{,}000e^{-0.0026t}$; 266.60 min   **3.** $A_t = 100e^{0.38t}$; 7.88 mo

4. 7 **5.** $6, 8, 10$ **6.** $\dfrac{7}{13}$ **7.** $_8P_5 = \dfrac{8!}{3!} = 6720$; $_8C_5 = \dfrac{8!}{3!5!} = 56$ **8.** $-\dfrac{1}{4}$

9. $-4, 8$ **10.** Refer to Lesson 90.   **11.** $\dfrac{\sqrt{2 - \sqrt{3}}}{2}$ **12.** $-\sin x$

13. $\dfrac{x^2}{16} + \dfrac{y^2}{25} = 1$ **14.** $-8, -6, -4, -2$

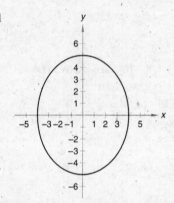

15. $\dfrac{\pi}{3}, \pi, \dfrac{5\pi}{3}$ **16.** $0, \dfrac{\pi}{3}, \dfrac{2\pi}{3}, \pi, \dfrac{4\pi}{3}, \dfrac{5\pi}{3}$ **17.**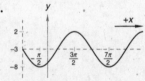

18. $\dfrac{\sin^4 \theta - \cos^4 \theta}{\sin^2 \theta - \cos^2 \theta} = \dfrac{\left(\sin^2 \theta + \cos^2 \theta\right)\left(\sin^2 \theta - \cos^2 \theta\right)}{\sin^2 \theta - \cos^2 \theta} = \sin^2 \theta + \cos^2 \theta = 1$

19. $\dfrac{\sec^2 x}{\sec^2 x - 1} = \dfrac{\sec^2 x}{\tan^2 x} = \dfrac{\dfrac{1}{\cos^2 x}}{\dfrac{\sin^2 x}{\cos^2 x}} = \dfrac{1}{\cos^2 x} \cdot \dfrac{\cos^2 x}{\sin^2 x} = \dfrac{1}{\sin^2 x} = \csc^2 x$

20. $44.36°$ **21.** $\dfrac{32}{3}$ **22.** $\sqrt{3} + i$; $-1 + \sqrt{3}i$; $-\sqrt{3} - i$; $1 - \sqrt{3}i$

23. $\dfrac{x^2}{50} - \dfrac{y^2}{32} = 1$; vertices: $\left(5\sqrt{2}, 0\right)$; $\left(-5\sqrt{2}, 0\right)$

asymptotes: $y = \dfrac{4}{5}x$; $y = -\dfrac{4}{5}x$

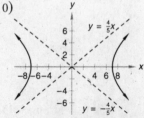

24. Area = 123.11 cm²; perimeter = 38.68 cm   **25.** No, Smith is not in the top 5%.

26. $\dfrac{9}{8}$ **27.** $\dfrac{11}{7}$ **28.** 1   **29.** 3   **30.** (a) $\dfrac{1}{25}$ (b) 25

**problem set
93**

1. $\dfrac{7}{9}$ **2.** $A_t = 400e^{-0.0096t}$; 72.20 hr   **3.** 5120   **4.** $4:27\dfrac{3}{11}$

5. $_9P_6 = \dfrac{9!}{3!} = 60{,}480$; $_9C_6 = \dfrac{9!}{3!6!} = 84$

6. $\dfrac{1 + \sin B}{\cos B} \cdot \dfrac{(1 - \sin B)}{(1 - \sin B)} = \dfrac{1 - \sin^2 B}{\cos B(1 - \sin B)} = \dfrac{\cos^2 B}{\cos B(1 - \sin B)} = \dfrac{\cos B}{1 - \sin B}$

7. $\dfrac{\tan B + 1}{\tan B - 1} = \dfrac{\dfrac{\sin B}{\cos B} + 1}{\dfrac{\sin B}{\cos B} - 1} \cdot \dfrac{\dfrac{1}{\sin B}}{\dfrac{1}{\sin B}} = \dfrac{\dfrac{1}{\cos B} + \dfrac{1}{\sin B}}{\dfrac{1}{\cos B} - \dfrac{1}{\sin B}} = \dfrac{\sec B + \csc B}{\sec B - \csc B}$

8. $(y \sin \theta + x \cos \theta)^2 + (y \cos \theta - x \sin \theta)^2$

$= y^2 \sin^2 \theta + 2yx \sin \theta \cos \theta + x^2 \cos^2 \theta + y^2 \cos^2 \theta - 2yx \cos \theta \sin \theta + x^2 \sin^2 \theta$

$= y^2 \sin^2 \theta + y^2 \cos^2 \theta + x^2 \cos^2 \theta + x^2 \sin^2 \theta$

$= y^2(\sin^2 \theta + \cos^2 \theta) + x^2(\cos^2 \theta + \sin^2 \theta) = x^2 + y^2$

9. 6, 18, 54 or –6, 18, –54   **10.** 20, 18, 16, 14   **11.** Refer to Lesson 90.

12. $\dfrac{\sqrt{2}}{2}(\sin x - \cos x)$ **13.** $\dfrac{-\sqrt{6} - \sqrt{2}}{4}$

14. $\dfrac{x^2}{9} + \dfrac{y^2}{16} = 1$

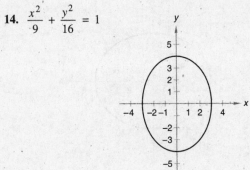

15. 120°, 240°   **16.** 40°, 100°, 160°, 220°, 280°, 340°

17.   **18.**

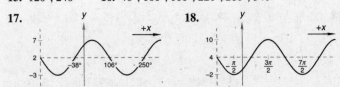

19. 4.50 cm   **20.** 2 cis 4°; 2 cis 76°; 2 cis 148°; 2 cis 220°; 2 cis 292°

21. $\dfrac{x^2}{8} - \dfrac{y^2}{18} = 1$; vertices = $(2\sqrt{2}, 0)$; $(-2\sqrt{2}, 0)$; asymptotes: $y = \dfrac{3}{2}x$; $y = -\dfrac{3}{2}x$

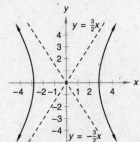

22. $x = \dfrac{6}{23}$; $y = \dfrac{67}{23}$ **23.** 4   **24.** $\dfrac{10}{3}$ **25.** $-\dfrac{13}{5}$ **26.** $\dfrac{5}{18}$ **27.** $-\dfrac{1}{2}$

28. (a) 36   (b) $\dfrac{1}{36}$ **29.** $\left(x + \dfrac{9}{2} + \dfrac{\sqrt{59}}{2}i\right)\left(x + \dfrac{9}{2} - \dfrac{\sqrt{59}}{2}i\right)$ **30.** 4.46%

**problem set
94**

1. $\dfrac{4}{5}$ **2.** $A_t = 4e^{0.20t}$ **3.** 1622.15 yr   **4.** 907,200   **5.** $\dfrac{180X}{PY}$ days

6. Refer to Lesson 94.   **7.** (a) $y = 4 + 4\sec x$ (b) $y = -2 + 4\csc x$

8. $\dfrac{1 + \cos x}{\sin x} \cdot \dfrac{(1 - \cos x)}{(1 - \cos x)} = \dfrac{1 - \cos^2 x}{\sin x(1 - \cos x)} = \dfrac{\sin^2 x}{\sin x(1 - \cos x)} = \dfrac{\sin x}{1 - \cos x}$

9. $\dfrac{\tan B + 1}{\tan B - 1} = \dfrac{\dfrac{\sin B}{\cos B} + 1}{\dfrac{\sin B}{\cos B} - 1} \cdot \dfrac{\dfrac{1}{\sin B}}{\dfrac{1}{\sin B}} = \dfrac{\dfrac{1}{\cos B} + \dfrac{1}{\sin B}}{\dfrac{1}{\cos B} - \dfrac{1}{\sin B}} = \dfrac{\sec B + \csc B}{\sec B - \csc B}$

10. $(1 + \sin x)^2 + (1 - \sin x)^2 = 1 + 2\sin x + \sin^2 x + 1 - 2\sin x + \sin^2 x = 2 + 2\sin^2 x$

$= 2(1 + \sin^2 x) = 2\left[1 + (1 - \cos^2 x)\right] = 2(2 - \cos^2 x) = 4 - 2\cos^2 x$

11. Refer to Lesson 90.   **12.** $\dfrac{\sqrt{2 + \sqrt{3}}}{2}$ **13.** $\dfrac{\sqrt{6} - \sqrt{2}}{4}$ **14.** $-\cos x$

15. $\dfrac{7\pi}{6}, \dfrac{11\pi}{6}$ **16.** $\dfrac{2\pi}{3}$ **17.**

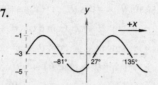

18. 7.21 ft

19. 3 cis 6°; 3 cis 96°; 3 cis 186°; 3 cis 276°   **20.** 4, −8   **21.** −2, 1, 4

22. $\dfrac{x^2}{25} + \dfrac{y^2}{16} = 1$

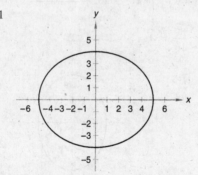

23. Perimeter = 120 in.; area = 1039.23 in.^{2} **24.** $\dfrac{3}{5}$ **25.** 7.84   **26.** 2   **27.** $\sqrt{2}$

28. (a) $\dfrac{1}{8}$ (b) $\dfrac{1}{9}$ **29.** $(x + 5 - \sqrt{5}i)(x + 5 + \sqrt{5}i)$ **30.** $\dfrac{9}{2}$

**problem set
95**

1. $\dfrac{1}{6}$ **2.** $\dfrac{1}{50}$ **3.** 249.04 min   **4.** 1226.75 min   **5.** 60 liters

6. 1.50 cis 13.28°; 1.50 cis 103.28°; 1.50 cis 193.28°; 1.50 cis 283.28°

7. 1.53 cis 18.77°; 1.53 cis 138.77°; 1.53 cis 258.77°

8.

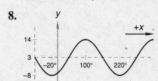

9. (a)   (b)

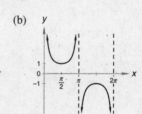

10. (a) $y = \tan \theta$ (b) $y = \cot \theta$

11. $\dfrac{\sin x}{1 + \cos x} + \dfrac{1 + \cos x}{\sin x} = \dfrac{\sin^2 x + (1 + \cos x)^2}{(1 + \cos x)\sin x} = \dfrac{\sin^2 x + 1 + 2\cos x + \cos^2 x}{(1 + \cos x)\sin x}$

$= \dfrac{2 + 2\cos x}{(1 + \cos x)\sin x} = \dfrac{2(1 + \cos x)}{(1 + \cos x)\sin x} = 2\csc x$

12. $(1 + \tan x)^2 = 1 + 2\tan x + \tan^2 x = \sec^2 x + 2\tan x$

13. $\dfrac{\sin^4 x - \cos^4 x}{2\sin^2 x - 1} = \dfrac{(\sin^2 x + \cos^2 x)(\sin^2 x - \cos^2 x)}{2\sin^2 x - 1} = \dfrac{\sin^2 x - (1 - \sin^2 x)}{2\sin^2 x - 1}$

$= \dfrac{2\sin^2 x - 1}{2\sin^2 x - 1} = 1$

14. Refer to Lesson 90.   **15.** $\dfrac{\sqrt{6} - \sqrt{2}}{4}$ **16.** $\dfrac{\sqrt{2}}{2}(\sin x + \cos x)$ **17.** $120°, 240°$

18. $11.25°, 56.25°, 101.25°, 146.25°, 191.25°, 236.25°, 281.25°, 326.25°$ **19.** $28.96°$

20. $_7P_2 = 42;\ _7C_2 = 21$ **21.** $-6, 12$ **22.** $-4, -\dfrac{4}{3}, \dfrac{4}{3}, 4, \dfrac{20}{3}$

23. $\dfrac{x^2}{25} + \dfrac{y^2}{4} = 1$

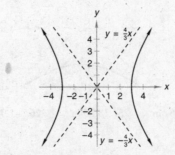

24. $\dfrac{x^2}{9} - \dfrac{y^2}{16} = 1$; vertices $(3, 0)$; $(-3, 0)$; asymptotes: $y = \dfrac{4}{3}x$; $y = -\dfrac{4}{3}x$

25. 90.85 in.^{2} **26.** 1 **27.** $\dfrac{7}{8}$ **28.** -1 **29.** $\dfrac{1}{3}$ **30.** $\sqrt[3]{x} - 1$

problem set 96

1. 415.89 units of time   **2.** 49.14 min   **3.** $5\dfrac{5}{11}$ min   **4.** 5 mph

5. $\dfrac{\cos^4 x - \sin^4 x}{\cos 2x} = \dfrac{(\cos^2 x + \sin^2 x)(\cos^2 x - \sin^2 x)}{\cos^2 x - \sin^2 x} = \cos^2 x + \sin^2 x = 1$

6. $(\sin x + \cos x)^2 = \sin^2 x + 2\sin x \cos x + \cos^2 x = 1 + 2\sin x \cos x = 1 + \sin 2x$

7. $\dfrac{1 - \cos x}{\sin x} \cdot \dfrac{(1 + \cos x)}{(1 + \cos x)} = \dfrac{1 - \cos^2 x}{\sin x(1 + \cos x)} = \dfrac{\sin^2 x}{\sin x(1 + \cos x)} = \dfrac{\sin x}{1 + \cos x}$

8. $A = 51.54°$; area $= 51.14$ cm^2 **9.** (a)   (b)

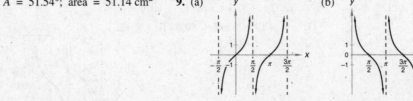

10. (a)   (b)   **11.**

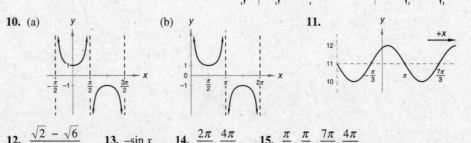

12. $\dfrac{\sqrt{2} - \sqrt{6}}{4}$ **13.** $-\sin x$ **14.** $\dfrac{2\pi}{3}, \dfrac{4\pi}{3}$ **15.** $\dfrac{\pi}{6}, \dfrac{\pi}{3}, \dfrac{7\pi}{6}, \dfrac{4\pi}{3}$

16. 2.24 cis 26.57°; 2.24 cis 206.57°   **17.** 1.12 cis 105°; 1.12 cis 225°; 1.12 cis 345°

18. $_8P_3 = 336$; $_8C_3 = 56$ **19.** 25, –125   **20.** –16, –12, –8

21. $\dfrac{x^2}{64} + \dfrac{y^2}{100} = 1$; length of major axis $= 20$; length of minor axis $= 16$

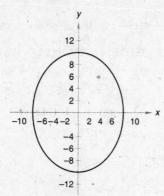

22. $\dfrac{y^2}{9} - \dfrac{x^2}{16} = 1$;

vertices $= (0, 3)$; $(0, -3)$;

asymptotes: $y = \dfrac{3}{4}x$; $y = -\dfrac{3}{4}x$

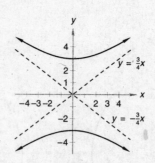

23. $x = \dfrac{1}{19}$; $y = \dfrac{68}{19}$ **24.** 403.06 cm^2 **25.** 18.85 in.^{2} **26.** –1.94   **27.** 1

28. $\dfrac{17}{25}$ **29.** 36   **30.** $x^2 - y^2$

problem set 97

1. $\dfrac{4}{13}$ **2.** $\dfrac{2}{5}$ **3.** 56.95 min   **4.** $H = 32$; $S = 56$; $C = 40$ **5.** 50 yd

6. 10.10; 2.38   **7.** No such triangle exists.

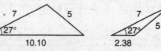

8. $\cos 2x + 2\sin^2 x = 1 - 2\sin^2 x + 2\sin^2 x = 1$

9. $\dfrac{\cos x}{1 - \sin x} - \dfrac{\cos x}{1 + \sin x} = \dfrac{\cos x(1 + \sin x) - \cos x(1 - \sin x)}{1 - \sin^2 x} = \dfrac{2\cos x \sin x}{\cos^2 x} = 2\tan x$

10. $\dfrac{2\sin x}{\sin 2x} = \dfrac{2\sin x}{2\sin x \cos x} = \dfrac{1}{\cos x} = \sec x$

11. $c = 4.18$ in.; area $= 0.083$ ft^2 **12.** 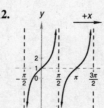   **13.**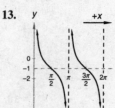

14.

15. $\dfrac{1}{2}$ **16.** 90°, 210°, 330°

17. 20°, 100°, 140°, 220°, 260°, 340°   **18.** 2.11 cis 40.67°; 2.11 cis 160.67°; 2.11 cis 280.67°

Advanced Mathematics, Second Edition

19. 4, 8, 16 or −4, 8, −16   **20.** −12, −9, −6

21. $\dfrac{x^2}{9} + \dfrac{y^2}{25} = 1$; length of major axis $= 10$; length of minor axis $= 6$

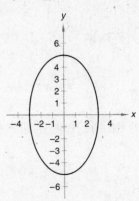

22. $\dfrac{x^2}{4} - \dfrac{y^2}{4} = 1$; vertices $= (2, 0)$; $(-2, 0)$; asymptotes: $y = x$; $y = -x$

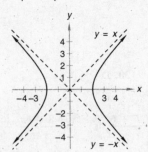

23. 65,449.85 cm^2 **24.** 70.53 cm   **25.** 2^{17} **26.** 2   **27.** $\dfrac{10}{3}$ **28.** −1

29. (a) $\dfrac{1}{216}$ (b) 216   **30.** $\left(x + \dfrac{5}{2} - \dfrac{\sqrt{43}}{2}i \right)\left(x + \dfrac{5}{2} + \dfrac{\sqrt{43}}{2}i \right)$

problem set 98

1. $\dfrac{9}{16}$ **2.** 168.75   **3.** 30,240   **4.** $\dfrac{mf}{f + m}$ hr   **5.** $\dfrac{m}{h + 3}$ mph   **6.** 450 laps

7. $_7P_6 = \dfrac{7!}{1!} = 5040$; $_7C_6 = \dfrac{7!}{6!1!} = 7$ **8.** 2.45   **9.** 10^4 **10.** 2^8

11. 1, 81   **12.** No such triangle exists.

13. 4.47; 14.33

14. $\dfrac{2 \cos 2x}{\sin 2x} = \dfrac{2(\cos^2 x - \sin^2 x)}{2 \sin x \cos x} = \dfrac{\cos^2 x}{\sin x \cos x} - \dfrac{\sin^2 x}{\sin x \cos x} = \dfrac{\cos x}{\sin x} - \dfrac{\sin x}{\cos x}$

$= \cot x - \tan x$

15. $2 \csc 2x \cos x = \dfrac{2 \cos x}{\sin 2x} = \dfrac{2 \cos x}{2 \sin x \cos x} = \dfrac{1}{\sin x} = \csc x$

16. $\dfrac{2 \tan x}{1 + \tan^2 x} = \dfrac{\dfrac{2 \sin x}{\cos x}}{\sec^2 x} = \dfrac{\dfrac{2 \sin x}{\cos x}}{\dfrac{1}{\cos^2 x}} = \dfrac{2 \sin x}{\cos x} \cdot \dfrac{\cos^2 x}{1} = 2 \sin x \cos x = \sin 2x$

17. $A = 36.42°$; $B = 71.79°$; $C = 71.79°$ **18.**

19. 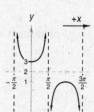   **20.** 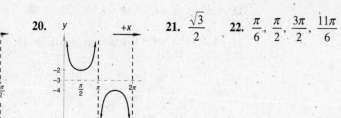   **21.** $\dfrac{\sqrt{3}}{2}$ **22.** $\dfrac{\pi}{6}, \dfrac{\pi}{2}, \dfrac{3\pi}{2}, \dfrac{11\pi}{6}$

23. $\dfrac{\pi}{12}, \dfrac{11\pi}{12}, \dfrac{13\pi}{12}, \dfrac{23\pi}{12}$ **24.** 1.85 cis 113.86°; 1.85 cis 233.86°; 1.85 cis 353.86°   **25.** 128

26. $\dfrac{x^2}{72} + \dfrac{y^2}{50} = 1$; length of major axis $= 12\sqrt{2}$; length of minor axis $= 10\sqrt{2}$

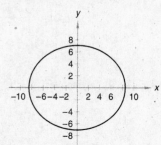

27. 16 in.   **28.** $\dfrac{81}{64}$ **29.** $\dfrac{4\sqrt{5}}{5}$ **30.** D

problem set 99

1. 1   **2.** 31.06 yr   **3.** 48   **4.** $\dfrac{F+6}{r+4}$ hr   **5.** $\dfrac{8-mt}{4t} \dfrac{\text{jobs}}{\text{hr}}$

6. Value was multiplied by 18   **7.** 16 ft   **8.** $(-3, -27)$ and $(27, 3)$ **9.** $17 + 12\sqrt{2}$

10. Arithmetic mean $= 15$; geometric mean $= \pm 4\sqrt{11}$ **11.** 2.54   **12.** 2.18   **13.** 16

14. 1, 2   **15.** $1, 3^9$ **16.** 2.01; 9.46

17. $\dfrac{\cos^3 x - \sin^3 x}{\cos x - \sin x} = \dfrac{(\cos x - \sin x)(\cos^2 x + \cos x \sin x + \sin^2 x)}{\cos x - \sin x}$

$\quad = 1 + \cos x \sin x = 1 + \dfrac{1}{2}\sin 2x$

18. $\dfrac{\cos 2x}{\cos^2 x} = \dfrac{\cos^2 x - \sin^2 x}{\cos^2 x} = \dfrac{\cos^2 x}{\cos^2 x} - \dfrac{\sin^2 x}{\cos^2 x} = 1 - \tan^2 x$

19. $\dfrac{2}{\cot x - \tan x} = \dfrac{2}{\dfrac{1}{\tan x} - \tan x} = \dfrac{2}{\dfrac{1 - \tan^2 x}{\tan x}} = \dfrac{2 \tan x}{1 - \tan^2 x} = \tan 2x$

20. $a = 624.50$ cm; area $= 151{,}554.45$ cm^2

21. 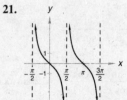   **22.**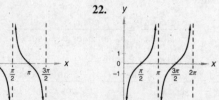

23. (a) $y = \cot \theta$ (b) $y = -3 + \sec x$ **24.** $\dfrac{\sqrt{3}}{2}$ **25.** 45°, 225°

26. 37.5°, 52.5°, 127.5°, 142.5°, 217.5°, 232.5°, 307.5°, 322.5°

27. 1.38 cis 53.42°; 1.38 cis 143.42°; 1.38 cis 233.42°; 1.38 cis 323.42°

28. $\dfrac{x^2}{25} + \dfrac{y^2}{21} = 1$

29. 19.31 cm^2

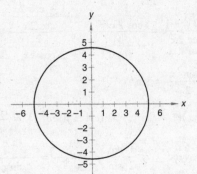

30. $\left(x + \dfrac{1}{2} - \dfrac{\sqrt{3}}{2}i\right)\left(x + \dfrac{1}{2} + \dfrac{\sqrt{3}}{2}i\right)$

problem set 100

1. 24 ft   **2.** $16\dfrac{4}{11}$ min   **3.** $\dfrac{R(m+5)}{m}\dfrac{\text{mi}}{\text{hr}}$ **4.** $\dfrac{14m}{d+km}$ items

5. No change in number of greens   **6.** $_{11}P_4 = 7920$; $_{11}C_4 = 330$

7. Refer to Lesson 100.   **8.** Refer to Lesson 100.

9. Refer to Lesson 100.   **10.** Refer to Lesson 100.

11. Arithmetic mean = 15; geometric mean = $\pm 3\sqrt{21}$

12. $(16, 4)$ and $(-4, -16)$ **13.** 1.88   **14.** 2.64   **15.** 3^9

16. 1   **17.** $\dfrac{6}{5}$ **18.** No such triangle exists.

19. $\cot x + \tan x = \dfrac{\cos x}{\sin x} + \dfrac{\sin x}{\cos x} = \dfrac{\cos^2 x + \sin^2 x}{\cos x \sin x} = \dfrac{1}{\cos x \sin x} = \dfrac{2}{2} \cdot \dfrac{1}{\cos x \sin x}$

$= \dfrac{2}{2\cos x \sin x} = \dfrac{2}{\sin 2x} = 2\csc 2x$

20. $\dfrac{\sin 2x}{\tan x} = \dfrac{2\sin x \cos x}{\dfrac{\sin x}{\cos x}} = 2\sin x \cos x \cdot \dfrac{\cos x}{\sin x} = 2\cos^2 x$

21. $(\tan^2 x)(1 + \cot^2 x) = \tan^2 x \csc^2 x = \dfrac{\sin^2 x}{\cos^2 x} \cdot \dfrac{1}{\sin^2 x} = \dfrac{1}{\cos^2 x} = \dfrac{1}{1 - \sin^2 x}$

22. $A = 33.17°$; $B = 46.83°$ **23.**   **24.**

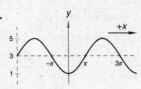

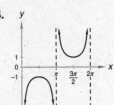

25. $\dfrac{1}{2}$ **26.** $\dfrac{\pi}{3}, \dfrac{5\pi}{3}$ **27.** $\dfrac{\pi}{12}, \dfrac{7\pi}{12}, \dfrac{13\pi}{12}, \dfrac{19\pi}{12}$

28. 1.50 cis 80.78°; 1.50 cis 170.78°; 1.50 cis 260.78°; 1.50 cis 350.78°

29. $x = \dfrac{11}{4}$; $y = \dfrac{1}{2}$ **30.** 1

problem set 101

1. 81 ft   **2.** $\dfrac{4}{33}$ **3.** 270.27 min   **4.** $B = 9$ mph; $W = 3$ mph   **5.** 60 mph   **6.** 36

7. 19   **8.** 3   **9.** Refer to Lesson 100.   **10.** Refer to Lesson 100.   **11.** 2 and 8

12. 20, 5 and $-20, -5$ **13.** (a) 2.21   (b) 2.06   **14.** e^2, e^{-2} **15.** 5   **16.** $1, 4^{16}$

17. 4.60; 10.44

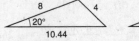

18. $\dfrac{\sec 2x - 1}{2 \sec 2x} = \dfrac{\dfrac{1}{\cos 2x} - 1}{\dfrac{2}{\cos 2x}} = \dfrac{\dfrac{1 - \cos 2x}{\cos 2x}}{\dfrac{2}{\cos 2x}} = \dfrac{1 - \cos 2x}{2} = \dfrac{1 - (1 - 2\sin^2 x)}{2}$

$= \dfrac{2\sin^2 x}{2} = \sin^2 x$

19. $(\cot^2 x)(1 + \tan^2 x) = (\cot^2 x)(\sec^2 x) = \dfrac{\cos^2 x}{\sin^2 x} \cdot \dfrac{1}{\cos^2 x} = \dfrac{1}{\sin^2 x} = \dfrac{1}{1 - \cos^2 x}$

20. $\dfrac{1}{2} \cot x \sec^2 x = \dfrac{1}{2} \dfrac{\cos x}{\sin x} \cdot \dfrac{1}{\cos^2 x} = \dfrac{1}{2 \sin x \cos x} = \dfrac{1}{\sin 2x} = \csc 2x$ 21. $3697.89 \ \text{m}^2$

22. 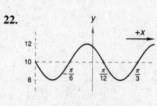   23. 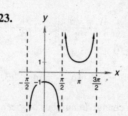   24. $\dfrac{\sqrt{2 - \sqrt{3}}}{2}$

25. $70°, 110°, 190°, 230°, 310°, 350°$ 26. $30°, 150°$

27. $1.65 \ \text{cis} \ 51.14°; \ 1.65 \ \text{cis} \ 171.14°; \ 1.65 \ \text{cis} \ 291.14°$ 28. $3\sqrt{2}$ 29. (a) $\dfrac{1}{64}$ (b) 64

30. 2.28%

problem set 102

1. 9 ft   2. $\dfrac{7}{13}$ 3. 28.71 s   4. $B = 18$ mph; $W = 9$ mph

5. $W = 47$ yr; $P = 23$ yr   6. $A_1 = 60°$; $A_2 = 20°$ 7. $-35x^4 y^3$

8. $8a^6 - 12a^4 b^3 + 6a^2 b^6 - b^9$ 9. 13   10. 1   11. Refer to Lesson 100.

12. Refer to Lesson 100.   13. 4 and 36   14. (a) 1.90   (b) 3.36   15. 1, 3   16. 3

17. 5   18. 1.70; 11.15

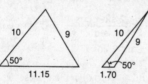

19. $\dfrac{\sin^2 x}{1 - \cos x} - \dfrac{1}{\sec x} = \dfrac{1 - \cos^2 x}{1 - \cos x} - \dfrac{1}{\sec x} = \dfrac{(1 + \cos x)(1 - \cos x)}{1 - \cos x} - \cos x$

$= 1 + \cos x - \cos x = 1$

20. $\dfrac{\cos 2x}{\sin^2 x} = \dfrac{\cos^2 x - \sin^2 x}{\sin^2 x} = \cot^2 x - 1$

21. $\dfrac{1 + \sin x}{\cos x} + \dfrac{\cos x}{1 + \sin x} = \dfrac{(1 + \sin x)^2 + \cos^2 x}{\cos x(1 + \sin x)} = \dfrac{1 + 2\sin x + \sin^2 x + \cos^2 x}{\cos x(1 + \sin x)}$

$= \dfrac{2 + 2\sin x}{\cos x(1 + \sin x)} = \dfrac{2(1 + \sin x)}{\cos x(1 + \sin x)} = \dfrac{2}{\cos x} \cdot \dfrac{2 \sin x}{2 \sin x}$

$= \dfrac{4 \sin x}{2 \sin x \cos x} = \dfrac{4 \sin x}{\sin 2x}$

22. $A = 101.54°$; area $= 63.21 \ \text{cm}^2$ 23.

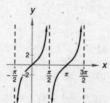

24. (a) $y = 6 + 8 \csc x$ (b) $y = \cot \theta$

25. $0, \dfrac{\pi}{5}, \dfrac{2\pi}{5}, \dfrac{3\pi}{5}, \dfrac{4\pi}{5}, \pi, \dfrac{6\pi}{5}, \dfrac{7\pi}{5}, \dfrac{8\pi}{5}, \dfrac{9\pi}{5}$ 26. $\dfrac{\pi}{3}, \dfrac{5\pi}{3}$

27. 1.52 cis 20.81°; 1.52 cis 92.81°; 1.52 cis 164.81°; 1.52 cis 236.81°; 1.52 cis 308.81°

28. 64.95 ft^2 29. $\left(x + \dfrac{5}{2} - \dfrac{\sqrt{15}}{2}i\right)\left(x + \dfrac{5}{2} + \dfrac{\sqrt{15}}{2}i\right)x$ 30. 1

problem set 103

1. $\dfrac{1}{2}$ ft   2. $\dfrac{1}{16}$ 3. 490.61 min   4. 20 atm   5. $\dfrac{12p}{k + sp}$ hr   6. 54 ml

7. $\log_3 \dfrac{x^{\frac{3}{5}}y^{\frac{1}{4}}}{z^3}$ 8. 1.80×10^{-5} 9. 4.28   10. $3.16 \times 10^{-7} \dfrac{\text{mole}}{\text{liter}}$ 11. $70x^4y^4$

12. $81a^8 - 108a^6b^3 + 54a^4b^6 - 12a^2b^9 + b^{12}$ 13. $-\dfrac{13}{7}$ 14. Refer to lesson 100.

15. Refer to Lesson 100.   16. (a) 1.92 (b) 1.24   17. ±3   18. $\dfrac{3}{4}$ 19. $\dfrac{1}{2}$

20. 4   21. 3.57; 10.93

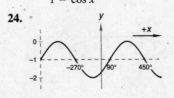

(triangle figures: 8, 5, 25°, 3.57; 8, 5, 25°, 10.93)

22. $\dfrac{\cos 2x + 1}{2} = \dfrac{2\cos^2 x - 1 + 1}{2} = \cos^2 x$

23. $\dfrac{2\cot x}{\tan 2x} = \dfrac{2\cot x}{\dfrac{2\tan x}{1 - \tan^2 x}} = 2\cot x \cdot \dfrac{1 - \tan^2 x}{2\tan x} = 2\cot x \cdot \dfrac{\dfrac{(1 - \tan^2 x)}{2}}{\cot x}$

$= \cot^2 x(1 - \tan^2 x) = \cot^2 x - 1 = \csc^2 x - 1 - 1 = \csc^2 x - 2$

24. Area = 0.0017 m^2; $a = 11.36$ cm   25.   26. $\dfrac{\sqrt{6} + \sqrt{2}}{4}$

27. 45°, 105°, 165°, 225°, 285°, 345°   28. 0°

29. 2.35 cis 37.54°; 2.35 cis 157.54°; 2.35 cis 277.54°   30. x

problem set 104

1. $\dfrac{7}{13}$ 2. $\dfrac{4200}{140 + s + f}$ gal   3. $N_W = 45$; $N_R = 20$; $N_B = 75$ 4. 45

5. (a) Refer to Lesson 104. (b) 2550   6. (a) Refer to Lesson 104. (b) 22

7. $\dfrac{2}{3}\log_4(s - 1) + \dfrac{1}{3}\log_4(t + 2) - \dfrac{3}{2}\log_4 s$ 8. 89.13   9. 3.2

10. $3.16 \times 10^{-9} \dfrac{\text{mole}}{\text{liter}}$ 11. $160x^3y^3$ 12. $x^6 - 6x^4y + 12x^2y^2 - 8y^3$ 13. $\dfrac{8}{3}$

14. 0   15. Refer to Lesson 100.   16. Refer to Lesson 100.   17. 2 and 18

18. (a) 2.12 (b) 1.06   19. 1, 16   20. 2   21. 9

22. $\dfrac{1 - \cos 2x}{2} = \dfrac{1 - (1 - 2\sin^2 x)}{2} = \dfrac{2\sin^2 x}{2} = \sin^2 x$

23. $\dfrac{1 - 3\cos x - 4\cos^2 x}{\sin^2 x} = \dfrac{1 - 3\cos x - 4\cos^2 x}{1 - \cos^2 x} = \dfrac{(1 - 4\cos x)(1 + \cos x)}{(1 - \cos x)(1 + \cos x)}$

$= \dfrac{1 - 4\cos x}{1 - \cos x}$

24.

25.   *y*

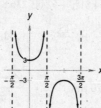

26. $\dfrac{\sqrt{3}}{2} + \dfrac{1}{2}i;\ -\dfrac{\sqrt{3}}{2} + \dfrac{1}{2}i;\ -i$

27. $\dfrac{\pi}{12}, \dfrac{\pi}{4}, \dfrac{3\pi}{4}, \dfrac{11\pi}{12}, \dfrac{17\pi}{12}, \dfrac{19\pi}{12}$ **28.** 0   **29.** 1   **30.** $\left(x + \dfrac{1}{2} - \dfrac{\sqrt{11}}{2}i\right)\left(x + \dfrac{1}{2} + \dfrac{\sqrt{11}}{2}i\right)$

**problem set
105**

1. 1 ft   **2.** 575.28 min   **3.** $5\dfrac{5}{11}$ min   **4.** $\dfrac{mhK}{560}$ workers   **5.** 210 teams   **6.** 7

7. 6   **8.** –3   **9.** (a) Refer to Lesson 104.   (b) 198

10. (a) Refer to Lesson 104.   (b) $\dfrac{21}{32}$ **11.** 68,699,634.76   **12.** 3.36   **13.** $240x^2y^4$

14. $27x^3 - 54x^2y + 36xy^2 - 8y^3$ **15.** $\dfrac{11}{17}$ **16.** Refer to Lesson 100.   **17.** $\dfrac{2 - \sqrt{3}}{4}$

18. 1, 81   **19.** 8   **20.** 6   **21.** $\dfrac{1}{2}\sin 2x \sec x = \dfrac{1}{2}\, 2 \sin x \cos x\, \dfrac{1}{\cos x} = \sin x$

22. $\dfrac{1 + \cos 2x}{\sin 2x} = \dfrac{1 + 2\cos^2 x - 1}{2 \sin x \cos x} = \dfrac{2\cos^2 x}{2 \sin x \cos x} = \dfrac{\cos x}{\sin x} = \cot x$ **23.** 20.48 cm^2

24.   *y*

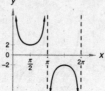

25. (a) $y = \tan\theta$ (b) $y = -7 + 4\sec x$

26. 15°, 105°, 135°, 225°, 255°, 345°   **27.** 45°, 225°

28. $\dfrac{\sqrt{2}}{2} + \dfrac{\sqrt{2}}{2}i;\ -\dfrac{\sqrt{2}}{2} + \dfrac{\sqrt{2}}{2}i;\ -\dfrac{\sqrt{2}}{2} - \dfrac{\sqrt{2}}{2}i;\ \dfrac{\sqrt{2}}{2} - \dfrac{\sqrt{2}}{2}i$

29. $\dfrac{y^2}{4} - \dfrac{x^2}{25} = 1$; vertices = (0, 2); (0, –2); asymptotes: $y = \dfrac{2}{5}x;\ y = -\dfrac{2}{5}x$ **30.** 0

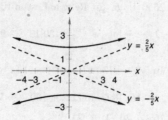

**problem set
106**

1. 270.27 min   **2.** 40,320   **3.** $\dfrac{300(100)}{(2.54)(12)(5280)}\ \dfrac{\text{mi}}{\text{min}}$ **4.** \$5600   **5.** 12 mph

6. $\dfrac{(x - 5)^2}{16} + \dfrac{(y + 1)^2}{1} = 1$; center = (5, –1); length of major axis = 8;

length of minor axis = 2

7. $\dfrac{(x+3)^2}{4} + \dfrac{(y-1)^2}{9} = 1$; center = $(-3, 1)$; length of major axis = 6;

length of minor axis = 4

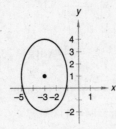

8. $\dfrac{(x+1)^2}{1} - \dfrac{(y-2)^2}{1} = 1$; center = $(-1, 2)$; vertices = $(-2, 2)$; $(0, 2)$;

asymptotes: $y = x + 3$; $y = -x + 1$

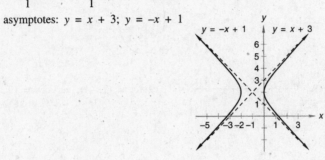

9. $\dfrac{(x+1)^2}{1} - \dfrac{(y+2)^2}{4} = 1$; center = $(-1, -2)$; vertices = $(0, -2)$; $(-2, -2)$;

asymptotes: $y = 2x$; $y = -2x - 4$

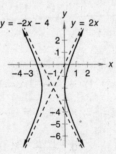

10. $(x+2)^2 + (y-3)^2 = 9$; $x^2 + y^2 + 4x - 6y + 4 = 0$　　**11.** 1

12. (a) Refer to Lesson 104.　(b) 72　　**13.** (a) Refer to Lesson 104.　(b) 172

14. $\log\left(\dfrac{x^8 z^{\frac{3}{2}}}{y^3}\right)$　　**15.** $3.16 \times 10^{-4} \dfrac{\text{mole}}{\text{liter}}$　　**16.** $4860x^4y^2$　　**17.** $\dfrac{7}{3}$

18. Refer to Lesson 100.　　**19.** $\dfrac{1}{4}$　　**20.** $\dfrac{25}{9}$　　**21.** $\sqrt{3}$　　**22.** 1, $e^{\frac{4}{9}}$

23. $\dfrac{\sin^3 x + \cos^3 x}{\sin x + \cos x} = \dfrac{(\sin x + \cos x)(\sin^2 x - \sin x \cos x + \cos^2 x)}{\sin x + \cos x}$

$= 1 - \sin x \cos x = 1 - \dfrac{1}{2}\sin 2x$

24. $\dfrac{\cot x + 1}{\cot x - 1} = \dfrac{\dfrac{\cos x}{\sin x} + 1}{\dfrac{\cos x}{\sin x} - 1} \cdot \dfrac{\dfrac{1}{\cos x}}{\dfrac{1}{\cos x}} = \dfrac{\dfrac{1}{\sin x} + \dfrac{1}{\cos x}}{\dfrac{1}{\sin x} - \dfrac{1}{\cos x}} = \dfrac{\csc x + \sec x}{\csc x - \sec x}$

25.

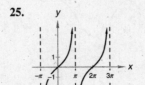

26.

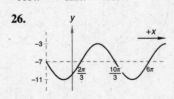

27. $0°, 180°, 240°, 300°$

28. 1.64 cis 36.58°; 1.64 cis 126.58°; 1.64 cis 216.58°; 1.64 cis 306.58°

29. 43.01 cm² **30.** $\dfrac{t}{t+1}$

problem set 107

1. $6:32\frac{8}{11}$ p.m. **2.** $\dfrac{2x}{x-2}$ days **3.** $2A - m$ **4.** 0.4 **5.** 60 boys **6.** 6 **7.** 8 mi

8. $\dfrac{(x+3)^2}{4} + \dfrac{(y-1)^2}{9} = 1$; center = $(-3, 1)$; length of major axis = 6; length of minor axis = 4

9. $\dfrac{(x-7)^2}{4} - \dfrac{(y+4)^2}{4} = 1$; center = $(7, -4)$; vertices = $(9, -4)$; $(5, -4)$; asymptotes: $y = x - 11$; $y = -x + 3$

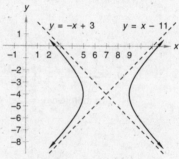

10. $(x-1)^2 + (y+3)^2 = 1$; $x^2 + y^2 - 2x + 6y + 9 = 0$ **11.** 25

12. $x = -2$; $y = 2$; $z = -1$ **13.** (a) $a_n = a_1 + (n-1)d$ (b) $\dfrac{n}{2}\big[2a_1 + (n-1)d\big]$

14. $3.16 \times 10^{-9} \dfrac{\text{mole}}{\text{liter}}$ **15.** 185.45 **16.** $280x^3$

17. (a) Refer to Lesson 100. (b) $\dfrac{2 - \sqrt{3}}{4}$ **18.** (a) Refer to Lesson 100. (b) $\dfrac{\sqrt{6}}{2}$

19. $\dfrac{\log 22}{\log e}$ **20.** $\dfrac{4}{3}$ **21.** 2^9 **22.** 4

23. $\sec x - \sin x \tan x = \dfrac{1}{\cos x} - \sin x \dfrac{\sin x}{\cos x} = \dfrac{1 - \sin^2 x}{\cos x} = \dfrac{\cos^2 x}{\cos x} = \cos x$

24. $\dfrac{\sec^2 x}{2 - \sec^2 x} = \dfrac{\dfrac{1}{\cos^2 x}}{2 - \dfrac{1}{\cos^2 x}} = \dfrac{\dfrac{1}{\cos^2 x}}{\dfrac{2\cos^2 x - 1}{\cos^2 x}} = \dfrac{1}{\cos^2 x} \cdot \dfrac{\cos^2 x}{2\cos^2 x - 1}$

$= \dfrac{1}{\cos 2x} = \sec 2x$

25. $c = 1.31$ ft; area = 1053.98 cm²

26. **27.** **28.** $\dfrac{\sqrt{6} + \sqrt{2}}{4}$

29. 40°, 280° **30.** $-\dfrac{\sqrt{3}}{2} - \dfrac{1}{2}i$; $\dfrac{\sqrt{3}}{2} - \dfrac{1}{2}i$; i

problem set 108

1. $\frac{3}{8}$ 2. 8.11%   3. $\frac{3W}{W+p}$ days   4. $J = 29$ yr; $K = 17$ yr

5. $A + B = \begin{bmatrix} 4 & 7 \\ -1 & 7 \end{bmatrix}$; $A - B = \begin{bmatrix} 2 & 7 \\ 3 & 1 \end{bmatrix}$; $2A = \begin{bmatrix} 6 & 14 \\ 2 & 8 \end{bmatrix}$

6. $A + B = \begin{bmatrix} -1 & 1 & 1 \\ 3 & 4 & 3 \\ 5 & 5 & 0 \end{bmatrix}$; $A - B = \begin{bmatrix} 3 & -1 & 1 \\ -3 & 0 & 3 \\ -3 & -3 & 0 \end{bmatrix}$; $2A = \begin{bmatrix} 2 & 0 & 2 \\ 0 & 4 & 6 \\ 2 & 2 & 0 \end{bmatrix}$

7. $A \cdot B = \begin{bmatrix} 2 & 3 \\ 3 & 7 \end{bmatrix}$; $B \cdot A = \begin{bmatrix} 7 & 9 \\ 1 & 2 \end{bmatrix}$ 8. $A \cdot B$ does not exist; $B \cdot A = \begin{bmatrix} 2 \\ 8 \end{bmatrix}$ 9. 2

10. $\frac{(x+2)^2}{3} + \frac{(y-3)^2}{5} = 1$; center $= (-2, 3)$; length of major axis $= 2\sqrt{5}$;
length of minor axis $= 2\sqrt{3}$; vertical

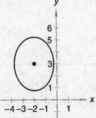

11. $\frac{(x-1)^2}{4} - \frac{(y+1)^2}{9} = 1$; center $= (1, -1)$;
vertices $= (3, -1)$; $(-1, -1)$;
asymptotes: $y = \frac{3}{2}x - \frac{5}{2}$; $y = -\frac{3}{2}x + \frac{1}{2}$

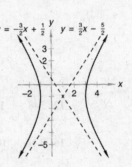

12. -144 13. -1 14. $5 + \frac{7}{3}(n-1)$ 15. 8.08

16. $2 + \frac{5}{3}\log_6 x + \frac{4}{3}\log_6 y + 3\log_6 z$ 17. y^9

18. (a) Refer to Lesson 100.   (b) $\frac{-2+\sqrt{3}}{4}$ 19. (a) Refer to Lesson 100.   (b) $-\frac{\sqrt{6}}{2}$

20. $\frac{\ln 50}{\ln 7}$ 21. e^{10} 22. 0.52   23. $\frac{2\sqrt{3}}{3}$

24. $\sec\theta - \cos\theta = \frac{1}{\cos\theta} - \cos\theta = \frac{1-\cos^2\theta}{\cos\theta} = \frac{\sin^2\theta}{\cos\theta} = \sin\theta \cdot \frac{\sin\theta}{\cos\theta} = \sin\theta\tan\theta$

25. 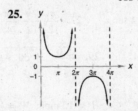   26. 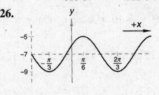   27.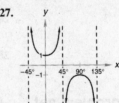

28. $0°, 180°$ 29. 1.66 cis 63°; 1.66 cis 135°; 1.66 cis 207°; 1.66 cis 279°; 1.66 cis 351°

30.

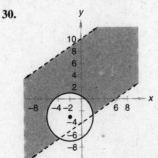

problem set 109

1. $\dfrac{1}{7}$ 2. 718.56   3. $\dfrac{400n}{d + 3n}$ 4. $\dfrac{10H - 15}{3H} \dfrac{\text{jobs}}{\text{hr}}$ 5. $M = 63$ yr; $J = 41$ yr

6. $\dfrac{31}{99{,}000}$ 7. $\dfrac{5957}{990}$ 8. 220 ft   9. $A + B = \begin{bmatrix} 2 & 2 & 3 \\ 7 & 5 & 9 \\ -1 & 1 & 7 \end{bmatrix}$; $A \cdot B = \begin{bmatrix} 7 & 13 & 31 \\ -4 & -4 & 20 \\ 1 & 4 & 15 \end{bmatrix}$

10. $\dfrac{(x - 2)^2}{\frac{1}{9}} + \dfrac{(y + 3)^2}{\frac{1}{25}} = 1$; center = $(2, -3)$;

length of major axis = $\dfrac{2}{3}$;

length of minor axis = $\dfrac{2}{5}$

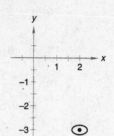

11. $\dfrac{(x + 3)^2}{1} - \dfrac{(y - 2)^2}{4} = 1$; center = $(-3, 2)$;
vertices = $(-2, 2)$; $(-4, 2)$;
asymptotes: $y = 2x + 8$; $y = -2x - 4$

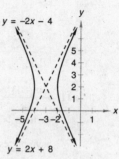

12. 348   13. 2   14. $\log_5 \left(\dfrac{x + 1}{x^2 - x} \right)$ 15. (a) $2(-2)^{11}$ (b) -2730

16. $3.16 \times 10^{-7} \dfrac{\text{mole}}{\text{liter}}$ 17. $90a^2 b^3 c^3$ 18. (a) Refer to Lesson 100.   (b) $-\dfrac{\sqrt{6}}{2}$

19. $\dfrac{\log 42}{\log e}$ 20. 10^9 21. No solution

22. $(\sin x - \cos x)^2 = \sin^2 x - 2 \sin x \cos x + \cos^2 x = 1 - 2 \sin x \cos x = 1 - \sin 2x$

23. $\dfrac{\tan^2 x}{\sec x + 1} = \dfrac{\sec^2 x - 1}{\sec x + 1} = \dfrac{(\sec x + 1)(\sec x - 1)}{\sec x + 1} = \sec x - 1$

24. $A = 60°$; area = 10.39 ft^2 25.

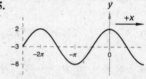

26. (a) $y = 10 + 6 \csc x$ (b) $y = -7 + 4 \sec x$ 27. $\dfrac{\pi}{12}, \dfrac{7\pi}{12}, \dfrac{3\pi}{4}, \dfrac{5\pi}{4}, \dfrac{17\pi}{12}, \dfrac{3\pi}{2}, \dfrac{23\pi}{12}$

28. $1.12 \text{ cis } 105°$; $1.12 \text{ cis } 225°$; $1.12 \text{ cis } 345°$ 29. $\dfrac{\sqrt{26}}{2}$ 30. $-x^3 - 3x^2 - 3x + 1$

problem set 110

1. $\dfrac{7}{13}$ 2. 49,382.72   3. $32 \dfrac{8}{11}$ min   4. $B = 12$ mph; $W = 4$ mph   5. $\dfrac{32}{9}$ hr

6. (a) Domain = $\{x \in \mathbb{R} \mid -1 \le x \le 1\}$

Range = $\left\{ \theta \in \mathbb{R} \mid -\dfrac{\pi}{2} \le \theta \le \dfrac{\pi}{2} \right\}$

Arcsin $\dfrac{\sqrt{3}}{2} = \dfrac{\pi}{3}$

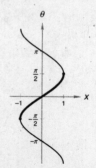

(b) Domain = $\{x \in \mathbb{R} \mid -1 \le x \le 1\}$

Range = $\{\theta \in \mathbb{R} \mid 0 \le \theta \le \pi\}$

Arccos $\left(-\dfrac{1}{2}\right) = \dfrac{2\pi}{3}$

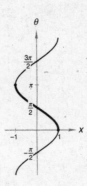

(c) Domain = $\{x \in \mathbb{R}\}$

Range = $\left\{\theta \in \mathbb{R} \mid -\dfrac{\pi}{2} < \theta < \dfrac{\pi}{2}\right\}$

Arctan $\left(-\dfrac{\sqrt{3}}{3}\right) = -\dfrac{\pi}{6}$

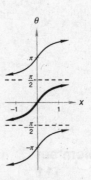

7. $\dfrac{241}{99,900}$ **8.** $\dfrac{1}{7}$ **9.** $A + B = \begin{bmatrix} 3 & 2 & 5 \\ -1 & 5 & 3 \\ 4 & 5 & -1 \end{bmatrix}$; $B \cdot A = \begin{bmatrix} 22 & 16 & 8 \\ -1 & 4 & 4 \\ -14 & 10 & 7 \end{bmatrix}$

10. $\dfrac{(x-4)^2}{9} + \dfrac{(y+1)^2}{25} = 1$; center $= (4, -1)$; length of major axis $= 10$;

length of minor axis $= 6$; vertical

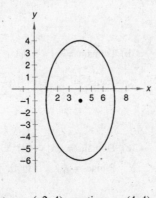

11. $\dfrac{(x+2)^2}{36} - \dfrac{(y-4)^2}{9} = 1$; center $= (-2, 4)$; vertices $= (4, 4)$; $(-8, 4)$;

asymptotes: $y = \dfrac{1}{2}x + 5$; $y = -\dfrac{1}{2}x + 3$

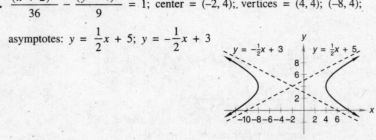

12. 2   **13.** 65,536   **14.** Arithmetic mean $= \dfrac{19}{2}$; geometric mean $= \pm 2\sqrt{21}$

15. 166.81   **16.** $x^6 - 6x^4y + 12x^2y^2 - 8y^3$

17. (a) Refer to Lesson 100.   (b) $-\dfrac{\sqrt{3}}{4} - \dfrac{1}{4}$ **18.** $\dfrac{\log 8}{\log 4}$ **19.** 16   **20.** $\pm\dfrac{1}{4}$

21. $\dfrac{1}{2}\sec x \csc (-x) = -\dfrac{1}{2}\sec x \csc x = -\dfrac{1}{2}\dfrac{1}{\cos x}\dfrac{1}{\sin x} = -\dfrac{1}{2\sin x \cos x} = -\dfrac{1}{\sin 2x}$

22. $\dfrac{\cos x}{\sec x - 1} - \dfrac{\cos x}{\sec x + 1} = \dfrac{\cos x(\sec x + 1) - \cos x(\sec x - 1)}{\sec^2 x - 1} = \dfrac{1 + \cos x - 1 + \cos x}{\tan^2 x}$

$= \dfrac{2 \cos x}{\dfrac{\sin^2 x}{\cos^2 x}} = \dfrac{2 \cos^3 x}{\sin^2 x} = 2 \cos^3 x \csc^2 x$

23. 88.98° **24.**

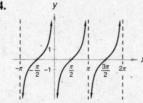

25.

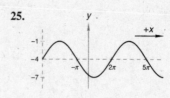

26.

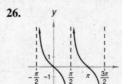
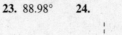

27. 70°, 110°, 190°, 230°, 310°, 350°

28. $1;\ -\dfrac{1}{2} + \dfrac{\sqrt{3}}{2}i;\ -\dfrac{1}{2} - \dfrac{\sqrt{3}}{2}i$ **29.** 6.18 in.

30. $(x - 1)\left(x + \dfrac{1}{2} + \dfrac{\sqrt{3}}{2}i \right)\left(x + \dfrac{1}{2} - \dfrac{\sqrt{3}}{2}i \right)$

problem set 111

1. 81 ft   **2.** $\dfrac{1}{4}$ **3.** 2.79 g   **4.** $\dfrac{ft}{t - 2}\dfrac{ft}{hr}$ **5.** 40°

6. $_8P_6 = 20{,}160;\ _8C_6 = 28$ **7.** $2 < x < 29$ **8.** $3 < x < 3\dfrac{1}{8}$

9. (a) Domain $= \{x \in \mathbb{R} \mid x \le -1 \text{ or } 1 \le x\}$

Range $= \left\{ y \in \mathbb{R} \mid 0 \le y < \dfrac{\pi}{2} \text{ or } \dfrac{\pi}{2} < y \le \pi \right\}$

(b) Domain $= \{x \in \mathbb{R} \mid x \le -1 \text{ or } 1 \le x\}$

Range $= \left\{ y \in \mathbb{R} \mid -\dfrac{\pi}{2} \le y < 0 \text{ or } 0 < y \le \dfrac{\pi}{2} \right\}$

(c) Domain $= \{x \in \mathbb{R}\}$

Range $= \left\{ y \in \mathbb{R} \mid 0 < y < \pi \right\}$

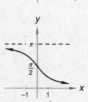

10. $\dfrac{431}{99{,}900}$ **11.** $2A - B = \begin{bmatrix} -1 & -3 & 5 \\ 2 & 4 & 6 \\ 2 & 0 & -6 \end{bmatrix};\ B \cdot A = \begin{bmatrix} 15 & 11 & 31 \\ 10 & 14 & 14 \\ 24 & 28 & 34 \end{bmatrix}$

12. $\dfrac{(x + 1)^2}{9} + \dfrac{(y - 2)^2}{25} = 1;$
center $= (-1, 2);$ length of major axis $= 10;$
length of minor axis $= 6;$ vertical

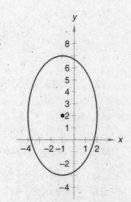

13. $\dfrac{(x-5)^2}{36} - \dfrac{(y-3)^2}{4} = 1$; center $= (5,3)$;

vertices $= (11,3)$; $(-1,3)$;

asymptotes: $y = \dfrac{1}{3}x + \dfrac{4}{3}$; $y = -\dfrac{1}{3}x + \dfrac{14}{3}$

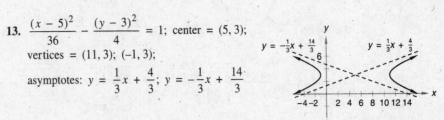

14. 0 **15.** $\log \dfrac{x-1}{x^2}$ **16.** 5.65×10^{-6} **17.** $16x^4 + 32x^3y + 24x^2y^2 + 8xy^3 + y^4$

18. ± 2 **19.** $-\dfrac{\sqrt{2}}{2}$ **20.** e^e **21.** 1

22. $\sec x \csc x = \dfrac{1}{\cos x} \cdot \dfrac{1}{\sin x} = \dfrac{1}{\cos x \sin x} \cdot \dfrac{2}{2} = \dfrac{2}{2\cos x \sin x} = \dfrac{2}{\sin 2x} = 2\csc 2x$

23. $\dfrac{2\tan\theta}{1+\tan^2\theta} = \dfrac{\dfrac{2\sin\theta}{\cos\theta}}{\sec^2\theta} = \dfrac{\dfrac{2\sin\theta}{\cos\theta}}{\dfrac{1}{\cos^2\theta}} = \dfrac{2\sin\theta}{\cos\theta} \cdot \dfrac{\cos^2\theta}{1} = 2\sin\theta\cos\theta = \sin 2\theta$

24. 16.93 cm   **25.**

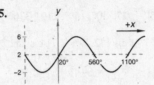

26.

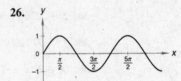

27. $\dfrac{\pi}{12}, \dfrac{\pi}{4}, \dfrac{5\pi}{12}, \dfrac{7\pi}{12}, \dfrac{3\pi}{4}, \dfrac{11\pi}{12}, \dfrac{13\pi}{12}, \dfrac{5\pi}{4}, \dfrac{17\pi}{12}, \dfrac{19\pi}{12}, \dfrac{7\pi}{4}, \dfrac{23\pi}{12}$ **28.** $0, \dfrac{\pi}{2}, \pi, \dfrac{3\pi}{2}$

29. 2; $2i$; -2; $-2i$ **30.** $(x+3)\left(x - \dfrac{3}{2} + \dfrac{3\sqrt{3}}{2}i\right)\left(x - \dfrac{3}{2} - \dfrac{3\sqrt{3}}{2}i\right)$

**problem set
112**

1. 256 ft   **2.** 0.8 **3.** 35 groups   **4.** $\$(0.9p - 0.5)$ **5.** $\$750$ **6.** $\$1920$

7. $-15{,}360x^{14}y^3$ **8.** $1120a^8b^4$ **9.** $2 < x < 127$ **10.** $x > -\dfrac{8}{9}$

11. Domain $= \{x \in \mathbb{R} \mid -1 \le x \le 1\}$

Range $= \left\{y \in \mathbb{R} \mid -\dfrac{\pi}{2} \le y \le \dfrac{\pi}{2}\right\}$

$\text{Arcsin}\left(-\dfrac{1}{2}\right) = -\dfrac{\pi}{6}$; $\text{Arcsin}\,\dfrac{1}{2} = \dfrac{\pi}{6}$; $\text{Arcsin}\,(-1) = -\dfrac{\pi}{2}$

12. $\dfrac{7}{900}$ **13.** $2A + 3B = \begin{bmatrix} 19 & 6 \\ 11 & 20 \end{bmatrix}$; $A \cdot 2B = \begin{bmatrix} 20 & 8 \\ 34 & 36 \end{bmatrix}$

14. $\dfrac{(x+10)^2}{64} + \dfrac{(y-4)^2}{4} = 1$;

center $= (-10, 4)$;

length of major axis $= 16$;

length of minor axis $= 4$; horizontal

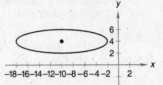

15. $\dfrac{(y+5)^2}{16} - \dfrac{(x-3)^2}{16} = 1$;

center $= (3, -5)$;

vertices $= (3, -1)$; $(3, -9)$;

asymptotes: $y = x - 8$; $y = -x - 2$

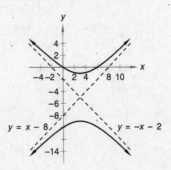

16. $\frac{3}{4}\log z - \frac{5}{4}\log x - \frac{1}{4}\log y$ **17.** $\frac{27}{7}$ **18.** $\frac{2-\sqrt{3}}{4}$ **19.** e **20.** e^{100}

21. $\tan 2x = \dfrac{\sin 2x}{\cos 2x} = \dfrac{2\sin x \cos x}{\cos^2 x - \sin^2 x} \cdot \dfrac{\frac{1}{\cos^2 x}}{\frac{1}{\cos^2 x}} = \dfrac{\frac{2\sin x}{\cos x}}{1 - \frac{\sin^2 x}{\cos^2 x}} = \dfrac{2\tan x}{1 - \tan^2 x}$

22. $\dfrac{1+\cos\theta}{\sin\theta} + \dfrac{\sin\theta}{\cos\theta} = \dfrac{\cos\theta(1+\cos\theta) + \sin^2\theta}{\sin\theta\cos\theta}$

$= \dfrac{\cos\theta + \cos^2\theta + \sin^2\theta}{\sin\theta\cos\theta} = \dfrac{\cos\theta + 1}{\sin\theta\cos\theta}$

23. 19.35 m   **24.**   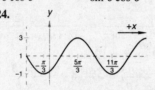   **25.**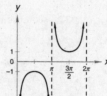

26. 210°, 270°, 330°   **27.** 30°, 150°, 210°, 330°

28. 1.71 cis 12.29°; 1.71 cis 132.29°; 1.71 cis 252.29°   **29.** $\dfrac{3\sqrt{2}}{2}$

30. $(x-2)(x+2)(x-2i)(x+2i)$

problem set 113

1. $\dfrac{14}{55}$ **2.** 18.51 yr   **3.** $(400 - hk)$ mi   **4.** $\dfrac{(k)(r)(2.54)(60)(60)}{100}\,\dfrac{\text{m}}{\text{hr}}$

5. $R_O = 60$ mph; $R_B = 20$ mph   **6.** $x^2 - 3x - 6$

7. $4x^3 - 12x^2 + 25x - 53 + \dfrac{108}{x+2}$ **8.** Yes   **9.** No   **10.** Yes

11. $2{,}795{,}520x^{22}y^{12}$ **12.** $-13{,}608x^{15}y^6$ **13.** $\dfrac{1}{2} < x < \dfrac{17}{2}$ **14.** $x > -\dfrac{4}{9}$

15. Domain $= \{x \in \mathbb{R} \mid -1 \le x \le 1\}$
Range $= \{y \in \mathbb{R} \mid 0 \le y \le \pi\}$
$\text{Arccos}\left(-\dfrac{1}{2}\right) = \dfrac{2\pi}{3}$; $\text{Arccos}\,\dfrac{1}{2} = \dfrac{\pi}{3}$; $\text{Arccos}(-1) = \pi$

16. $\dfrac{13}{990}$

17. $\dfrac{(x-3)^2}{9} + \dfrac{(y-0)^2}{36} = 1$;
center $= (3, 0)$;
length of major axis $= 12$;
length of minor axis $= 6$; vertical

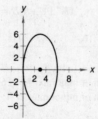

18. 1   **19.** $\ln\dfrac{z}{x(y+1)}$ **20.** $-\dfrac{1}{4}$ **21.** $1, e^4$

22. $\dfrac{\tan x}{\tan x - 1} - \dfrac{\cot x}{\cot x + 1} = \dfrac{\tan x \cot x + \tan x - \cot x \tan x + \cot x}{\tan x \cot x + \tan x - \cot x - 1} = \dfrac{\tan x + \cot x}{\tan x - \cot x}$

23. 2.65 cm   **24.**   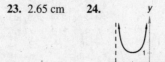   **25.** $\dfrac{\pi}{3}, \dfrac{2\pi}{3}$

26. $1;\ \dfrac{1}{2} + \dfrac{\sqrt{3}}{2}i;\ -\dfrac{1}{2} + \dfrac{\sqrt{3}}{2}i;\ -1;\ -\dfrac{1}{2} - \dfrac{\sqrt{3}}{2}i;\ \dfrac{1}{2} - \dfrac{\sqrt{3}}{2}i$ **27.** $a - 2$

28.

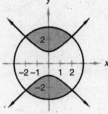

29. $\sqrt{2}$ **30.** $(x + i)(x + i)(x - i)(x - i)$

problem set 114

1. $\dfrac{1}{216}$ **2.** 99   **3.** 4900   **4.** 132 pages   **5.**

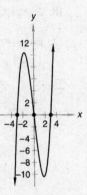

6.

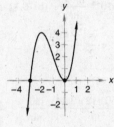

7.

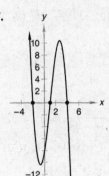

8. A   **9.** D

10. $3x^4 + 6x^3 + 10x^2 + 20x + 20$ **11.** $2x^2 - 6x + 17 - \dfrac{51}{x + 3}$ **12.** Yes

13. $16x^4 - 32x^3y^3 + 24x^2y^6 - 8xy^9 + y^{12}$ **14.** $x > \dfrac{101}{100}$

15. Domain $= \{x \in \mathbb{R}\}$

Range $= \left\{ y \in \mathbb{R} \mid -\dfrac{\pi}{2} < y < \dfrac{\pi}{2} \right\}$

Arctan $(-\sqrt{3}) = -\dfrac{\pi}{3}$; Arctan $\sqrt{3} = \dfrac{\pi}{3}$; Arctan $1 = \dfrac{\pi}{4}$

16. $\dfrac{(x - 1)^2}{4} + \dfrac{(y - 2)^2}{16} = 1$; center $= (1, 2)$;

length of major axis $= 8$;

length of minor axis $= 4$; vertical

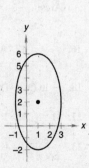

17. $\dfrac{(y+1)^2}{16} - \dfrac{(x-1)^2}{16} = 1$; center $= (1, -1)$;

vertices $= (1, -5)$; $(1, 3)$;

asymptotes: $y = x - 2$; $y = -x$

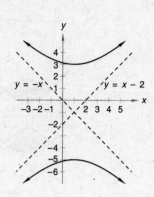

18. 2 **19.** $\log \dfrac{c}{a-b}$ **20.** $\dfrac{\sqrt{2}}{2}$ **21.** 4

22. $\tan^4 x + 2\sec^2 x - 1 = \left(\tan^2 x\right)^2 + 2\sec^2 x - 1 = \left(\sec^2 x - 1\right)^2 + 2\sec^2 x - 1$

$\qquad = \sec^4 x - 2\sec^2 x + 1 + 2\sec^2 x - 1 = \sec^4 x$

23.

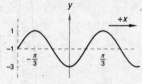

24.

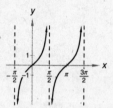

25. $0°, 180°, 210°, 330°$ **26.** (a) $3.98 \times 10^{-8} \dfrac{\text{mole}}{\text{liter}}$ (b) 6.11 **27.** 1074 **28.** 8 and 12

29. 8 **30.** $x(x-5)\left(x + \dfrac{5}{2} + \dfrac{5\sqrt{3}}{2}i\right)\left(x + \dfrac{5}{2} - \dfrac{5\sqrt{3}}{2}i\right)$

**problem set
115**

1. $\dfrac{4}{13}$ **2.** $\dfrac{mk}{m-pk}$ mph   **3.** $\dfrac{(60)(60)(12)(2.54)}{35} \dfrac{\text{rad}}{\text{min}}$ **4.** $N_R = 10$; $N_W = 2$; $N_P = 7$

5. $R = \$140$; $T = \$60$ **6.** $f(-2) = -50$ **7.** -14 **8.** No

9. $x^5 - 4x^4 - 4x^3 - 2 - \dfrac{1}{x-1}$ **10.**

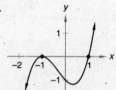

11.

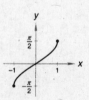

12. A   **13.** $210x^{16}y^{18}$ **14.** $\dfrac{2}{3} < x < \dfrac{7}{9}$

15. Domain $= \{x \in \mathbb{R} \mid -1 \le x \le 1\}$

Range $= \left\{y \in \mathbb{R} \mid -\dfrac{\pi}{2} \le y \le \dfrac{\pi}{2}\right\}$

$\text{Arcsin} \dfrac{\sqrt{3}}{2} = \dfrac{\pi}{3}$; $\text{Arcsin } 1 = \dfrac{\pi}{2}$; $\text{Arcsin}\left(-\dfrac{\sqrt{3}}{2}\right) = -\dfrac{\pi}{3}$

16. $\dfrac{3}{4}$ **17.** Arithmetic mean $= 15$; geometric mean $= \pm 12$

18. $\dfrac{1}{2}\ln(x+1) + \dfrac{3}{4}\ln(y-2) - \ln x - \ln(y+2)$ **19.** -251.48 **20.** $\dfrac{\sqrt{6} - \sqrt{2}}{4}$

21. 81 **22.** $1, 16$

23. $\dfrac{\cot x}{\cot x - 1} - \dfrac{\tan x}{\tan x + 1} = \dfrac{\cot x \tan x + \cot x - \tan x \cot x + \tan x}{\cot x \tan x + \cot x - \tan x - 1} = \dfrac{\cot x + \tan x}{\cot x - \tan x}$

24. $A = 36°$; area $= 35.15 \text{ yd}^2$ **25.** 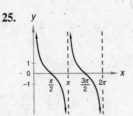 **26.**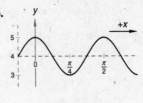

27. $30°, 90°, 270°, 330°$ **28.** $22.5°, 112.5°, 202.5°, 292.5°$

29. $1.07 \text{ cis } 45°$; $1.07 \text{ cis } 117°$; $1.07 \text{ cis } 189°$; $1.07 \text{ cis } 261°$; $1.07 \text{ cis } 333°$ **30.** $x = 2$; $y = -1$

problem set 116

1. $\dfrac{1}{4}$ **2.** 1111.19 **3.** $21\dfrac{9}{11}$ min **4.** $\dfrac{7c(5 + w)}{2(m + 4)}$ hr **5.** 55

6. $r = 6$ **7.** $r = 7$

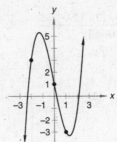

8. **9.** **10.** B **11.** $x^3 + 2x + 3 + \dfrac{13}{x - 3}$

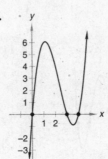 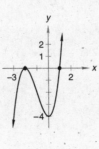

12. $x^4 - x^3 + x^2 - x + 1 - \dfrac{2}{x + 1}$ **13.** 5 **14.** $-25{,}344x^{21}y^{15}$

15. $-\dfrac{1}{2} < x < 40$ **16.** $x > 99$

17. Domain $= \{x \in \mathbb{R} \mid -1 \le x \le 1\}$

Range $= \{y \in \mathbb{R} \mid 0 \le y \le \pi\}$

$\text{Arccos } \dfrac{\sqrt{3}}{2} = \dfrac{\pi}{6}$; $\text{Arccos } \left(-\dfrac{\sqrt{3}}{2}\right) = \dfrac{5\pi}{6}$; $\text{Arccos } 0 = \dfrac{\pi}{2}$

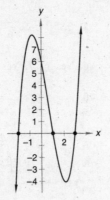

18. $\dfrac{71}{33}$ **19.** $-\dfrac{1}{5}$ **20.** $\begin{bmatrix} -20 & 1 & 4 \\ 0 & 0 & 0 \\ -11 & 5 & -1 \end{bmatrix}$

21. $\dfrac{(x - 3)^2}{9} - \dfrac{(y + 2)^2}{4} = 1$;

center $= (3, -2)$; vertices $= (6, -2)$; $(0, -2)$;

asymptotes: $y = \dfrac{2}{3}x - 4$; $y = -\dfrac{2}{3}x$

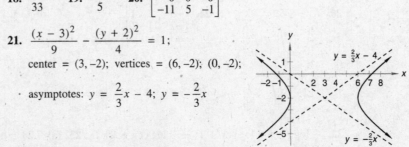
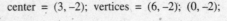

22. $x = -4$; $z = 1$ **23.** (a) $6.31 \times 10^{-10} \frac{\text{mole}}{\text{liter}}$ (b) 7.89 **24.** 1 **25.** $1, 10$

26. $\dfrac{\cos^2 x}{1 - \sin x} = \dfrac{1 - \sin^2 x}{1 - \sin x} = \dfrac{(1 + \sin x)(1 - \sin x)}{1 - \sin x} = 1 + \sin x = 1 + \dfrac{1}{\csc x} = \dfrac{1 + \csc x}{\csc x}$

27. $2 + \sqrt{3}$ **28.** $\dfrac{5\pi}{12}, \dfrac{7\pi}{12}, \dfrac{13\pi}{12}, \dfrac{5\pi}{4}, \dfrac{7\pi}{4}, \dfrac{23\pi}{12}$ **29.** 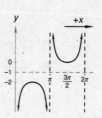   **30.** 2

problem set 117

1. 0.85 **2.** $\dfrac{2}{9}$ **3.** $\dfrac{m(5280)(12)(2.54)}{c(60)(60)} \dfrac{\text{rad}}{\text{s}}$ **4.** $\dfrac{20m}{k}$ hr   **5.** $\dfrac{1800h + 30m}{m + k}$ min

6. Yes   **7.** Yes   **8.** $\pm 1, \pm 5, \pm \dfrac{1}{2}, \pm \dfrac{5}{2}$ **9.** $\pm 1, \pm 3, \pm \dfrac{1}{2}, \pm \dfrac{3}{2}, \pm \dfrac{1}{4}, \pm \dfrac{3}{4}$

10. $r = 4$ 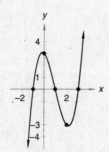   **11.** $r = 3$ 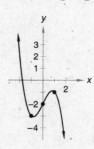   **12.**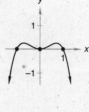

13. $(x - 2)(x + 2)(x - 1)(x + 1)$ 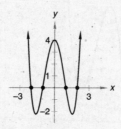   **14.** B

15. $2x^3 + 4x^2 + 5x + 6 + \dfrac{13}{x - 2}$ **16.** -4

17. $x^{10} + 10x^8 y + 40x^6 y^2 + 80x^4 y^3 + 80x^2 y^4 + 32y^5$ **18.** $x > \dfrac{17}{3}$

19. Domain $= \{x \in \mathbb{R}\}$

Range $= \left\{ y \in \mathbb{R} \mid -\dfrac{\pi}{2} < y < \dfrac{\pi}{2} \right\}$

Arctan $\dfrac{\sqrt{3}}{3} = \dfrac{\pi}{6}$; Arctan $\left(-\dfrac{\sqrt{3}}{3} \right) = -\dfrac{\pi}{6}$; Arctan $(-1) = -\dfrac{\pi}{4}$

20. 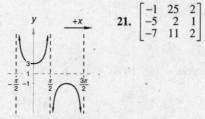   **21.** $\begin{bmatrix} -1 & 25 & 2 \\ -5 & 2 & 1 \\ -7 & 11 & 2 \end{bmatrix}$

22. $\dfrac{1}{3} \log_2 y + 3 \log_2 (x + 1) - \dfrac{1}{2} \log_2 (y + 2)$ **23.** (a) 7.28 (b) $3.98 \times 10^{-11} \dfrac{\text{mole}}{\text{liter}}$

24. $\dfrac{(x+1)^2}{4} + \dfrac{(y-2)^2}{5} = 1$;

center = $(-1, 2)$;

length of major axis = $2\sqrt{5}$;

length of minor axis = 4; vertical

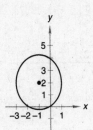

25. $y = -1$; $z = 1$ **26.** 3 and 75   **27.** $\dfrac{1}{32}$

28. $\dfrac{\csc x + \cot x}{\tan x + \sin x} = \dfrac{\dfrac{1}{\sin x} + \dfrac{\cos x}{\sin x}}{\dfrac{\sin x}{\cos x} + \sin x} \cdot \dfrac{\sin x}{\sin x} = \dfrac{1 + \cos x}{\sin^2 x + \sin^2 x \cos x} = \dfrac{1 + \cos x}{\dfrac{\sin^2 x(1 + \cos x)}{\cos x}}$

$= \dfrac{\cos x}{\sin^2 x} = \dfrac{\cos x}{\sin x} \cdot \dfrac{1}{\sin x} = \cot x \csc x$

29. $60°, 150°, 240°, 330°$ **30.** $\left(x + \dfrac{1}{2} + \dfrac{\sqrt{7}}{2}i\right)\left(x + \dfrac{1}{2} - \dfrac{\sqrt{7}}{2}i\right)$

**problem set
118**

1. $\dfrac{1}{6}$ **2.** 47.75 yr   **3.** $R_W = 50$ mph; $T_W = 8$ hr; $R_B = 70$ mph; $T_B = 16$ hr

4. $\dfrac{12}{11}$ hr   **5.** $N_F = 10$; $N_S = 140$ **6.** $-3, 2$ **7.** $\dfrac{1}{2}, \dfrac{3}{2}$ **8.** $-1, \dfrac{1}{2}, \dfrac{3}{2}$

9. No, they have the factor of 12 in common.   **10.** $\pm 1, \pm 2, \pm 3, \pm 6, \pm\dfrac{1}{2}, \pm\dfrac{3}{2}, \pm\dfrac{1}{4}, \pm\dfrac{3}{4}$

11. $r = \dfrac{9}{4}$
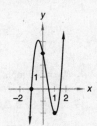

12. $r = 2$
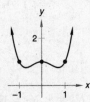

13.
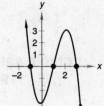

14. $y = (x - 2)(x - 3)(x + 3)$ **15.** D   **16.** -1

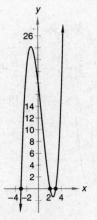

17. $3x^4 - 10x^3 + 19x^2 - 19x + 7 - \dfrac{5}{x + 1}$

18. $x^{15} - 5x^{12}y^2 + 10x^9y^4 - 10x^6y^6 + 5x^3y^8 - y^{10}$ **19.** $x > \dfrac{17}{8}$ **20.** $\dfrac{127}{300}$

21. Domain = $\{x \in \mathbb{R} \mid -1 \le x \le 1\}$

Range = $\left\{y \in \mathbb{R} \mid -\dfrac{\pi}{2} \le y \le \dfrac{\pi}{2}\right\}$

Arcsin $\dfrac{\sqrt{2}}{2} = \dfrac{\pi}{4}$; Arcsin $\left(-\dfrac{\sqrt{2}}{2}\right) = -\dfrac{\pi}{4}$; Arcsin 0 = 0

22. $\begin{bmatrix} 12 & 6 \\ 4 & 2 \\ 8 & 4 \end{bmatrix}$

23. $\dfrac{(y+2)^2}{9} - \dfrac{(x+3)^2}{25} = 1$; vertices $= (-3, -5)$; $(-3, 1)$;

asymptotes: $y = \dfrac{3}{5}x - \dfrac{1}{5}$; $y = -\dfrac{3}{5}x - \dfrac{19}{5}$

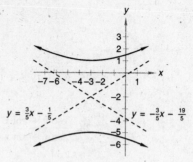

24. $672x^8$ **25.** $2\log_3(x+1) + \dfrac{1}{3}\log_3(x+2) - \log_3(x-3)$ **26.** 2^{16} **27.** 5

28. $\cos 2x + \sin 2x + 2\sin^2 x = \cos^2 x - \sin^2 x + 2\sin x \cos x + 2\sin^2 x$

$= \cos^2 x + 2\sin x \cos x + \sin^2 x = (\sin x + \cos x)^2$

29. 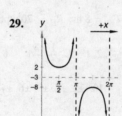   **30.** $\dfrac{7\pi}{6}, \dfrac{11\pi}{6}$

problem set 119

1. 150 ft   **2.** $\dfrac{7}{13}$ **3.** 247.05   **4.** $R_C = 40$ mph; $T_C = 6$ hr; $R_W = 20$ mph; $T_W = 8$ hr

5. $N_R = 5$; $N_B = 12$ **6.** 1 or 3   **7.** 1   **8.** 0, 2, or 4   **9.** 1

10. Upper bound $= 2$; lower bound $= -4$ **11.** Upper bound $= 3$; lower bound $= -1$

12. $-2, -1, 1$ **13.** $3, 2i, -2i$ **14.** $2 + i, 2 - i$ **15.** $-\dfrac{1}{3} + \dfrac{\sqrt{11}}{3}i, -\dfrac{1}{3} - \dfrac{\sqrt{11}}{3}i$

16. $\pm 1, \pm 3, \pm\dfrac{1}{2}, \pm\dfrac{3}{2}, \pm\dfrac{1}{4}, \pm\dfrac{3}{4}, \pm\dfrac{1}{8}, \pm\dfrac{3}{8}$ **17.** Yes

18. $r = 3$ **19.** $r = 3$ **20.**

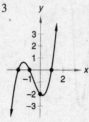   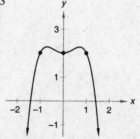   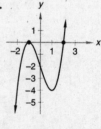

21. $y = (x+2)(x+1)(x-1)$ **22.** -26 **23.** $x^3 + 3x + \dfrac{3}{x} + \dfrac{1}{x^3}$

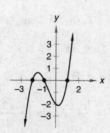

24. $1, e^{\frac{1}{2}}$ **25.**

26. $\cos^2\theta \dfrac{(1 - \cos 2\theta)}{(1 + \cos 2\theta)} = \cos^2\theta \dfrac{(1 - 2\cos^2\theta + 1)}{(1 + 2\cos^2\theta - 1)} = \cos^2\theta \dfrac{(2 - 2\cos^2\theta)}{2\cos^2\theta}$

$= \dfrac{2(1 - \cos^2\theta)}{2} = 1 - \cos^2\theta = \sin^2\theta$

27. $45°, 135°, 225°, 315°$ **28.** $x > 102$ **29.** cis 67.5°; cis 157.5°; cis 247.5°; cis 337.5°

30. $\dfrac{\log 72}{\log 6}$

**problem set
120**

1. $\dfrac{19}{34}$ **2.** 4.64 days   **3.** 2720   **4.** $\dfrac{H_1 H_2 - H_2}{H_2 + H_1}$ hr   **5.** $\begin{bmatrix} -2 & 1 \\ \frac{3}{2} & -\frac{1}{2} \end{bmatrix}$

6. $\begin{bmatrix} -\frac{1}{4} & -\frac{1}{8} \\ \frac{1}{8} & -\frac{3}{16} \end{bmatrix}$ **7.** $x = -2;\ y = 3$ **8.** $x = 1;\ y = -4$ **9.** (a) 0 or 2   (b) 0 or 2

10. (a) 1   (b) 0 or 2   **11.** Upper bound = 2; lower bound = -3 **12.** $-2, -1, 1, 1$

13. $-2, 1$ **14.** $r = 4$ **15.**

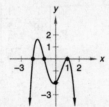

16. $216x^2y^2a^8$ **17.** $x > 1$

18. (a) Domain = $\{x \in \mathbb{R} \mid -1 \le x \le 1\}$
    Range = $\{y \in \mathbb{R} \mid 0 \le y \le \pi\}$

   (b) Domain = $\{x \in \mathbb{R}\}$
    Range = $\left\{y \in \mathbb{R} \mid -\dfrac{\pi}{2} < y < \dfrac{\pi}{2}\right\}$

   (c) Domain = $\{x \in \mathbb{R} \mid -1 \le x \le 1\}$
    Range = $\left\{y \in \mathbb{R} \mid -\dfrac{\pi}{2} \le y \le \dfrac{\pi}{2}\right\}$

19. $\dfrac{181}{90}$ **20.** $A - B = \begin{bmatrix} -3 & -6 & -1 \\ -1 & -6 & 4 \\ -1 & 4 & -2 \end{bmatrix}$; $A \cdot B = \begin{bmatrix} 14 & 13 & 6 \\ 5 & 8 & -1 \\ 20 & 53 & -9 \end{bmatrix}$ **21.** 32   **22.** e, e^{-1}

23. $\sec^2\left(\dfrac{\pi}{2} - \theta\right) + \csc^2\left(\dfrac{\pi}{2} - \theta\right) = \csc^2\theta + \sec^2\theta = \dfrac{1}{\sin^2\theta} + \dfrac{1}{\cos^2\theta}$

$= \dfrac{\cos^2\theta + \sin^2\theta}{\sin^2\theta \cos^2\theta} = \dfrac{1}{\sin^2\theta \cos^2\theta} = \sec^2\theta \csc^2\theta$

24. 9.85 ft   **25.** 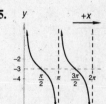   **26.** 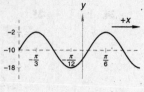   **27.** π

28. $\dfrac{\ln 10}{\ln 5}$ **29.** 2 cis 45°; 2 cis 105°; 2 cis 165°; 2 cis 225°; 2 cis 285°; 2 cis 345°   **30.** 3 in.

problem set 121

1. $\dfrac{2}{9}$ **2.** 54.57 hr   **3.** $\dfrac{(85)(60)(2)}{(191)(2\pi)}$ m   **4.** $\dfrac{30}{7}$ atm

5. (a) $\begin{cases} y = -1 & \text{if } x \le 0 \\ y = x & \text{if } 0 < x \le 1 \\ y = 1 & \text{if } x \ge 1 \end{cases}$ (b) $\begin{cases} y = -2 & \text{if } x \le 1 \\ y = x - 1 & \text{if } 1 < x \le 3 \\ y = 2 & \text{if } x \ge 3 \end{cases}$

6. 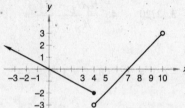   **7.**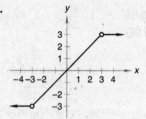

8. 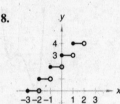   **9.** $\begin{bmatrix} \dfrac{1}{10} & \dfrac{1}{5} \\ \dfrac{3}{10} & -\dfrac{2}{5} \end{bmatrix}$; $x = \dfrac{11}{10}$; $y = \dfrac{13}{10}$ **10.** (a) 1   (b) 0 or 2

11. Upper bound = 1; lower bound = –3   **12.** $\pm 1, \pm 2, \pm\dfrac{1}{2}, \pm\dfrac{1}{4}$ **13.** $-2, -\dfrac{1}{2}, \dfrac{1}{2}$

14. Yes   **15.** –30   **16.** $r = 3$ **17.**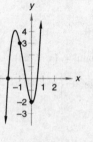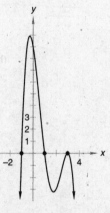

18. $x^4 + 3x^3 + 7x^2 + 21x + 59 + \dfrac{178}{x - 3}$ **19.** $-\dfrac{1760}{p^3}$

20. $-\dfrac{2}{3} < x < -\dfrac{7}{12}$ **21.** 4   **22.** $1, 6^9$

23. $(\sec\theta + \tan\theta)^2 = \sec^2\theta + 2\sec\theta\tan\theta + \tan^2\theta = \dfrac{1}{\cos^2\theta} + \dfrac{2\sin\theta}{\cos^2\theta} + \dfrac{\sin^2\theta}{\cos^2\theta}$

$= \dfrac{1 + 2\sin\theta + \sin^2\theta}{1 - \sin^2\theta} = \dfrac{(1 + \sin\theta)(1 + \sin\theta)}{(1 + \sin\theta)(1 - \sin\theta)} = \dfrac{1 + \sin\theta}{1 - \sin\theta}$

24. $\dfrac{1 - \tan^2 x}{1 + \tan^2 x} = \dfrac{1 - \dfrac{\sin^2 x}{\cos^2 x}}{\sec^2 x} = \dfrac{\dfrac{\cos^2 x - \sin^2 x}{\cos^2 x}}{\dfrac{1}{\cos^2 x}} = \dfrac{\cos^2 x - \sin^2 x}{\cos^2 x} \cdot \dfrac{\cos^2 x}{1} = \cos 2x$

25.   **26.** 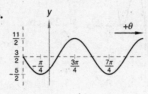   **27.** 30°, 120°, 210°, 300°

28. 45°, 135°, 225°, 315°   **29.** $4i$; $-2\sqrt{3} - 2i$; $2\sqrt{3} - 2i$ **30.** No

problem set 122

1. $\dfrac{1}{3}$ **2.** 3   **3.** $\dfrac{k + 5}{p + 2}$ mph   **4.** 1, 3, 5, 7

5. 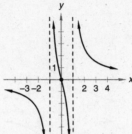   **6.**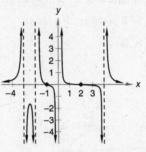

7. 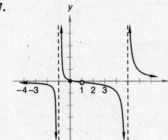   **8.**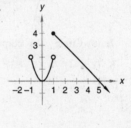

9. (a) $\begin{cases} y = x + 1 & \text{if } -\infty < x \le -1 \\ y = -2 & \text{if } -1 < x < 1 \\ y = x - 1 & \text{if } 1 \le x < \infty \end{cases}$ (b) $\begin{cases} y = -1 & \text{if } -\infty < x < -2 \\ y = -x - 2 & \text{if } -2 \le x \le 0 \\ y = 2x & \text{if } 0 < x \le 1 \\ y = 2 & \text{if } 1 \le x < \infty \end{cases}$

10. $\begin{bmatrix} \dfrac{5}{34} & \dfrac{1}{17} \\ \dfrac{7}{34} & -\dfrac{2}{17} \end{bmatrix}$; $x = 2$; $y = 1$ **11.** (a) 0 (b) 1   **12.** (a) 1 or 3   (b) 0

13. Upper bound = 5; lower bound = -2 **14.** Upper bound = 2; lower bound = -1

15. $-1, \dfrac{2}{5}, 1$ **16.** $-1, \dfrac{1}{5} \pm \dfrac{\sqrt{39}}{5}i$ **17.** $-\dfrac{5}{2} \pm \dfrac{\sqrt{7}}{2}i$ **18.** $i, -2, 2$

19. No, 15 is a common factor.   **20.** $r = 7$

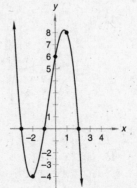

21.

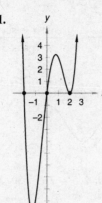

22. C   **23.** –1   **24.** $8x^3 + 36 + \dfrac{54}{x^3} + \dfrac{27}{x^6}$

25. $5 < x < 10$ **26.** $\dfrac{28}{9}$ **27.** 1, 1000   **28.** 2

29. $\cos 3x = \cos(2x + x) = \cos 2x \cos x - \sin 2x \sin x$

$= (2\cos^2 x - 1)\cos x - 2\sin x \cos x \sin x$

$= 2\cos^3 x - \cos x - 2\cos x \sin^2 x$

$= 2\cos^3 x - \cos x - 2\cos x(1 - \cos^2 x)$

$= 2\cos^3 x - \cos x - 2\cos x + 2\cos^3 x = 4\cos^3 x - 3\cos x$

30. $0, \dfrac{2\pi}{3}, \dfrac{4\pi}{3}$

problem set 123

1. 150 units   **2.** 100 ml 10%, 200 ml 40%   **3.** 300 mi   **4.** 2, 4, 6

5. B = 46 yr; J = 36 yr

6. (a)   (b)

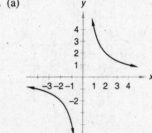
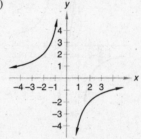

7. (a) Circle (b) Ellipse (c) Hyperbola (d) Parabola (e) Circle

8. $(x + 4)^2 + (y - 3)^2 = (\sqrt{40})^2$

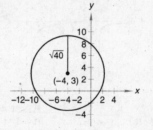

9. (a) Ellipse (b) Hyperbola (c) Circle (d) Parabola (e) Circle

10. $y = -2(x - 3)^2 + 2$ **11.**

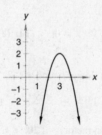
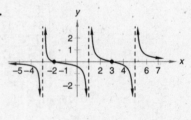

12.   **13.**   **14.**

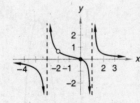
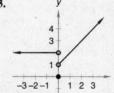

15. (a) $\begin{cases} y = -x - 1 & \text{if } -\infty < x \le -1 \\ y = -2 & \text{if } -1 < x < 1 \\ y = x - 1 & \text{if } 1 \le x < \infty \end{cases}$ (b) $\begin{cases} y = -4 & \text{if } -\infty < x \le -3 \\ y = -2 & \text{if } -3 < x \le 0 \\ y = x & \text{if } 0 < x \le 2 \\ y = 3 & \text{if } 2 < x < \infty \end{cases}$

16. $\begin{bmatrix} -\dfrac{1}{16} & \dfrac{3}{16} \\ \dfrac{3}{16} & -\dfrac{1}{16} \end{bmatrix}$; $x = 2$; $y = -1$ **17.** (a) 0 or 2   (b) 0 or 2

18. Upper bound $= 3$; lower bound $= -3$ **19.** $-2, -2, 1, \dfrac{5}{2}$

20. $r = 7$ **21.**

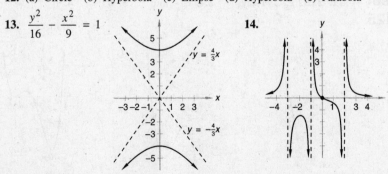

22. $x^3 + x^2 - 2x - 4 - \dfrac{3}{x - 1}$ **23.** $\dfrac{924}{m^6}$ **24.** $x > \dfrac{25}{8}$ **25.** $10, \dfrac{1}{10}$

26. $\dfrac{\cot^2 x + \sec^2 x + 1}{\cot^2 x} = \dfrac{\csc^2 x + \sec^2 x}{\cot^2 x} = \dfrac{\dfrac{1}{\sin^2 x} + \dfrac{1}{\cos^2 x}}{\dfrac{\cos^2 x}{\sin^2 x}}$

$= \dfrac{\cos^2 x + \sin^2 x}{\sin^2 x \cos^2 x} \cdot \dfrac{\sin^2 x}{\cos^2 x} = \dfrac{1}{\cos^4 x} = \sec^4 x$

27. 3.13 in.   **28.**

29. $40°, 100°, 160°, 220°, 280°, 340°$

30. $(x + \sqrt{2}i)(x - \sqrt{2}i)\left(x + \dfrac{1}{2} + \dfrac{\sqrt{3}}{2}i\right)\left(x + \dfrac{1}{2} - \dfrac{\sqrt{3}}{2}i\right)$

problem set 124

1. 208.05 min   **2.** $B = \dfrac{9}{2}$ mph; $W = \dfrac{3}{2}$ mph   **3.** 200 atm

4. $N_R = 4$; $N_B = 8$; $N_G = 11$ **5.** $A = 10°$; $B = 40°$ **6.** $\left(\dfrac{1}{4}x_1 + \dfrac{3}{4}x_2, \dfrac{1}{4}y_1 + \dfrac{3}{4}y_2\right)$

7. $\left(\dfrac{7}{11}x_1 + \dfrac{4}{11}x_2, \dfrac{7}{11}y_1 + \dfrac{4}{11}y_2\right)$ **8.** $\left(3, \dfrac{9}{2}\right)$ **9.** $\left(-\dfrac{19}{5}, \dfrac{6}{5}\right)$

10. (a) Circle   (b) Hyperbola   (c) Hyperbola   (d) Parabola   (e) Ellipse

11. $\dfrac{x^2}{25} + \dfrac{(y - 6)^2}{16} = 1$

12. (a) Circle   (b) Hyperbola   (c) Ellipse   (d) Hyperbola   (e) Parabola

13. $\dfrac{y^2}{16} - \dfrac{x^2}{9} = 1$ **14.**

15.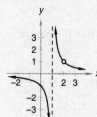

16.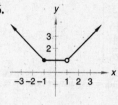

17. (a) $\begin{cases} y = -1 & \text{if } -\infty < x < -3 \\ y = x - 1 & \text{if } -3 \le x \le 1 \\ y = 1 & \text{if } 1 < x \le 3 \\ y = 3 & \text{if } 3 < x < \infty \end{cases}$ (b) $\begin{cases} y = -1 & \text{if } -\infty < x < -1 \\ y = x + 1 & \text{if } -1 < x < 0 \\ y = x & \text{if } 0 < x < 1 \\ y = x - 1 & \text{if } 1 < x < 2 \\ y = -1 & \text{if } 2 < x < \infty \end{cases}$

18. $\begin{bmatrix} \dfrac{1}{33} & \dfrac{7}{99} \\ -\dfrac{4}{33} & \dfrac{5}{99} \end{bmatrix}; \; x = -\dfrac{116}{33}; \; y = -\dfrac{97}{33}$ **19.** (a) 0 or 2 (b) 1

20. Upper bound = 4; lower bound = –2 **21.** –2, 2, $\dfrac{7}{3}$

22. $r = 5$ 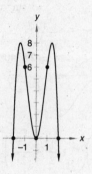 **23.** 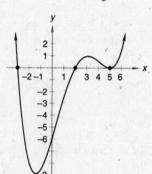 **24.** $x > 27$ **25.** $1, 3^{16}$

26. $\sin 3x = \sin(2x + x) = \sin 2x \cos x + \cos 2x \sin x = 2\sin x \cos x \cos x + (1 - 2\sin^2 x)\sin x$

$= 2\sin x \cos^2 x + \sin x - 2\sin^3 x = 2\sin x (1 - \sin^2 x) + \sin x - 2\sin^3 x$

$= 2\sin x - 2\sin^3 x + \sin x - 2\sin^3 x = 3\sin x - 4\sin^3 x$

27.   **28.**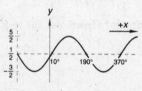

29. $\dfrac{\pi}{8}, \dfrac{3\pi}{8}, \dfrac{5\pi}{8}, \dfrac{7\pi}{8}, \dfrac{9\pi}{8}, \dfrac{11\pi}{8}, \dfrac{13\pi}{8}, \dfrac{15\pi}{8}$ **30.** y^2

problem set 125

1. 21.52 g; 2.71 days **2.** $32\dfrac{8}{11}$ min **3.** 455 **4.** 6

5. 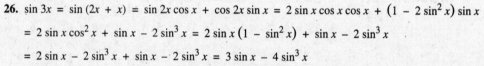 **6.**  **7.**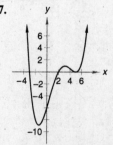

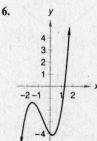

8.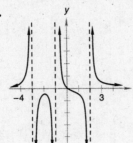

9.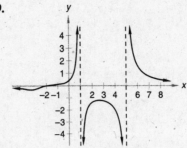

10. (−1.5538, −0.5538); (1.5538, 2.5538)   **11.** (−1.1478, 1.3173)

12. (−0.7454, 0.4745); (0.4918, 1.6352)   **13.** (1.3553, 6.1632)   **14.** −1.4142, 1.4142

15. −0.4142, 1, 2.4142   **16.** −2.8846, 1.0815   **17.** −2, 2   **18.** $\left(\dfrac{13}{8}, \dfrac{31}{8}\right)$

19. (a) Parabola (b) Parabola (c) Hyperbola (d) Ellipse (e) Circle

20. $y = \dfrac{1}{4}(x - 1)^2 - 2$

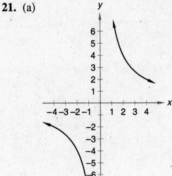

21. (a) 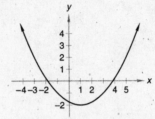   (b)

22. 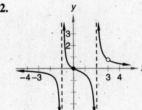   **23.** 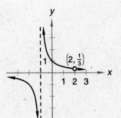   **24.**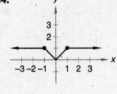

25. (a) $\begin{cases} y = \dfrac{1}{2}x & \text{if } -2 < x \le 0 \\[2mm] y = -\dfrac{1}{2}x + 1 & \text{if } 0 < x \le 2 \\[2mm] y = 1 & \text{if } 2 < x < \infty \end{cases}$ (b) $\begin{cases} y = -1 & \text{if } -\infty < x < 1 \\ y = x - 1 & \text{if } 1 < x < 2 \\ y = 3 - x & \text{if } 2 < x < 3 \\ y = 1 & \text{if } 3 \le x < \infty \end{cases}$

26. (a) 1 (b) 0 or 2   **27.** Upper bound = 1; lower bound = −3   **28.** $-\dfrac{3}{2}, -1, \dfrac{1}{4}$

29. $1, 1 + i, 1 - i$ **30.** 30°, 90°, 150°, 270°